THE BIG BOOK OF MONSTERS

VOLUME 1

JOSH NANOCCHIO

Published by Beyond The Fray Publishing

ISBN 13: 978-1-954528-52-9

Cover design: Disgruntled Dystopian Publications

Beyond The Fray Publishing, a division of Beyond The Fray, LLC, San Diego, CA

www.beyondthefraypublishing.com

BEYOND THE FRAY

Publishing

DEDICATION

I dedicate my channel, my passion and my life to Jesus, my amazing children and my incredible wife who has supported me through everything.

CONTENTS

Introduction vii

1. Alien Abductions & Ufo Encounters & Sightings 1
2. Bigfoot/Sasquatch Encounters & Sightings 27
3. Chupacabra Encounters & Sightings 51
4. Creature Encounters & Sightings 65
5. Dogman Encounters & Sightings 109
6. Flying Humanoid Encounters & Sightings 147
7. Goatman Encounters & Sightings 167
8. Reptilian Encounters & Sightings 207
9. Sea/Lake Encounters & Sightings 235
10. Skinwalker Encounters & Sightings 251
11. Thunderbird Encounters & Sightings 285
12. Wendigo Encounters & Sightings 305

Afterword 337
About the Author 339

INTRODUCTION

First off, I wanted to say thank you so much for your support and desire to purchase this book. I promise you that with over one hundred encounters to sift through, you'll be spending late nights reading through these stories in enjoyment. I remember when I first got into the concepts of monsters and cryptids and how fascinating I thought it was. I would've paid TONS of money at the time for a book like this, or as some *crude* commenter on YouTube pointed out: *a compendium of reddit posts*. 😉

However, this is much more than that. What I've compiled for you in this book is very special. These are eyewitness encounter stories from various platforms detailing strange, supernatural entities. Everything from the traditional Bigfoot to more exotic beings.

As you might notice, there are some sections with more stories than others. This wasn't intentional, as sifting through the literal *thousands* of stories I have at hand, I just had to pick and choose ones to fit **volume one**. I tried to pick a large variety of story types. Short ones, long ones, different writing styles, etc.

I do want to give a few words of caution before you start though. Firstly, some of these stories are incredibly disturbing. I would recommend not reading them before bed, as a few of them definitely gave me nightmares when I first read them. Secondly, while I have done my best to vet these stories, I can't guarantee that they are 100% true.

In fact, one of the biggest flaws people will hold against this book is that it's just *stories*, stories with no pictures, "hard" evidence or multiple credible eyewitnesses. This is why I can only present them as is and encourage you to take them with a grain of salt. While they are good reads and incredibly entertaining, I have no way to prove their authenticity. However, if you step back for a moment and think, any "firsthand account" of anything in life can't be proved unless you have evidence. This is something I've been thinking about to those naysayers who are so anti-cryptid sighting stories. Think about it: If you tell me some of your personal life stories, I literally just have to believe what you say. Most of the time, due to them being personal experiences, you can't challenge them. However, most of our life experiences don't deal with the supernatural, so most people don't bat an eye. Just an interesting take and a new way to think about it. ANYWAYIf you do enjoy this book, please leave a review on Amazon, or go ahead and subscribe to my YouTube channel, What Lurks Beneath for storytelling of the mysterious and supernatural! It really does help me out a ton, and I appreciate every single one.

These stories are pulled from original emails and cleaned up to maintain authenticity and rawness.Thank you again, and I hope you enjoy.

Sincerely,
Josh Nanocchio

1
ALIEN ABDUCTIONS & UFO ENCOUNTERS & SIGHTINGS

THERE ARE many people who claim to have been abducted by aliens or to have had encounters with unidentified flying objects (UFOs). While some of these reports may be hoaxes or the result of mistaken identity, there are a number of cases that remain unexplained.

Abductions by aliens are often described as involving being taken aboard a UFO, sometimes against one's will. There, the abductee may undergo medical procedures or be subjected to tests and experiments. Many also report being given messages or warnings by their captors.

UFO encounters, on the other hand, generally involve sightings of strange aircraft or lights in the sky. These objects may be observed for a short period of time before disappearing or moving off at high speed. In some cases, people have reported following or being followed by UFOs.

Whether or not one believes in alien abductions or UFO encounters, there are many people who have reported such experiences. And while some of these may be explainable, others remain a mystery. Especially the ones dealing with time anomalies, like missing time.

Some experts believe that these reports may offer clues about the nature of reality itself.

These stories serve as a varied collection to the real harrowing experiences of eyewitnesses.

Encounter 1
Submitted By: Dawn
Time: 1999
Location: Portland, Oregon

LET me start by saying that I believe I had contact with alien life and was sent back in time a few hours. That's the short version. Here's the long version: I am a former military officer now living in Portland, Oregon. My encounter was in 1999. I had been to work and returned home to my apartment. It was late at night, right after one in the morning, and I decided to sit on my porch and watch the stars. It was a clear night with a full moon. As I sat on my porch, a humming sound started behind me, and I turned to see a large black triangular craft, complete with lights, land on my street. The sound that it made was that of a metal scraping, and it was loud. I stood up slowly, trying to see what was going on, and I suddenly felt as though my body was being pulled into the craft.

I felt my body was being weighed down like someone had put weights on my body. I felt my arms and legs being pulled towards the craft. I was not able to move. I was terrified, and suddenly, the feeling was gone, and I could move freely. As soon as I was able to move, I was immediately enveloped in a blinding hot light. I'm pretty sure I lost consciousness because I had no sense of time or how long I'd been out when I awoke. The whole thing felt like a dream. When I looked at my watch, there was something very wrong. It was 10:03 p.m. I checked the date, and I checked everything, even the channel two guides where it shows the local time. I was trying to understand what had happened. Had I somehow gone back in time for three hours? I have no idea how to explain what happened or how it happened, but I'm in a desperate search for answers.

Encounter 2
Submitted By: Jonas E.
Time: 2016
Location: Green Bay, Wisconsin

I HAVE BEEN GOING through many issues over the last three years. I have seen a few things myself but was unsure what I was looking at. In 2016, this was the week of the fourth, I was driving home around 9:30 p.m., coming out of the south end of Green Bay, Wisconsin. Just after the airport, I saw something darting across a field just to my right. I slowed down and looked for it in my side mirror as I went farther down the road. I looked in my rearview mirror as well. I did not want to see it again, so I kept my eyes moving.

I saw a large, black-headed creature running on all fours, coming out of the field and into a wooded area. It was not a bear, as I thought it might be, but it was a large animal. I have seen many bears in the woods, and this was not a bear. This animal was running with ease, jumping over a small creek. I have seen many deer, and there was no chance this animal was one. I don't know what it was, but I believe it had something to do with what was about to happen. I had my windows rolled down maybe twenty minutes after this, still trying to wrap my brain around what I had just seen, and the air started to smell heavily like a thunderstorm. Do you know what I'm talking about? I would describe it as a wet smell... if that makes sense. The night was clear as a whistle. No overcast or anything in sight for miles. I see these four bright white lights pop up in the sky, almost lined up perfectly in a rectangle. They then swerved in a choreographed pattern of flashing blue, pink, and red-green lights.

Within seconds, my car died, and I drifted off slowly to the pull-off lane.

I was half panicking, trying to get my car off the road while trying to get it back going. The lights in the sky persisted for some time before they appeared to get bigger and brighter; then they'd retract and shrink in size. They would dart around each other and continue to grow in size. The more they grew, I felt like I was freezing to death. Panic set in, the car started back to life, and I sped home. I pulled onto my driveway, got out, and told myself I wouldn't let this happen again. I'm not sure what happened, but it was very apparent the lights in the sky did something to my car. I have never heard of this kind of thing happening to anyone. It scared me so much that I avoided driving in the dark for a while. Not sure what I saw or what happened to me, but it seemed like something was watching me. I'm curious to know if anyone else has seen these lights or has experienced something like this.

Edit: Just recently, I learned that electronic failure is common with alien and UFO encounters. I can't say for sure that's what I experienced, but all things point to that. I also believe that the being I saw twenty minutes before this happened had something to do with the craft I saw that night. They have to be related somehow, someway.

Encounter 3
Submitted By: Ada Sheen
Time: 2000
Location: N/A

I AM WRITING to you because of a personal experience I had in the summer of 2000. I have never told anyone about this due to their disbelief or thought that no one would believe me; however, now that I have read other people's stories, it seems that my experience is not as unusual as I once thought.

I was on my way home from a drive to the state park with my husband and children. My husband was driving, and my kids were in the back seat, asleep. It had been a hot day, and we were eager to get home. It was about 10 p.m., and we were driving near the town of Vernon, New Jersey, heading down a straight stretch of road. There is not much light on this road at all because there are trees on each side of the road. My husband was paying attention to the car's speed, and I was looking out the passenger-side window with my head turned to look at my husband when I saw something right on the side of the road.

There are no streetlights on this road, so there is not much light, but I saw a figure I could not identify at first. When my eyes caught it, I glanced and saw several small black things in the field right by the road on the right. A fence separates most of the land from the road, and it is a field with trees on each side. A creek runs along the back of this land, and it is all raised so that, at times, the stream is over six feet deep. When I first saw it, the small black objects were crouched near a tree on the other side of this fence. It was about ten feet from the road. As I watched, it stood up and walked across the field towards the road on two legs. This was black, and I would say it was about six feet tall and skinny.

As I watched it, I said to my husband, "What is that?" He replied that he did not know. I asked, "What is it doing?" and he said, "I don't know. I can't tell." Then it walked across the road and out of sight. I could see it clearly when it was on our side of the road. It walked on two legs and had no arms. At first, it seemed to have a big head, but as it moved, I realized that the head was not large but more like a human skull with a flat top. I could not see any features, eyes, nose, or mouth. However, I could see that it was dark and had hair. It stood at least six feet tall and had a skinny body. When it walked on the road, I could see that the road was about four feet wider than his body, and it had very long legs. After crossing the street and disappearing into a wooded area around the corner, I immediately got the urge to vomit and felt dizzy.

As if looking at this thing set off my entire body. I would not call this experience horrible, but it was odd. I had never seen anything like it before, and I have never seen one since. My husband said he did not want to look at it anymore. He asked me what it was, and I could not tell him. He said he would look at the road. I asked him why he did not look at it; he just said he did not want to. It has been about six months since this happened, and I have thought about it often. My husband asked me about it again tonight, and I told him we needed to check out what it might have been. He was unhappy about this but said we could look on the internet.

I am writing this to you because my husband was watching a story on your site and said it sounded like something we saw. When I heard this, my jaw dropped, and we both realized it was similar to what other people had seen. I am not saying that this is what people have seen, but we did see something unusual. I want to find out what it was, and I want to know if other people have seen this. I have found several sightings online that are similar to what we saw. Thank you for your time, and have a great day!

Encounter 4
Submitted By: Anonymous
Time: 2017
Location: N/A

THIS WAS the summer of 2017. I was sitting on my porch, enjoying a beer after work, when suddenly something caught my attention from across the street. I had no idea what it was. I saw a bright light like some UFO.

Of course, I wasn't sure, so I stayed seated and watched as it came closer to my house, nearly hovering over the garage roof. At this point, I was not dealing with a conventional aircraft or drone because there was no sound, and the light just hung over me for several minutes. Then, without warning or any noise, it began moving up and away at a breakneck speed. It shot off into the horizon, leaving behind nothing more than a long glowing trail that lasted for several seconds before evaporating completely.

I was stunned. I don't think it's possible not to be perplexed when something like that happens. And the way it just vanished without a trace? It was freaky.

I was so shocked I didn't have the presence of mind to take pictures or video, and it was long gone when I got inside for my camera. Overcome by curiosity, I researched the next day and came across incidents similar to mine all over the country.

I want to think there's a possibility it might've been some alien spacecraft that just lost power and was trying to access my electricity or something, but that could easily be wishful thinking. Although the way it came in without warning and left just as abruptly seems suspiciously similar to how people describe UFO sightings.

When I lived in Australia, there were so many reports of UFOs around Perth that the media ran specials about them every other week. We even had our *X-Files*-type TV show where they followed different groups of Australians who hunted for UFOs on weekends called *The Outback UFO Hunters*. It was pretty cool! But seriously, I doubt aliens would waste their time hovering over my house if they took a break from a party on the moon or something. I mean, that trail of light was incredibly bright and long-lasting for that amount of time. If it had been some drone with a powerful spotlight, I would have heard at least some engine sound.

Anyway, while there is no evidence (besides myself) to back any of this up, I still think it's worth mentioning these incidents because it wouldn't be the first time somebody came forward with proof after seeing something like this in their backyard.

I've given up on the idea of finding out what it was. I mean, why would they leave behind any evidence if it was some secret government experiment or alien aircraft? And even if there had been something to photograph, all that trail had already disappeared by the time I got my camera. Nowadays, when I see planes crossing the sky at night filled with passengers who are blissfully unaware of the power above them, I get a chill down my spine. Who knows how often this has happened during my lifetime without anybody knowing it? Even more frightening is wondering whether or not these things have ever caused harm to people on Earth...

Encounter 5
Submitted By: Taylor Adante
Time: Spring 2011
Location: Green Bay, Wisconsin

I HAD a UFO sighting back in the spring of 2011. I was visiting my sister in Green Bay, Wisconsin, and was outside looking at the stars before bed. While watching the sky, an extremely bright light caught my attention. I stared at this for a few seconds before it began to take off across the sky, moving extremely fast until out of sight within seconds.

I immediately went inside to tell everyone what I saw, thinking they would probably think I was nuts, but no one did. My fiancé said he had seen that same object only about five minutes prior but decided not to say anything because he didn't want me to get mad. Other people there claimed they had never seen anything like that before, so I was shocked. They said it looked like the object was moving towards me as I watched it cross the sky.

My fiancé and I have been together for over ten years; we both grew up on a farm with a lot of farmland around us. Later that summer, we moved from Illinois to Wisconsin, so I didn't know if I would have another chance to have an encounter soon. But all I know is that what I saw was something real and has forever changed me.

I've read about various things like swamp gas and orbs of light, but nothing that could move that fast or change direction the way this did. My fiancé thinks there may be parallel universes or dimensions next to our own (which may be why we have never seen any proof of aliens before). Maybe these beings can choose when they want to pop in and out of different universes/dimensions, so they'll always stay one step ahead of us. I don't know. All I do know is what I saw with my own eyes. If I hadn't seen it myself, I would think they were crazy, but I know better. I also don't know if it's something they want us to see, or maybe they didn't even realize we were there.

I think it might be a little of both. I've always believed that this particular type of thing was never meant to be seen by anyone. But perhaps no one else saw it. So they came back because they probably thought no one had seen them. Who knows for sure? Now, I can wait and see if anything happens again, because what happened that night has changed my life forever. It makes me wonder how many people have spotted UFOs/aliens without realizing it. Or might have even been abducted without even knowing it.

Encounter 6
Submitted By: Anonymous
Time: N/A
Location: N/A

I SAW something one night that is hard to describe, and I'm pretty sure this was an alien craft of some kind. I was out on the lake fishing like I always do on Wednesday evenings when I saw this bright light in the sky.

At first, I thought it was an airplane, but then it stopped in midair and disappeared for a while. Then right after that, another one of these lights appeared at the same spot. Before long, there were five lights right next to each other, hovering in place. Then I saw them off in the distance, starting to descend in unison together.

Then something more strange occurred; they started making this weird sound that vibrated every part of my body, especially my chest area. The next thing I knew, I couldn't control my hands; it was like someone else was in charge of them and forced me to let go of my fishing rod.

I couldn't move or scream either; all I could do was watch. They then came closer and closer to where I was standing on the lake's edge. At this point, I had closed my eyes out of fear and was unsure of what might come next.

Suddenly, I could feel my body moving against my will, but I fell asleep. When I opened my eyes again, everything seemed bright and foggy around me, even though I could see somehow. The next thing I remember is I woke up in bed and found myself staring at the ceiling in disbelief and confusion about what had just happened to me. I was in my bed, but I was still in the clothes I had gone out in earlier that evening. The time was 3:34 in the morning. My left leg hurt like I had kicked a brick wall. It hurt bad, but I couldn't find anything wrong with it. No marks or nothing.

I have no way to account for what happened to me out there. I wonder if anyone else has had this happen to them.

Encounter 7
Submitted By: Anonymous
Time: N/A
Location: N/A

I HAD GONE to bed like any other night. Around midnight, I woke up from a strange light shining in my window. I remember being in a daze and feeling a presence enter my room. As I was trying to come to, I saw these shapes materialize in my room. Have you ever seen the movie *The Predator* with Arnold Schwarzenegger? Do you remember how in that movie, the predator took on this weird translucent cloaking device that made the light around its body warp? That's kind of how these figures looked. Like human beings but like the light was bending around their bodies.

I was worried for my safety while trying to grasp what I was looking at. I'm not sure how long it had been before I mustered up enough courage to scream out of fear, but when I did, that was when they all vanished into thin air.

I ran downstairs and grabbed a baseball bat—prepared to defend myself against whatever might be lurking in the shadows. The only thing on my mind was getting assistance from someone else so they could witness what had just happened upstairs. I'm not sure what happened after I ran downstairs, but my dad and I found strange footprints on the carpet when we went back upstairs to investigate. The prints were bizarre looking and shaped with a webbed foot. Something had been in my house, and I wasn't sure what.

That experience has scarred me for life, and I fear something may return one night to finish me off or do worse things to me. I have no idea what those creatures' intentions were, or even if these were aliens or demons. Whatever their desire was for me, it was nefarious, I believe.

I'm not exactly sure what these things were or what they wanted with me, but it's been a little over a year since this happened, and I've only told my story to one other person.

The only thing that really sticks out from this encounter is that I got a scratch on my arm that did not heal for a long time. I've even had X-rays done to see if there was anything stuck in my arm or ribs. X-rays have been negative so far, though, and nothing unusual has shown up. My mind is still plagued with questions about what entered my room that night! And why?

Encounter 8
Submitted By: Anonymous
Time: 2014
Location: White Pine State Park, Nevada

AT THE BEGINNING OF 2014, I was planning on taking a trip to visit a friend in Utah. My friend told me about a place called Newcastle and said it was fun to see, and he said it actually had buildings designed like old English castles.

I got up early on the morning of the trip, around 6 a.m., after packing some essentials into my pack, such as clothes, compass, knife, etc. I left Reno, Nevada, at about 8 a.m. I had checked the route on a map, knowing it would be about an eight-hour drive, and I wasn't in a hurry to get there. I decided that if I felt tired along the way, I would stop and maybe get some hiking in.

I had been driving for about five hours when I got to the White Pine State Park area. So I thought that I would enjoy taking a hike there.

I'd been walking through the hills for an hour when I came to an excellent place to take a break. So I set up my hammock and took out some beef jerky before settling for a nap. I must have been more tired than I thought because I slept for two hours. I ate some more beef jerky and hiked back to my car. I figured Newcastle was about four hours away from where I currently was. So I thought I would take a back road I saw on the map that would get me there sooner.

Thirty minutes later, I realized that I probably should have stayed on the highway. I reached this bridge that had been abandoned long ago, there were rusted cars everywhere, and everything smelled like rotting flesh. It gave me goosebumps, but I pushed through and kept going. I realized that not far away from me were shapes and figures moving towards my car at incredible speed. A feeling of dread came over me as they came closer. And I knew something was off, and I stopped the car.

I can barely remember what happened because I blacked out. The next thing I know, the car is running, and I'm driving away from these things.

I drove for a little while with my music on full blast before it happened again. One of them appeared in front of me on the road almost instantaneously! It stood there looking at me, and I was frozen in fear. All I could do was stare into its eyes, which seemed like they were gazing into my soul. It then disappeared, but I didn't know if it was gone for good. So I sped off at full speed. I knew by now I had to be getting close to the highway. There it was, the turnoff to get back on the highway. I barely made the turn because I was going so fast.

Had these beings caught up to my car, there's no telling what they would have done to me, but it couldn't have been good. When I got to my friend's house, I didn't mention anything about what had happened.

It's been years since the encounter. But still, I am haunted, remembering those eerie black eyes staring at me. It scares the living daylights out of me.

Encounter 9
Submitted By: Geoff
Time: N/A
Location: Chihuahuan Desert Area

BETWEEN CONSTANT CAREER CHANGES, extensive travel, and an unusual upbringing, I can safely say I've led an exceptionally rich life. This being said, I have lots of stories, albeit a few probably appropriate for this channel's horror theme. Still, I figured I share one of the things that happened to me and see if there's any desire for more.

They say everyone's Army experience is different. Some people engage the enemy in close combat, and others never even deploy. People have various job assignments, and there's no way to sum them up in a single sentence or phrase for people who haven't experienced them. Oddly enough, I feel like this story is the best illustration of my life as to how real that phrase is.

I was stationed at a base in the Chihuahuan desert during my enlistment. It was a boring place with nothing besides dunes, long stretches of sun-shattered highway, scalding heat, and many impoverished people surrounding the base. That said, there wasn't much to do unless you got off the post. It was at this duty station where I met my friend Forest.

Forest was a great guy. Like myself, he'd signed up for the Army because he legitimately wanted to serve his country. While he was brilliant, he was in the infantry out of dedication. Anyway, being such a nice dude, Forest was inclined to give those of us who didn't have a vehicle at the time rides into town. Driving in his sports car was always fun, so I'd ride along on boring weekends whenever he felt like going somewhere.

I don't remember where we went on this particular day, but we went down an open highway. Since we were off post cruising through a little Latino area, Forest was going faster than he usually might under other circumstances. You see, on the post, they pull you over for going even one mile over the speed limit, and that means guys would book it when they got off the post.

We were bolting down this desert freeway and noticed a box in the distance. Looking back, the conversation as I remember it was only a few seconds. I heard Forest's voice through the piercing wind as he began steering the car towards the box.

"Hey, see that box in the road? I'm gonna hit it."

Laughing, I responded how that would be funny, but whatever was inside might screw up his car, so he shouldn't.

With a defeated smile, he swiftly steered away and said I was probably right. The desert was littered with junk, and hitting it at that speed might not be as fun as it could seem to two bored privates.

As I said, the conversation took maybe six seconds. As Forest passed by and nearly hit the box, we immediately saw movement in the rearview mirror. However, we weren't prepared for what happened next. It looked like a person, but its body shape wasn't human, and it was moving unnaturally fast. It leaped out of the way at the last moment before impact, then turned to watch us leave. We both just sat in shock as we stared at each other, neither of us wanting to believe what we had seen. Then I slowly started nodding my head yes, and he responded with an affirmative nod. Neither of us said a word for the next few miles until we got back on base and reported the incident up the chain of command. We were interrogated for hours, but no one could explain what we had seen. The box in the road was gone when they went to check it out, and there were no signs of anything else in the area. Eventually, we were just told to forget about it and move on with our lives. But I know what I saw, and so does Forest: an inhuman figure that saved itself from a high-speed impact by leaping out of the way at the last second.

But a few days later, a civilian reported something similar, except it was reported that a being was seen running to some kind of craft off the side of the road. And then it was all over the news. The papers called them "UFOs," and people talked about aliens visiting our planet. Later the same night that the news coverage about the UFO was aired, there was an incident on the base.

It was 11 p.m. when sirens on the base went off. When that happens, everyone is alerted and sent to their assigned post on the base. Forest and I were assigned to add to the security team on base. So, grabbing our gear, we headed toward the command center for guard duty. As we were running to that position from our barracks, we saw in the sky above the base four disclike objects. They seemed to be floating across the sky right above the base. We stopped for a second to gaze at these things, then continued to our post. Our security detail placed us inside the command center, so our view of what happened outside was null and void. The all-clear signal was given after about three hours had passed. We were relieved of our assignment and sent back to our barracks.

The next day we were called back into the command center for a debriefing. We were reminded not to say anything about what we had seen on the road that day. And what had happened during the night. The Army is closed about that stuff, and we never heard another word about what took place that night.

So when I think back to that phrase about how everyone's military experience is different, I can't help but figure out where this story fits in the narrative of my life.

Encounter 10
Submitted By: Anonymous
Time: Summer 2012
Location: N/A

IT'S ALWAYS the small things that creep back into your mind as you try to lull yourself to sleep; maybe that's why I'm writing this so late, to try to get it off my mind. Anyway, I'm here to tell the story of the only paranormal, otherworldly, extraterrestrial, unexplained experience I've ever had.

I want to start by saying I wouldn't call myself a skeptic. Still, I'm not gullible regarding UFO stories, which is why my experience keeps me up sometimes. It's been about seven years since this happened, but I remember it clear as a bell.

In the summer of 2012, a group of friends gathered at my best friend's house for a pool party. To provide some context, we live in a small farming town that's been slowly built up over time. My best friend lived in a historic farmhouse, but neighbors' houses were right next to hers, and the town hall was across the street. The street was lined with homes. Her long backyard bordered a field, and you could see the tops of cars on the highway next to the field from her yard. The five or six of us all arrive, and we swim for hours, having the best time a kid can hope for during their summer break.

It's about 8:00, and the sun is starting to set. As we're all relaxing in the pool, someone says, "Guys, what is that?" We all turn to gaze where a finger points up into the air. About ten feet above and thirty feet from where we are is a little orange globe, about the size of a golf ball—just... floating there. It lazily bobs through the air for about ten seconds, moving a few feet horizontally. Then it just sort of fades out of existence. If you blinked, it wasn't there anymore.

We were a little freaked out but tried to write it off as a big firefly, not wanting to get out of the pool and ruin our evening. We all continue the merriment for another hour until something else happens.

It's about 9:00, and the sun is set, but there's still some residual sunlight on the horizon. We aren't entirely in the dark. We're splashing around when my friend says, "Guys, there it is again!" We turn and see another golf-ball-sized orb, about the same height and distance as the last one, but this time it's blue. It doesn't lazily bob past you either. The movements it made were exact and calculated. It, too, moved a few feet horizontally but in the most perfectly straight line, and then it paused in midair for a couple of seconds.

Then... it zoomed away. It moved so fast away from us that it left a blue light trail as it zipped between nearby houses in a straight line.

We screamed. We immediately fled to the house, trying to rationalize something to explain what had happened. Truthfully, I'm tearing up typing this because this memory comes back to my mind from time to time. It terrifies me that we have no idea what floated by us that night.

Encounter 11
Submitted By: Quiet_Mouse_2234
Time: Fall 2015
Location: Minnesota

TO START, I live in a small town in the middle of Minnesota. It was the middle of October 2015 when my dad, brother, and I went to our backyard to stargaze at around ten o'clock. Even though trees surround our backyard, there is enough clearance to see the sky in all directions. We were out there for about fifteen minutes and only saw one or two shooting stars. After about five minutes of not seeing anything more, I noticed things around us got silent. My brother then got scared, and my dad said he hadn't noticed. We were about to go back inside, but my eye caught something moving in the tree line. When it came into full view, we could see this thing was only about a hundred feet off the ground, no higher—moving in silence. We watched as its five rotating, orange lights passed beyond our view. Once it was gone, we tried to discuss what it was. During that time, another one came from the same spot as the first one. It looked identical. I told my dad, "Let's see if another one comes." And sure enough, another one did.

We waited a little longer to see if there were any more to come, but none did. My dad thought they were drones, but I've seen and heard drones, and they're pretty dang noisy and small for what we saw. I said I wished I had an iPhone with a camera and could have taken some pictures.

A few days later, my parents bought me an iPhone. This new phone had a great camera when it was released, and I was excited to take a slew of images. I was, let's just say, now addicted to taking selfies.

Not to deter from the story, the same day, my sister wanted me to go with her to the local Walmart to pick up her new prescription glasses. And I happily obliged. It was maybe 7 p.m. when she asked me, and we both knew the eye center at the Walmart would close soon, so we got in her Jeep, and she rushed.

In my hometown, we have a plethora of back roads to get to your destinations, so instinctively, she took one that would be a nearly straight shot to the store. At this point, it was near 7:30, and it was starting to get dark out. The back roads are quick but get lonely and creepy at night. Nonetheless, she continued driving on this road because she knew we were only about five more minutes away.

That was when we noticed it. Near the road, this object hovering over the tree line was probably only two hundred feet away in the distance. It was an odd shape and reminded me of a giant Coke can. It was quiet and had some lights on the top and bottom of the object. My sister stopped, and we got out of the Jeep and stood there watching this thing. Immediately I grabbed my new iPhone and started to take pictures. Only, the phone began to glitch. It wouldn't take any images, and the few I was able to take were pitch black. I found this odd, as just hours before, I had been taking pictures like there was no tomorrow, so it would glitch when I needed proof of something.

After nearly ten minutes of this thing hovering over the tree line, my sister said we still needed to pick up her glasses. So we got back in her Jeep and sped towards the Walmart. I couldn't wait to return home and tell my dad and brother that we had seen more UFOs.

As soon as we got home, I told my dad what we'd seen. And about the new iPhone not being able to take pictures of it. He seemed to think that that was odd. "But," he said, "when it comes to UFOs, anything or everything strange happens." I was excited about what we saw, and it took a while to get to sleep that night.

Because we live in one of those areas far out in the country, everyone's phones are always roaming for a signal. Luckily, if I positioned my phone correctly on the table next to my bed, I could get full service. That is country life.

Late in the night, maybe around 2 a.m., I awoke to the vibration of my phone. I received a text from my friend that read, "Wake up, please."

I was still in a daze from abruptly waking up and was worried about why she needed me to wake up.

After I put my phone back down, I realized I could not move a single muscle in my body. It was like I was being held down, and only my eyes could look around. I questioned if I was enduring sleep paralysis or if this was real. That was when I noticed my door beginning to open slowly. I saw this black figure start coming close to me, and within an instant, it was gone, and I was then able to move. I didn't know what had happened. I didn't blink. I didn't wake up in a jump from a deep sleep. I was awake this whole time. And when I looked at my phone, my friend... had never texted me.

I always wondered if seeing those UFOs and that nighttime incident were related.

Encounter 12
Submitted By: Anonymous
Time: N/A
Location: Northern California

IT WAS A SLOW, hot day in the summer. I was at the beach of a lake with my family, swimming, boating, and having fun. It had been burning all day, but when the sun began to set, I was tired of being in the water and decided to sit on the shore.

I found a small rock outcropping stuck into the lake near our picnic. A bit of shade from some trees nearby made this a perfect spot to relax without overheating. I sat down facing the lake, using my sweatshirt as a pillow.

I must have dozed off because the next thing I knew, something was just outside my field of vision at the water's edge. Things around me suddenly got very bright. I was so disoriented that it took me a few seconds to realize I wasn't looking at the setting sun any longer. Something warm and armored had my shoulders in its grip.

I must have panicked because whatever was holding me squeezed hard enough for it to hurt. I screamed, but the light was too bright for me to see anything except a silhouette. I was trying to fight it off me, but I woke up on a cold steel medical table before I could free myself from its grip.

I couldn't move because of the restraints around my wrists and ankles. My head was held in place by a helmet/mask apparatus covering my head, with only my nose exposed. I couldn't see anything, but I could hear and feel the sound of some kind of fluid being pumped into my nasal passages.

Then I noticed several large creatures looming over me, speaking in a harsh, unintelligible language. I could only see their silhouettes against the bright lights shining on me. The one holding my shoulders was large and dark, its head just a giant shadow obscuring any details.

The ones examining me had some kind of scanners that moved around me in a blur. Their bulky exoskeletons and strange appendages made them look like giant praying mantises.

Time after that seemed to be a blur. I tried to resist as best I could, but whatever sedative they were pumping into my system made it hard for me to think enough. I had never felt so drugged up before. It was incredibly traumatizing.

I remember them taking what appeared to be a small metal tool and inserting it into the right side of my arm. They were jamming a hot iron poker into my veins and arteries. It felt like a burning sensation. It caused tremendous agony unlike anything else I've ever experienced. I can't even begin to explain how it made me feel. It was excruciating. I faded out after that.

The next thing I know, I'm waking back up on the shore of the lake near our picnic site. I was screaming. The light was gone, and everything seemed dark after that unbearable brightness. Everyone was staring at me like I was a lunatic. I was screaming and crying uncontrollably, trying to explain what had happened. They must have thought I'd hit my head because nobody else saw anything happen!

I nervously looked around, scratching at my arm, which was still hurting, but there were no visible marks. My family tried their best to comfort me and explained I had probably just had a horrible nightmare.

I'm not a believer in UFOs or aliens. But there is no other explanation for what happened to me. That was not any kind of nightmare; it was real! I don't believe this was a nightmare. I believe I was abducted and experimented on. I am not the only one who has had this happen to them; there are others just like me. Someone needs to take these aliens seriously before they experiment on anyone else.

I don't know if it's relevant, but while I was slipping in and out of consciousness on the medical table, I was able to catch a glimpse. I saw some kind of symbol burned into the skin on the upper part of my stomach. It was something no human could have done to me, and it must have been burned there while I was passed out. I don't know if anyone will believe me, but that same symbol will still randomly appear on my stomach at night and then go away.

I was in terrible shape for the following weeks after this happened. I was extremely sick. Some kind of flu or something going around, but it felt different. Whatever the aliens did to me made it harder for my body to recover from sicknesses like it usually would have. Maybe they planted a disease in my body, I feel that even the thought of that is so ridiculous, but I can't explain that horrible flu I had. It was the worst sickness I've ever endured.

I've had vivid nightmares after that night. Explicit enough that I am too scared to sleep. These dreams will happen randomly, but they mainly focus on what happened in the ship when I was drugged. The part about how I was abducted seems to fade in and out. But I'll get a recap of what happened when I was on that table. In these dreams, I see my perspective of the room where they kept me. When this happens, it starts with them operating on me and doing things to me. It was like surgical torture! I know it sounds weird, but the most prominent dreams are when they would give me something through an IV... My body would be shaking involuntarily like I was having a seizure of some kind!

Seeing these things happen to me in my dreams is very disturbing. It's hard not to wake myself up every time this happens. I don't know what else to say. They were experimenting on me.

I dreamt about the symbol again last night. Exactly like it was in reality after the abduction. I'm probably being paranoid, but I feel that I have proof of alien abduction. All I want is someone to believe me. I want someone who will finally take these things seriously!

Whatever this was ruined part of me that night, I pray God never lets it happen to me again. The pain was unbearable. I'm still unsure what happened to me that day, and I haven't told anyone because it sounds like a crazy hallucination.

If anyone out there has had this happen to them or knows what happened that day, please help me. I'm unsure if I'll ever feel safe living in my home again. If you have any information about where I can go for verification on the symbol burned into my stomach, anything at all, it would be great.

Encounter 13
Submitted By: Jimmy Janssen
Time: October 7
Location: Walton County, Florida

I WAS DRIVING my car into town at approximately 11 a.m. It was a Friday morning, and I recall the exact date was October 7. It is an important day for me because it is also my birthday.

I was driving down Old Hwy 52 in Walton County, Florida. The road is not well maintained, and there are many cracks and potholes throughout the old dirt road. Many people often take this shortcut instead of Highway 331 (the main highway) because it is faster and much less traveled by traffic.

I suddenly noticed that my odometer was going backward. "It's impossible," I said to myself. "What is happening here?" Confused, I lowered the volume on the radio and listened for any sound that might have been out of the ordinary coming from the motor. There didn't appear to be any issues with my car.

I looked up at the sky through the driver's side window and saw the sky turning from blue to dark gray. I turned, looked out the passenger window, and saw it was still clear on that side of the sky. A few moments later, what appeared to be a rip in space opened above my car, which rippled up the entire road length. By then, I had started going uphill towards Highway 331 (the main road). The so-called "rip in space" looked like an eerie glowing light and was perhaps no more than fifty feet above me, and it appeared to be more of a flat rectangular shape.

As I passed under this "rip in space," everything around me became dark. I couldn't see anything for a brief moment, and then everything became visible again, except it was now nighttime. Specifically, at 10:14 p.m., I was in the same spot on the road as I was when this happened. No more than ten seconds had passed since everything had turned dark.

I pulled over on the side of the road, completely shocked, trying to comprehend what had just happened. I checked my phone, and it read 10:14 p.m., and the date was still the same. I pulled up my Instagram; there had been posts that had been made by people I was following hours ago, which would have been earlier in the evening. I was in utter shock.

How is it that I just fast-forwarded eleven hours? I don't know how long it took me to get my bearings together, but I know it was more than ten minutes, probably closer to thirty minutes.

A few days later, I searched online to see how common this type of event is. And it turns out that people have been reporting missing time worldwide, and it seems to happen most frequently with people who live in rural areas.

The most common explanations are:

A glitch in the Matrix.

Interdimensional travel.

People have a "moment of clarity" when they come across some fundamental truth about themselves, the universe, or reality.

Alien abduction.

Because I was under the assumption that this is a rare phenomenon, I'm not sure what compelled me to look it up on Instagram, of all places. But after doing quite some research, I've come across many people who have reported these "time jumps."

Let me know if you have any stories about this, as I'm trying my best to comprehend it.

2

BIGFOOT/SASQUATCH ENCOUNTERS & SIGHTINGS

MADE famous by the Patterson-Gimlin film, Bigfoot is said to be a large, hairy, apelike creature that inhabits the forests of North America. There have been many sightings and encounters with this elusive creature over the years. Some people believe that Bigfoot is a real, undiscovered species, while others believe it to be a legend or myth. Whatever your belief, there is no denying that the idea of Bigfoot is fascinating, and these stories are sure to send a chill down your spine.

What I find really interesting about this section of the book is that two of the encounters here really ring special. The first being my very own father's account. He swears up and down that it happened to him when he was younger. He believes he had a run-in with a Florida skunk ape. And, while we're on the topic of the Florida skunk ape, another harrowing tale is from a gentleman whom we'll call *Briggs*. His story involves getting attacked by a group of them while hunting on private land in the state of Florida. These stories really stay with you.

I encourage everyone to take the time to read through these pages and see if anything jumps out at you. Chances are, if you're a believer, you'll find something that solidifies your convictions. And if you're a skeptic, perhaps one of these tales will give you pause and make you reconsider your stance. Either way, it's always fun to read about Bigfoot encounters!

Encounter 1
Submitted By: Orin
Time: 1992
Location: Oregon

IN 1992, I used to go hunting with my brother all the time near Mount Hood National Forest. In fact, for many years, we roughed it out there in the backcountry with minimal gear. I guess you could call it the survivalist in me. We would go for days at a time and never see another person. We were very familiar with the area, knew all the good spots to hunt, and had seen many strange things in our years of exploring. One night I was sleeping in my tent about twenty feet from my brother's tent. It was late fall, so it got real cold fast once the sun went down.

I woke up around 2 a.m. to use the restroom; I always tried to go before bed. As soon as I stood up, something caught my eye that made me freeze mid-stride... about fifty yards away, standing next to a tree, was this massive hairy creature staring right back at me! The moonlight lit him up perfectly!

He looked like he could have been eight feet tall if he stood straight, but his posture seemed hunched over slightly, so maybe six feet? His arms hung way past his knees, and his head turned slowly from side to side, looking directly into my eyes and then back again as if sizing me up really good. Then he took off running on all fours super-fast towards some thick forest brush/trees on top of a hill near us, which led into an old logging road area that no one used anymore. Reminded me of the way a gorilla runs on all fours when charging... I didn't know what exactly what it was. Still, I knew it wasn't human or anything else known by man!

After seeing him run away like that, I noticed how quiet everything became just seconds after seeing him! Like every animal stopped moving all at once. It creeped me out big time! My heart felt like it would explode out of my chest!

So naturally, being scared sh*tless, I ran over, shaking uncontrollably, telling my brother, "Wake up, wake up, wake up." He sat upright, rubbing sleep from his eyes and asking, "What's wrong?" And that's when I told him what happened! He laughed, saying, "You're crazy!" But I'm sure you can imagine how frustrated that made me feel.

I finally got him to listen, so we both grabbed our flashlights and loaded rifles and walked outside together, shining lights everywhere, searching for any sign of movement anywhere; only we saw nothing unusual except some deer grazing peacefully nearby, which surprised us because they are usually spooked easily by even slight noises. We decided to call off the search mission until morning light came since neither one wanted to be alone outside.

Once morning arrived, we scoured the entire area and found nothing unusual besides some tracks leading down the hillside through heavy brush areas, which elk or other large animals do travel during their nightly trips... but something tells me the thing I saw that night also used that game trail too.

Encounter 2
Submitted By: Bradley
Time: Unknown
Location: Washington State

CALL ME CRAZY, but it's about time I share my story. I was twenty-two when this happened. I'm forty now. This was outside the Seattle area when I was visiting a good friend, and we were going for a hike with my big brother, my cousin, and his friend. We were all young adults, twenty-two to thirty years old. We hiked up a trail about three miles long with a river down below us on our left side and thick woods to our right side. I remember it was around noon when we started the hike because I had just finished eating lunch with my friend's family before we went hiking. We had been walking for about an hour when my brother said he needed to stop for a minute to rest his leg from hurting him since he had injured his knee the previous year. So we stopped in this small clearing by trees growing and weaving together. My brother sat down while my cousin and I stood there talking while waiting on my bro, who was sitting on the ground resting his leg as he complained of it hurting him pretty badly. I felt bad, but there was nothing we could do but allow him to rest.

I figured I'd take the time to scout the clearing out and see if I could find any high vantage points near me for scenery. However, there were none. At least, not in this particular spot. We chatted a bit before deciding it was about time to move farther down the trail when I saw something moving through the nearby trees. It looked humanlike but much larger and black. It moved like one solid mass, not gracefully at all. It sounds bizarre, but I thought there's a gorilla out here! But apes don't walk upright, do they? Its shoulders were far broader than mine are now, even though I'm six feet one inches tall. And its head seemed incredibly large. Then suddenly, whatever this thing is stepped out into full view... Right next to where my brother was just sitting, I'll say I've never seen my brother move that fast in his life, even with his injured knee. Call me fortunate or unfortunate, but I believe that what I bore witness to was a living, breathing Sasquatch in the flesh. We saw it from head to toe in the light. It must've not liked our reaction to seeing it because it let out this reckless scream that was almost bloodcurdling but very deep. The hair on my body stood right up.

The sound kinda reminds me of what lions sound like, only louder and deeper sounding. I think it was trying to intimidate us, but either way, we didn't stick around. We took off running. We could hear this thing behind us throughout the trail beyond the trees. It was making this awful-sounding breathing/huffing noise. I could hear it pounding its feet against the ground as it chased us. We made it back in record time to my friend's house. We were all out of breath and scared out of our minds. We told his family what had happened, and they were kind of skeptical. They said it was probably just a bear. I know what I saw, and it wasn't a bear. It was the keeper of the forest, I called him. Bigfoot. Sasquatch. I know he's real. We all do now.

Anyway, I've never been back to that area since. I don't think I'd ever want to. It was one of the most terrifying experiences of my life. While it was fascinating, and I'd love to see it again, I don't think I'd ever want to encounter it again. I'm not sure what it was going to do to us. I don't think it would hurt us, but I'm not sure. I think it was just trying to scare us off. I'm glad it did. I don't know what would've happened if it had caught us. I'm not sure if it would've eaten us or not, LOL.

Encounter 3
Submitted By: Rick Shawford
Time: 2000
Location: Oregon

I WAS bow hunting for elk in the Umatilla National Forest near Pendleton. I was on a ridge that overlooked a large meadow. It was about 6:30 p.m., and I had been sitting there for about an hour and a half when I heard something walking through the brush below me to my right (east). At first, it sounded like two people walking together, but then it stopped moving and started making these strange grunting sounds. The sound of its breathing was hefty. So I turned on my headlamp and shined it down into the brush. I saw this giant, hairy creature standing with its back facing me. It was about nine feet tall and had reddish-brown hair all over its body. I could see that it had a massive chest and shoulders but no neck. Its arms were extended.

In reaction to the light, it turned to look in my direction, and that was when I saw its face for the first time. The face looked like a cross between an ape and a human—flat nose, wide mouth with big teeth showing in the light from my headlamp. It stood there for several seconds, looking at me through his yellow eyes glowing. It seemed delirious or confused. Then it turned around slowly without making any noise or grunting sounds and quickly moved to the trees about fifty yards away. To be honest, I think I startled it. That was the impression I got from its reaction. With the light shining on its face, it didn't seem to know what to do or how to react. It walked upright like a man, but it was so tall that its head brushed the tops of the trees as it walked by them.

I watched until I couldn't see it anymore.

I couldn't believe what I was seeing. It was like something out of a movie. I was terrified and amazed all at the same time. This creature was so big and hairy, and it looked nothing like any animal I had ever seen before. My jaw was on the floor. I couldn't believe I had just seen an actual Bigfoot. There was no other explanation that would've made sense. So, after about ten minutes, I got up and ran off the ridge toward my truck.

I've been hunting and fishing in the woods all my life. I know what a bear looks like, and this wasn't one. I didn't tell anyone about this for several months because I thought they'd think I was crazy. But then someone else came forward with their own story about seeing something similar in the same area, so now I'm telling you. Hiding it doesn't make sense anymore. This was no bear, and it wasn't a person in a costume. I know what I saw, and there's no denying it. There are Bigfoots out there in the wild.

Oregon, well, the whole Pacific Northwest, is Bigfoot territory. I'm not the only one who's seen one. There have been many reports of sightings in this area for years now. I'll admit that for the longest time, I didn't buy into the idea of it. That was, of course, until I had this experience.

I've got some relatives who are part of the Umatilla tribe down here, and boy oh boy, do they have some pretty harrowing stories. They've been dealing with these creatures for generations. They have a name for them too, although I don't know it. I don't know much about their legends or folklore, but I do know that they're not to be trifled with.

Encounter 4
Submitted By: Gus L.
Time: Unknown
Location: Texas

I'M FORTY-FOUR. I grew up in East Texas and currently reside in the state. I have been an avid outdoorsman all my life. I have spent countless hours in the woods of East Texas, both as a child hunting and fishing and as an adult hiking, camping, and kayaking. I am very familiar with the woods and the animals that live there. I am also a firm believer in Bigfoot. I have read every book and article I can find on the subject. I have followed all the reports and sightings. I am convinced that Bigfoot is real and that they live in North America's woods. With that said, I will now relate my own personal Bigfoot encounter.

It was early spring, and my friends and I were camping near the river. We had been hiking and fishing all day and sat around the campfire, enjoying a cold beer. It was getting dark, and we started talking about turning in for the night. The river flowed slowly and calmly, and the woods were alive with the sounds of the animals that came out at night. It was a dark, moonless night. The only light came from the campfire and the stars. Through the trees, we could see the lights from the houses on the other side of the river. As we were talking, we heard a loud, long howl. It was a high-pitched howl, like a wolf, but much more prolonged and more deafening. It sounded like it came from the other side of the river. We all stopped talking and listened. The howl came again, this time sounding farther away. We listened for a few more minutes but heard no more howls. None of us could place the sound. It didn't sound like any animal we had ever heard before.

A few minutes passed when one of my friends tossed a piece of wood into the fire. He kept his 9 mm close by his side but talked in hushed tones about what we had just heard. We were both pretty unnerved by all of this and, after a time, decided to try to retire to our tents. However, retiring just meant lying there for an undisclosed amount of time. I couldn't tell you exactly when it was, but I was awoken by something hitting the side of my tent. I was lying at the back side of my tent and could tell something large and heavy had struck the side next to me. It sounded like a baseball hit the tent. I heard a massive crash and a tree coming down fast not far from our campsite. At that point, I remember saying screw this, grabbed my sleeping bag, and jolted out of my tent. My friend was already outside, looking like he'd seen a ghost. Without speaking, we both gave each other this mutual look that said let's get out of here. And we did. We left our tents and other supplies that we could just return in the morning and grab. Luckily we parked not too far away from where we were camping.

The following afternoon we came back and retrieved our stuff. It felt EERIE. The entire spot where we had our tent set up. Like we were being watched as we dismantled and packed up everything.

We talked about it the following day. We were both pretty shaken up by the whole experience. We had no idea what could have caused the howling or the tree to come crashing down. We still don't know for sure what happened that night. But we both agree that it was a Bigfoot.

Encounter 5
Submitted By: Thomas Bailey
Time: 1974
Location: Pennsylvania

I WAS SPENDING the weekend with my mother at her home in the mountains of north-central Pennsylvania. It was the summer of 1974. I was twelve years old. My mother's house was near a large state forest. I was riding my bicycle along a dirt road in the woods when I came upon a large clearing. I stopped to rest and looked around when I noticed a large, dark figure moving about a hundred yards away through the trees. I watched it for a few minutes, trying to figure out what it was. It was about seven feet tall and covered with dark brown hair. It was walking upright, but it was not a man. I didn't see any clothing... I watched it for about five minutes, and then it disappeared.

I was so frightened that I ran home and told my mother. She didn't believe me and thought I was playing a joke on her. I never told anyone else about it. I've always wondered what I saw that day. I haven't seen anything like it since. I've spent many years researching. I have found that there are a lot of sightings in the Pennsylvania mountains. I have also found that there are a lot of strange sounds in the mountains of Pennsylvania. I have heard some of the sounds on YouTube. They sound similar to the sounds I have heard.

As it turns out, my brother had an encounter in the mountains in the same region about nine years after I did. My brother saw a Bigfoot in the early 1980s. He was camping with friends in the mountains. They were in a tent. He woke up in the middle of the night and saw a large, dark figure trying to get into his tent, and he fired several rounds off at this thing only to have it scream and run off. He said it was not a bear or a man. He said it was large and walked on two legs. He said it had a deep, guttural scream unlike anything he had heard. He said it was very frightening. He said it was about 3 a.m. and a full moon. He said he could see it very clearly. He said he didn't tell anyone about it for years. He was ridiculed and thought to be crazy. I believe him 100% and believe that what I saw was the same thing he saw.

He and I grew up differently because he spent more time living with our father, and I spent more time living with our mother. We spent a lot of time in the mountains and forests of Pennsylvania. We both know the mountains and forests very well. We both know what we saw and heard. I think there is something in the Pennsylvania mountains that is similar to the one seen in the Patterson film. I can't say for sure that it is Bigfoot, but I'll stand by my words that it wasn't a person or a bear.

Encounter 6
Submitted By: Angelo
Time: 1970s
Location: Florida

MANY PEOPLE HAVE HEARD stories about Bigfoot. Well, in Florida, they call it the skunk ape.

Why? Because whatever this creature is, it has a really nasty smell like a skunk, albeit different.

So this story takes place in South Florida. West Hollywood, to be more precise. West Hollywood is a small town that lies between Miami and Fort Lauderdale on the east coast of Florida. Although it happened many years ago, I remember it like it was yesterday.

It was the middle of summer and unbearably hot and humid. The air was thick and heavy like you could almost cut it with a knife. During the day, the sun would be beating down mercilessly from a cloudless sky. You could actually fry an egg on the sidewalks. Forget going to the beach. The water was so warm it felt like a hot bath. Even the beach sand would burn your feet if you didn't wear shoes right to the water's edge.

My cousin Gary had moved to a house that sat right in the middle of an orange grove about ten miles west of Hollywood. His house was surrounded by hundreds of acres of orange, grapefruit, and tangelo trees. Beyond that was the Everglades swamp. It's full of gators, deer, snakes, and all kinds of creepy-crawly things.

Some friends and I went to Gary's house on this particular night. There was Steve, Bill, Dallas, myself, Gary, and his girlfriend just hanging out. We had heard on the news that the skunk ape had reportedly been seen close by in the Everglades. So, needless to say, we were armed, just in case. We had a couple of pistols, a .38 Special, a .357 Magnum, and a few hunting rifles.

We were sitting on the front porch, trying to stay cool because it was too warm to sit in the house. Gary didn't have air conditioning.

All of a sudden, an awful smell filled the air. If you ever smelled a skunk, you know how potent the air can get, and you can't escape the smell. Well, this was like that. Except the scent was different than a skunk but just as nasty. It seemed to get stronger as we sat there deciding if we should go inside and try to avoid the odor.

Then we heard something that sounded like heavy footsteps coming from the direction of the orange grove behind the house. Almost simultaneously, we all looked at each other and said, "Skunk ape." We ran into the house, and each of us grabbed a gun. Then Gary turned on the back-door porch light. It was so dark, though, that the light only penetrated about thirty feet into the grove; beyond that, total darkness.

We all stood there looking out the back door, guns at the ready. None of us said a word. Then we heard what sounded like twigs snapping and leaves rustling as if something was coming closer. We all tensed up and gripped our guns tighter. The smell was so bad by now that it was making our eyes water.

We stepped out of the house into the backyard very slowly. Then we heard what sounded like a tree branch crashing down to the ground just beyond the reach of the light.

Then we saw it. The skunk ape. It was about seven or eight feet tall and covered in dark fur. Its long arms ended in sharp claws, and its face was long and narrow with glowing red eyes.

Then it let out a bloodcurdling scream that sounded like a woman being murdered. I felt scared and excited at the same time. My heart was pounding in my chest, and my hands were shaking. I was afraid that the creature would hurt us, but I was also curious to see it up close. When it let out that chilling scream, I felt a wave of terror wash over me. But I didn't hesitate to open fire. I just wanted to get rid of the thing. So even though we were scared, we kept shooting until it ran away. We don't know if we hit it or not, but it ran off into the darkness. And even after it was gone, the smell lingered for days.

Some days later, a news report mentioned that a farmer had found his horse dead. Not far from where Gary lived. Supposedly something had ripped the horse's head right off its body. What beast has that kind of strength?

But the story doesn't end there. A few weeks later, my brother and some of his friends were out in the Everglades hunting for deer when they found what looked like a made cave. And it had animal bones inside, and it stank awful. They even took pictures to prove to everyone what they found. They thought it was the skunk ape's cave.

I genuinely believe that what we saw that night was the skunk ape.

Encounter 7
Submitted By: Villify009
Time: N/A
Location: N/A

I WAS CAMPING one evening by a large lake, all by myself. The night was beautiful, and it was a serene quiet evening. All of a sudden, it got freezing. I felt a presence walk up beside me but saw nothing. As the presence got closer, I could hear heavy breathing. I assumed it was a bear and turned on my flashlight to look around. I didn't see anything, but I could feel something. I could hear the breathing, but there was no sign of movement beside me. Entirely unnerved by this newfound experience, I sat up and decided it was time to retire to my tent. I quickly jumped into my tent, afraid of what I was experiencing. I stayed in my tent the rest of the night, holding a flashlight and a tiny pocketknife should anything happen. Attempting to calm myself, I distracted myself with thoughts of remembering camping trips as a child. Then I heard two loud screeches just outside my tent and then nothing.

Shortly after that, I started hearing these loud noises approaching my tent at night. They sounded large, whatever it was that I was hearing. I was panicking, thinking two huge men would come and kill me. The sounds would stop abruptly outside my tent, then walk away and return at another angle. Several times this went on. I could hear three separate footsteps and sounds. The whole encounter lasted for over three hours. It felt like an eternity. I felt like I was going crazy. I just wanted it to stop. They were all sorts of strange sounds and noises. Some were screams and growls, while the others were weird stomping noises. Then it went silent for a moment, and I heard what sounded like a large branch being ripped off a tree right by me. Then, I listened to it getting kicked off into the forest. Now, not only was I scared because of what I was experiencing, but I felt like whatever this was was trying to intimidate me and wanting to hurt me.

Finally, it stopped, and I could not keep it together. I tried calling out for help, just hoping someone else was around. But I heard nothing but me. I felt as though I was utterly helpless and all alone. I knew I was doomed. This had been going on for hours now, and these things were coming back and forth around my campsite. They were constantly circling my tent, waiting for the right moment to strike. I was on edge like crazy. Finally, the noises eventually ceased for some time, and I wasn't sure what would happen. They could still be out there watching me, but I was not going to take any chances or risks. I figured staying put in my tent was the best course of action until sunrise.

I waited the entire night in my tent, frozen in fear. Morning eventually came, and I had not slept at all. Thoroughly exhausted, I decided to hike my way out as soon as possible. Upon exiting my tent, the area around me was trashed. Huge branches were ripped off the large fir tree about ten feet away from my tent! My supplies were thrown all over the campsite. Frightened but intrigued, I grabbed my stuff and hit the trail, looking for a clear spot where I could escape because I couldn't precisely remember the section of trail where I had hiked in. I only had the salvageable backpack and my tent; everything else was destroyed.

Upon getting to my car, more than a mile away, I opened my trunk to put my gear inside so I could drive away. At the time, I had no idea what had happened the night before, but right as I closed my trunk, I heard this horrific scream in the distance. It sounded like a man's yell but deep and loud. It sounded like a massive set of lungs. I froze in place, listening for a few seconds; then out of nowhere, these strange noises started sounding off all around me. I felt immediate danger, just like the night before, and I realized that my life would be in danger if I didn't get in my car at that very moment. Terrified, I jumped in my vehicle, locked all the doors, and left as fast as I could, still hearing these noises echoing off in the distance.

What did I hear the previous night? What did this all mean? I can only say that this experience left me completely overcome with fear, confusion, and amazement. I've never had an experience like that before. It leaves me feeling shaken about how such a large creature could move about at night, surround a tent and scare someone without ever being seen. There are theories and explanations for what it could be, but I have my doubts about most of them. I just don't think everybody who has come up with a plausible answer is aware of how loud, intimidating, and ferocious this thing is. Whatever it is.

Encounter 8
Submitted By: Anonymous
Time: n/A
Location: N/A

LATELY, all of the animals in our neighborhood have started to act strangely. We can attribute these behaviors to none other than supernatural forces. At random times all of our animals will start acting strangely, barking and acting crazy in the woods surrounding our houses. Our cats recently have gone missing and so have our small dogs. While some of us believe it's a pack of coyotes or something on the loose... I know better. Whatever is there has taken an interest in our pets for unknown reasons. If this is, in fact, paranormal, entering an aggressive, directly territorial combat response is illogical, as in nature, defense-based aggression is rarely the first response. Based on the research, I believe this is a being that is purposefully waiting for the right moment to strike. They know how we behave, yet we do not know their behaviors. It's incredibly patient, cunning, and intelligent. It's not a coyote, fox, or wolf.

I've seen the wandering of coyotes, and there appears to be a kind of intelligence guiding the behavior. Based on emotional inference, drawing from memory, coyotes, even in packs, seem apprehensive when coming into certain territories of neighborhoods due to the population. We live in areas with a lot of wildlife and birds, so it's very natural to assume that coyote behavior is simply fear of the human being. These cats that are being snatched away and small dogs aren't animals straying far away from our populated areas and neighborhood. They're being snatched up from their yards or back porch. Something is taking them, and no one is sure what it is. From other experiences alone in the woods, we know it's not your typical animal in nature. This has to be the work of something else entirely. What, I'm not quite sure. Is it possible this is a dogman or Bigfoot?

Absolutely, since they are usually the ones to be a little more aggressive when it comes to coming in for food based on stories and experiences from others. But at what scale do we call this a dogman or Squatch? This has to be something else that we are not experiencing or understanding.

What's creepy is this is happening primarily at night, when everyone's asleep in the early morning hours. That's when these animals disappear, and no one finds a trace of them. One night, my girlfriend asked me if I saw movement in the yard, but I didn't see what she was talking about. She looked out of bed and said she could've sworn she saw a giant shadow running around, dashing between yards, but I dismissed her outright. You know, maybe there is truth to what she had to say. So far, we've never found a trace of any animals, any blood trail clues, and never any animal bones. I do not think we will ever see the remains, so this is probably something completely different. What that is, I have no idea.

Encounter 9
Submitted By: Anonymous
Time: N/A
Location: N/A

I WAS WALKING BACK to my car in an area of the woods that I had been in before. It was a one-mile hike from the parking lot. It was about 6:30 p.m. I was walking because I had just finished a seven-mile run. I was a little more exhausted and kind of just dragging my feet. It was dusk; it hadn't quite gotten dark yet. I heard the sound of something following me in the woods next to me. I turned to look and saw a Bigfoot about fifty feet away from me. It was on the side of the trail and standing on the side of a hill. It was looking at me, but at the same time, it appeared to be looking at something on the ground. I was too in shock to look at it for too long. It was about six feet tall and had dark brown hair. I knew what it was right away because nothing else out here looks like that. It had to be a Bigfoot. It was freaky looking and just kept glaring at me. It had a tall pointed head, looked down at the ground, and had something small in its hands, maybe a dead rabbit or something. It stared at me for maybe a few more moments before it turned and ran off into the woods behind it.

That was enough for me, and I ran toward my car. I didn't stop running until I got to my car, which was about a half mile down the trail. I got in my car and drove off as fast as I could. But this would spark a long and endearing relationship between me and cryptids and Bigfoots. I was initially scared, but now I'm intrigued by their existence.

I've heard some other eyewitness reports from people in the area. There was an incident in the summer of 1983 where a truck driver was driving down a logging road. He said he came across a family of Bigfoots. He said they were crossing the road in front of him. When he stopped to see what they were, they ran into the woods. He said he saw at least four of them. He said they were all big and were running very fast. He was shocked and didn't know what to do. This is only the second sighting I know of in the area.

I have been hiking and running in this area for a few years. It's a remote spot and far from any type of civilization. I have heard of other sightings in the area. Wild black bears are in the area, but they are nothing like the Bigfoot I saw. I saw it with my own eyes, knowing what I saw.

Encounter 10
Submitted By: Briggs
Time: November 2001
Location: Florida

I DECIDED to tell a story that is only known by two people—one of my best friends and me. I am a firearms/tactics instructor, prior law enforcement, I am also a gunsmith who owns a gun shop, and I would beg you not to give my real name because I can't dare have anyone think I am not mentally sound to hold the licenses and certifications that I do—it isn't hard to get harassed by the government on these matters. I can't imagine how this might go over if someone wanted to be an ass and make a complaint.

My story:

I live in Florida, just north of Ocala. Back in November 2001, the day before the second half of deer hunting season in Florida was to open, I received a phone call I had been waiting for for a long time—exclusive permission to hunt one thousand acres of private land owned by a well-known paper and wood products manufacturer. This opportunity was a hunter's dream score because this land has been completely untouched for thirty years, strictly off-limits to trespassers, and has never been hunted. The trees had been harvested in the mid-'60s, replanted, and then left pretty much untouched the entire time except for the crews that this company hired to keep up the dirt roads. Trails are halfway maintained, and professional arborists check the tree growth and overall replanting progress—even then, this only happens three to five times a year. I was permitted to hunt this area because it was set to be harvested and replanted the following spring. Because this land butted up to a national forest, it was a haven for hunted deer, and because it was located near the Georgia-Florida line—it was a haven for really BIG deer.

I called my best friend and hunting partner, I'll just call him Dave for this story, and let him know the good news. He was as excited as I was, and we made plans to pack up that night so we could leave early the following day. The night before we left, I met up with one of the company's land managers, and I was given the keys to the gates and a map of the road system.

Dave and I decided this was a rare opportunity, and we would make every bit of it count. Since the property was two hours away, we decided to bring the camper and stay for seven days. We loaded up my hunting UTV side-by-side and all the other supplies we would need. My trailer is called a toy hauler, so the UTV goes inside the camper via the back portion, which has a big ramp operated by a winch; the ramp comes down to load and hauls a pretty good-sized ATV/UTV until you get to where you're going, and then you unload it while you stay in the camper. That night Dave decided to stay at my house so we could get an early start the following day.

I want to be clear, every part I have told you so far, I did so for a reason—the story needs to make sense later. To continue:

When we get to the property, we come to the main gate, unlock it, get the truck and camper inside, and lock it behind us. The map showed a thick row of trees and a clearing where we could set up the trailer. We got everything set up and decided to take the UTV side-by-side out and explore. There was a road set up to go completely around the property perimeter and then there were four roads equally spaced connecting to each side of the loop and one more road that ran in the middle of those roads connected to each of the other sides of the loop—kind of like massive city blocks.

We decided to start exploring this place by taking the long trip around the perimeter road, and then we would venture into the cross-roads. As soon as we started, we both felt we were being watched. I can't explain that feeling—everyone feels like they are being watched in the woods now and again, but this was different. This felt like we were being glared at more than watched; that's the best way I can explain it.

As we spent the rest of the day exploring, we noticed many crude shelters built off the trail. We probably passed five or six of them, seemingly evenly spaced throughout the entire property. We stopped and looked at the first one we had seen, and we thought there were a bunch of vagrants living on the property, and they had made it—only the shelters were so crude, made by bending a bunch of small trees down over each other and then covered with palm leaves and other debris. The smell was so horrible as we approached it we didn't want to look inside. It smelled like a scorching dirty wet dog and skunk mixed. It was nauseating, and we both joked about the vagrants needing to take a bath. My heart sank a little because I was wondering how many of the deer these vagrants had poached, and it seemed like this wasn't the forgotten hunting oasis I was hoping it would be. But it was a thousand acres, and we weren't THAT deterred.

We found a couple of places to set up our stands, and the following day, I dropped Dave off at his stand, and I went to mine, climbed up, and got settled to watch the sunrise and play the still game until lunch.

As 10:00 a.m. rolled around, I had not seen anything. Then as I thought about it, I hadn't seen ANY wildlife. The woods were dead quiet—no bugs, birds, wind, squirrels, and not the first deer. Then I started to get a natural uneasy feeling like I was being glared at again. By the time 11:00 a.m. rolled around, I got a call from Dave on his walkie—he was getting the same feeling, and we both decided to hang it up for the rest of the morning, which is highly unusual for us to give up so quickly.

We started back to the camper to have some breakfast and relax until the evening hunt. Dave had had the same experience I'd had, not seeing or hearing any wildlife, and we both had never encountered that before—not that quiet. This property has been untouched for thirty years, it should be TEEMING with wildlife, and there just didn't seem to be any. We decided if we had the same experience in the evening, we would relocate to the other end of the property. I picked up Dave, and we headed back to the camper.

As we were driving along down the trail and talking about how weird it was, this place was so quiet—out of nowhere, I yelled, "FU**

SON OF A BITCH," because I just got smacked directly in the forehead with a rock—I was struck pretty damn hard too—hard enough I had to immediately stop to figure out what in the hell just happened. Hard enough, I was bleeding pretty good. At the time, we didn't know it was a rock, and Dave asked, "Did something fly up off the road?" and I said, "Hell no, someone shot me with something; no way anything flew off the road and hit me that hard." That was my reasoning at the time because to me it was the only possible conclusion for something to hit me so hard, directly in the forehead, and at a moving target. We confirmed it was a rock because it was lying on the UTV side-by-side's floor. I said, "Someone has a slingshot and doesn't like us bothering their squatting."

As I was talking sh*t about what I would do to them when I caught them, yelling at nothing in the woods, mind you, we both smelled that same putrid smell we had experienced at the shelter we had found. We both got an uneasy feeling—like a dreaded feeling almost, and we both decided to get to the camper. We chose not to go out for the evening hunt and just relax, and besides that, my head was pounding too much to go out that evening.

When we returned to our campsite, we were shocked to see everything we had set up outside—the grill, containers with cooking pans and utensils—everything just dumped and thrown all around. It wasn't only abandoned, but a lot of the pans were dented, our grill was demolished, and we had no food sitting outside. What made me upset most of all was my camper looked like someone had just gone around punching the outside of it, leaving dozens of huge dents.

I told Dave to come where I was standing and pointed at the ground—all around my camper were bear footprints—massive. Now Dave and I are both hunters, and we know what a track that is imprinted really deep means—it means it's big, and by how far these tracks were depressed in the ground, we concluded that whatever left these prints not only had damn big feet but was also really damn heavy eight hundred to a thousand pounds. We again smelled that putrid smell. It seemed to be all over everything.

It took us an hour to clean everything up, and we decided to just cook inside the camper with what cooking utensils we had inside; we hooked the truck up to the trailer and decided we would leave first thing in the morning. I would have left that night, but Dave wasn't comfortable driving my big truck and trailer, and my head was pounding and hurting too much from the earlier incident to drive. After dinner, we went ahead and loaded up the UTV side-by-side and got everything secure so that in the morning, we could jump in the truck and just go.

After we were done, we talked about what could have left those tracks, and we were hoping this was all just a massive bear, and he'd stepped inside his tracks, which would make a footprint-like track, but we both knew that wasn't the case. Neither one of us said it at the time, but we both thought it was a Sasquatch, or what we call down in Florida a skunk ape. We both went to bed around 9:00 p.m. so we could leave at first light—I don't mind saying we were both unnerved by the day's events. I fell asleep with an icepack on my head and my rifle beside me.

Dave and I both woke up around 1 a.m. to something crashing into the side of the camper. I asked, "Dave, what the hell was that?" He said, "I don't know. Did a car hit us?" We were both asleep and out of it, and then the side of the trailer got hit again, only this time we could feel the side of the trailer lift and drop. This isn't a tiny camper—it was thirty-five feet long and cumbersome to pull. Things started to fall out of the cabinet doors that had security locks to keep that from happening as you traveled down the road—and it's weird what you think during something like that. I thought, *Damn, I am glad we hooked up to the truck because the locked hitch to the truck is the only thing keeping this thing from going over.* Had it just been on the jacks, it would have gone over; I am sure of that.

As Dave and I were grabbing our rifles, trying to navigate the situation, we heard the door trying to be pried open. As that was happening, I looked out the window and was about to evacuate my bowels when I saw it. It was indeed a Sasquatch—it was damn big, and I could not believe what I saw. Dave had come beside me to look, and he said quietly, "Holy sh*t—look at the size of that thing," and then it stopped what it was doing and looked directly at us. The small porch light that was on shone directly on this thing, a humanlike face with a wide blunt nose, and it had these soulless pure black eyes, and it just shuddered a cold streak directly through our nerves.

Then it started to try to pry the front door of the camper open—Dave said, "Look, he has his hand in," and I knew it was only a matter of seconds before he pulled the camper door off; let's be honest, I am surprised it held on as long as it did. I took my rifle, cycled a round in the chamber, pointed at the door, and fired. Now, my rifle is chambered in 7 mm—which is a pretty sizeable round, and I had fully expected this thing to step back and die—it didn't. It did drop to the ground and let out this gut-wrenching, bloodcurdling yell as it lumbered back into the woods. Ever shot a rifle with a huge round in an enclosed space? Well, it leaves you with ringing ears, and you are most certainly deafened quite a bit for a while, and even at that, we could still hear it scream for an hour.

Dave and I were trying to figure out do we just go for it and leave now, or do we wait until we know it's clear, or are there others? Can we drive through the gate? Because we goddamn sure weren't getting out to open it—all these weird things you think and talk about in a situation like this.

About an hour later, the screams stopped, and everything seemed to die down. Just to be safe, we decided to wait until daylight, and we both sat on a long wall with no windows.

About 3 a.m., we were startled again to hear what sounded like a herd of buffalo running around my camper. We peeked out the window and were horrified to see three or four of these things just running around the trailer punching it. They did this for over an hour, and I will tell you, if they do this as a tactic to scare what's inside to just run out—it almost worked.

Then we were horrified to hear the back gate of the camper—you know, the one where we load the UTV in and out, and again we see this large hand trying to pry it open. I did the same thing as before, chambered another round, and fired through the door—I don't think I hit it as square as the other one—but it stopped him—but it pissed him off. They just kept running around and punching the camper until daylight.

After the sun rose, we didn't see anything, but we were both too scared to go outside. About noon, we decided to look around—we didn't see anything—so we just ran for the truck, jumped in, fired it up—got to the gate, Dave got out and quickly threw it open, and we hauled ass the hell out of there and didn't stop until we were a good hour away from that place.

I haven't been hunting since, and neither has Dave, and I doubt very seriously we ever will. We decided not to tell anyone because, at the time, cell phones weren't a thing, not with cameras anyways, and we had absolutely no proof it happened. Plus, I just graduated from the police academy and didn't want to be known as the weird "Bigfoot" guy. Because we shot at them, we debated calling the FWC—wildlife officers—but decided not to.

3
CHUPACABRA ENCOUNTERS & SIGHTINGS

IN PUERTO RICO, the chupacabra is said to be a dangerous creature that attacks livestock and sucks their blood. The name "chupacabra" comes from the Spanish words "chupar" (to suck) and "cabra" (goat). There have been many reports of chupacabra sightings in Puerto Rico, Mexico, and the United States. Some people believe that the chupacabra is a real creature, while others think it may be a myth.

There are many different descriptions of the chupacabra. Some say it is a small, hairless creature with large eyes and sharp teeth. Others describe it as a large, furry creature with horns. Some people believe that the chupacabra is a type of vampire, while others think it may be a mutant or an alien.

What I find fascinating is the various descriptions of the creature. In the United States, it is said to look like a coyote with mange, while in Cuba, it has been described as looking more demonic and evil. Eyewitnesses have reported that the chupacabra is anywhere from three to five feet tall, and its body is covered with spikes. It has large claws and red eyes.

Despite the creature variations and how long I can make this section, I've decided to only pick a few encounters for this section and make it shorter to shine light on other cryptids. Enjoy!

Encounter 1
Submitted By: Anonymous
Time: N/A
Location: Arizona

I USUALLY DON'T TELL many people this, but I believe I've seen a dead chupacabra on the side of the road. Years ago, before the invention of cell phones, my job entailed driving to different locations across the United States. Specifically, the southwest like New Mexico, etc. I've been to Nevada and around the area; I prefer that my job details stay more private, as I'm not comfortable sharing any of that sensitive information. I will say, though, at the time, I smoked like a chimney and could not smoke in the company vehicle I drove. I would often make frequent stops along the side of the road to light one up. It wasn't what I wanted to do, but I didn't have a choice.

I do remember this event quite well, though. I was probably about eighty miles outside Tucson, headed east, and it was getting a little dusky outside. I pulled over on the side of the road for a smoke, and I thought I would sit outside my car and enjoy the cool evening breeze. Well, who am I kidding? It's Arizona; there isn't anything remarkably "cool" about it. But it was at least a breeze.

Nonetheless, it had been at least four or five hours since my last smoke break. Anyway, I was trying to make good time to my following location. I had five minutes to spare because I was exceeding the speed limit. I was sitting there, smoking my cigarette, looking off in the distance, when my eye caught something on the ground, probably about fifty feet away from me in the dirt. I didn't know why I didn't see it at first, but it looked like a dead animal. Not anything surprising, since animals die all the time out here; the conditions are extreme. This is also a bustling road. But the more I looked at it, my brain had difficulty registering what animal this could be. My brain couldn't configure the puzzle pieces. I was confused after about thirty seconds of trying to figure this out. I said screw it in my mind and threw my cigarette down.

I walked on over there to see precisely what animal this was. I was surprised that coming up close to it, I wasn't able to rightfully say it was just a mangled coyote that had gotten run over by a big truck. This was an animal I was not familiar with. I have a couple of close Native friends whom I told the story. They said it sounds like I saw a dead skinwalker that had gotten hit by a semitruck. I don't know; all the depictions I've seen of skinwalkers don't look anything like what I saw. This thing was freakier and built strangely. I don't want to say smaller because it was still a larger animal.

I'd guesstimate the size of a dog because that makes the most sense, but more like a pit-bull-sized dog—a large mastiff. The only problem was it had short back legs and long gangly forearms that formed into tiny three-fingered hands that looked to even have claws on the ends of them. It was very humanoid looking. The face was also much flatter than a dog's. It had two big fangs protruding from its mouth, with sharper rigid teeth. It looked to be whatever animal it was probably had mange or something. It looked like the body had perhaps been run over in the last twelve to fifteen hours, if I had to guess. Part of its body was contorted and crushed. It looked like it's lower half was the spot that had been run over or crushed; this part of its body had been destroyed entirely. I'm presuming that's how it died, and then it was knocked off the road in the dirt.

I want to talk about the fangs quickly because I've never seen an animal with three-to-four-inch canine fangs hanging out of its mouth. This thing looked like a little mini vampire. Although physically, it seemed like a mixture of a dog and a human, if that makes sense. I'm not talking about no werewolf or anything like that. It looked more like a science experiment gone wrong. Like somebody was trying to make a monster-infused dog featuring DNA from humans and somehow got screwed up and died. I don't know; between the general abnormality of the beast and the fact that it was mangled from death by a semitruck, I couldn't give you an actual answer. Skinwalker or not, this thing was freaky to look at.

I probably stood there and spent more time observing than I should have. I probably freaked myself out too much. The more questions I had, the more I wanted to examine it. The more I tried to look at it, the more questions I had. I had probably sat there for about ten minutes before I left. It wasn't until a little later that I put two and two together and realized it was perhaps a chupacabra. This wouldn't be till years and years after, though. After watching this show, I saw the resemblance and put it in my head that that is what it had to be. I didn't think they were real. But this must have been traveling at night and somehow got smacked by an oncoming truck. I guess I'm lucky that I saw it before the vultures and other wildlife ate through it. The weird thing was that no flies or anything were buzzing around it. There was also no smell or odor, and it was a blazing hot day. Just two things that stick out to me that are odd. I'll let you be the judge. Make of it what you will. That's my experience, one of those things that will forever creep me out.

Encounter 2
Submitted By: Fredrick
Time: 2010
Location: New Mexico

ABOUT TEN YEARS AGO, I used to do some minor ranch handling and help around a few farms in the general New Mexico area, where I lived for a short period.

One farm that I remember very distinctly had a problem of supernatural proportion. They had a chupacabra problem, to put it bluntly. And I'm not afraid to come out and say it. I have never believed in ghosts or supernatural nonsense before this. I never paid attention to Bigfoot or any of that stuff. What I encountered and experienced on that ranch, along with several others, I can't deny it anymore. It's changed how I view and think about the things around me. There's nothing else this creature could have been because no animal does what these things did. It's unnatural. I know that no predator on this god-given earth drains the blood of animals as these things did for whatever reason. I say things because there were several of them. It wasn't just one of these creatures acting by itself. They would target the horses and show up early in the morning. I'm talking around 1 a.m. to 3 a.m. Usually, they would show up in groups of three to four and break into the barn and stables. They managed to take and kill two of our horses successfully.

When we found them the following morning, they had two large holes in their lower neck, and their bodies were completely drained of all blood. It was chilling to know that such an animal could do such a thing.

I'll tell you what, though, that event made our owner up his firepower tenfold. And before you know it, we had a bunch of extra hired guards walking around fully armed with semiautomatic rifles. Even with all that hired muscle, I don't think we managed to kill even one of those things. I can tell you that I probably heard several gunshots almost every night, if not every other night; I would always know they were around because the horses would start going crazy in the stalls. You could tell they were freaked out by something. Sure enough, the guards would go by and shine their lights, and there would be these little buggers. I shouldn't say little buggers because these things weren't tiny. If I had to estimate, I'd say the child's size; they were hunched over. These things were gray and had a short snout with gargantuan canines. Their eyes were large and dark and sunken in.

I couldn't tell exactly what color, if any, because the only time I saw them was when they generally reflected eye shine late at night. They were a genuine nuisance, and we dealt with them for quite some time. Things died down after a few months, but it was quite a while there that they tried to get more horses, and they couldn't.

Surprisingly, they never came after any of our other livestock. We had chickens, pigs, and several other types of livestock that, in my opinion, were in a much more vulnerable location than our horses. Maybe these things have it out for horses. Perhaps they have a taste for horse meat. I don't know what you want to call it.

When we found the two horses' bodies, there wasn't a lick of flesh or blood anywhere on the horse. These things had not only been drained of all their blood but the meat had been peeled off their bodies. Very meticulously. It appeared to be done with almost surgical precision and was not done carelessly. There were no signs of a struggle, no broken bones or gashes of any kind, just the two large puncture holes in its neck with its flesh missing. That's the kind of stuff that keeps you up at night. When you realize this sort of thing, it's like I'm living in the *X Files*. It makes you sit back and wonder what else they tell you is a lie that is out there and exists right now. These things never attacked us to try to go after me or anyone else, to my knowledge. I feel like given a chance if they were backed into a corner, who knows what they would be capable of?

Encounter 3
Submitted By: Mark Suárez
Time: N/A
Location: Cuba

MY NAME IS MARK, and I'm part Cuban. My father is a full-blooded Cuban and currently lives in Cuba. My mother is half Italian, half Portuguese. My mother and father met, had me, and then separated when I was young. I didn't grow up knowing my father since I moved to the United States with my mother when I was very young. She remarried very quickly to an American man. I didn't have much of a relationship with my real father growing up. It wasn't until my later teens; I'm now in my early thirties. I visit my father sometimes, but he mainly comes up here to see me now and then, and we have a fantastic relationship.

All of the family matters aside, he deals with a common problem that many local farmers in his area deal with: chupacabras. To give a little lesson to those that know nothing about the chupacabra, it's Spanish for goat sucker. These beings steal and kill livestock and suck the blood out of their bodies. My father has lost well over a dozen goats and several other livestock to these creatures. I know this because when I call him, he's often complaining about it, not having the money and means to barter for more.

I didn't start listening to creepypastas and scary stories until I was older. So once I began learning about this stuff, it rang a bell in my head while my dad's thing was going on. I've always believed in cryptids and stuff you can't see. Especially in the spiritual realm. I've had some near-death experiences I could tell you about, but I'll save that for another time.

Anyway, having this happen firsthand is just downright terrifying. Even though I'm not experiencing it, my father is, and it is genuine for him. He's just a simple man trying to get by in life. These creatures are coming and killing off his animals. I don't think I started to talk to him about them and get his side of the story until I watched some chupacabra stuff myself, read some research and reports, and watched anything I could on the subject matter. Unfortunately, there's not a whole lot.

I decided to talk to my father more about it since he believes they are real. He knows nothing of them beyond what he experiences with them. He hasn't read any encounters and hasn't been exposed to our American pop culture. He doesn't watch any documentaries or any sort of thing like that. He explains that they have huge black eyes and long droopy fangs that tell him they are of the devil. He's convinced they come from hell, and I can't blame him. He'll often know they're around because of the sickly smell of sulfur in the night air. These are the descendants of the night, and they're here to scare and torment. As I explained, I'm agnostic-ish but leaning towards belief in the supernatural. But my father is Catholic and tells me he prays against them daily.

Not too many months after all this started happening, a few of them, I guess, tried to break into his house by scratching at the windows and doors. Petrified with fear, all my father could do was pray that these things would leave him alone. They still will come during the night to try to get into his house, wiggling his door handle and looking for weak spots to enter. My father doesn't believe these things wouldn't try to kill him. I'm worried about him because this is still an ongoing occurrence. Even as I write this to you, I've tried to get him out here to the United States, but he just doesn't want to leave his farm. I don't know what to do.

Encounter 4
Submitted By: Anonymous
Time: N/A
Location: Nevada

THREE YEARS AGO, I went on a vacation, with one of my best friends taking care of my dog. At the time of this, I lived in Nevada and was taking a road trip to see a girlfriend who lived in northern California at the time; I was going to be gone for a week. All was well. I should mention that before this, I had never had any experiences that were weird in any way, shape, or form. Life for me had been relatively normal, and I've enjoyed that until now. I don't want strange and creepy things to happen to me. I guess you don't ask for these things. They just come to you.

I called my friend every few days to check in to ensure everything was okay and that my dog was doing well. I trusted my best friend, and everything had gone great until the very last day when I didn't hear from her. I didn't think much of it. When I finally returned to my house later in the evening, my friend was crying on the front porch. I got out of the car to greet her, and she was visibly shaking. I tried to talk to her, but she was not responding. I could see in her eyes there was something wrong with my dog. I asked her if my dog was okay, and she just shook her head, saying that she didn't know what had happened to her.

I started to panic and began asking, "What do you mean you don't know? Where is she?" Before totally breaking down and sobbing, she looked at me and told me she was dead. Before I had a mental breakdown, I kept begging her to tell me where she was. She finally pointed back and told me that she was there and she'd found her dead this morning and didn't know what got her.

After running to the back with everything I had in me, seeing my dog dead on the ground was one of the most heartbreaking experiences I wouldn't wish on anybody, not even my worst enemy. My dog was my best friend, and it took a long while for me to ever truly get over it. I still miss her so much to this day. I thought maybe a pack of coyotes had killed her, but she wasn't eaten at all. She looked peaceful like she had just fallen or collapsed to the ground and died.

I tried to move her body around to see if I could find any reason she would have suddenly died. When I moved her, her neck moved. These two large holes showed right back at me; there wasn't a drop of blood. There were puncture wounds on her neck. Both spots, I would say, were roughly the size of a number two pencil. *What makes two puncture marks in an animal's neck like this?* I thought to myself. Well, at the moment, it was more of an emotional meltdown and a lot of tears than fear or wondering what killed my dog.

Fast-forward about six months, and the friend who watched my dog ended up moving into that house because I moved to northern California with my friend I visited. We went in on the house together to roommate since it fit for both of our jobs. My best friend and I are in Nevada and still stay in very close contact. Sometimes we talk, and she would try to confide in me that she'd been having strange experiences in that house. She had mentioned that she had been hearing banging against her back windows and walls at night and even went so far as to have a security surveillance system installed. Then she told me she had seen this tiny, gray person with claws trying to break into the back window. She kept saying, "I know, I know, it sounds crazy, but I promise this is what's happening." I asked her if she had any of the surveillance footage to show me, and she said that the police had taken it. Shortly after, she began to see this short gray humanoid with claws. Several neighbors had also been calling the police, complaining about similar circumstances. The police force confiscated her entire surveillance system, computer, and hard drive.

Next thing you know, I stopped getting phone calls from her. Now I can't even reach her. I haven't gotten ahold of her in a long time. I even sent her a card not too long ago and never heard anything back. I would usually always at least get a text message or phone call, but nothing. Her Facebook was also deactivated. We weren't family, so it's not like I can reach out to her relatives, but it's disturbing...

I've been listening to your channel for months and don't want to be a Doomer. Everything I've heard in your stories and things that have happened to people in your accounts is happening to me in real life. I feel like I'm in some sort of fictional horror story. Maybe there's more to my dog being killed than I would think. Maybe there's a reason that the police confiscated her equipment, and God only knows what happened to her. I hope she's okay.

Encounter 5
Submitted By: Blake h.
Time: 2015
Location: Central Oregon

HI, I live out in Central Oregon. Central Oregon is a vast, high desert full of rattlesnakes, punishing high temperatures, and tons upon tons of dust. However, there's so much beauty where I live that it makes up for all the potential dangers of living out in the desert. Coyotes can be dangerous; I know they will kill livestock, animals, and horses. But one thing I'm not sure about is creatures that suck the blood out of other animals. I'm talking vampires. Okay, well, maybe not vampires in a traditional sense because they are fictional. However, my dad and I are finding dead wild horses in groups, and we found one lone one dead.

Each features multiple sets of holes along its neck and is drained of all blood. I'm talking zero blood throughout the entire carcass. There's no blood on the ground. Whatever poked a hole in the neck was so clean and precise. The same sets of pricks on their neck can be found in the exact locations on the other horses. We have discovered deceased horses alone with these puncture wounds. And we have also seen them in large groups, all dead. It's almost as if something walked right up to them, poked a hole in their neck and walked away, and just let them bleed out.

Except there's no blood, or evidence of any bleeding out for that matter. I'm not sure how I'm going to explain it. It's just a weird supernatural phenomenon because my mind goes to vampires. I have to stop that. It's been programmed that way because of pop culture; I know that vampires don't exist and that there isn't a vampire drinking the blood of horses. It's just... I cannot explain why we're finding these wild horses dead over the past couple of months, all of a sudden. It's been about the same time that we went into quarantine. So probably late March. Yeah, I would say about two months.

Now, I want to say we've been probably finding up to about thirty to forty dead wild horses in total, all having their blood drained. I know people talk about UFO stuff, alien stuff, and all that weird abduction nonsense out in the middle of nowhere. What even drains the blood of a horse? We are close with the neighbors around us, and we've checked in with them. They've been experiencing strange things too, but no animals are killed or blood drained from anything.

The one connection I could potentially piece together is that in the last sixty days, not only have more wild horses been showing up dead more than ever, but the dogs around the area have gone missing.

I know that because I've been asked on several occasions already if I have seen several of our neighbors' animals and dogs. There are the same dogs that I've seen around the area for years because I've been here for so long. I've gotten to know my neighbors and the people around us; they've had the same animals forever. Something happens when the same animals just get up and go missing within sixty days. Now, all of a sudden, these horses just drop dead in the middle of the night. Something just doesn't add up.

I've thought about calling the cops, but what will they do? If it's somebody doing this? They're gonna get caught eventually. But I don't know who goes out and murders random wild horses. You would think that if they kidnapped the dogs, why don't you find them somewhere? I guess I'm just thinking out loud at this point. See, my dad is a stickler just like me and firmly stands by that it's a coyote. I'm a skeptic just as much as anybody, but even I think that's total bollocks. He's just in denial about something more here.

What does more even mean? That is what I'm trying to figure out. Could it be that there's some unknown animal out of the desert, draining these horses' blood?

Why hasn't anybody seen it? I suppose a pack of rabid coyotes can be killing all the local dogs. I still feel like we would find carcasses with how much my dad and I travel in the outback around here. There's always evidence of a kill, it seems. Nature is messy, and few predators go to any lengths to hide their work. Coyotes just simply aren't one of them. Even looking around the area of these horses, there are zero tracks of anything. No tracks of any kind; it's very perplexing.

My dad tells me I'm putting far too much of my mental energy and focus into figuring out what's happening. He says I should just let whatever happens occur. And nature will sort itself out. I don't feel like this is an act of nature, though. I feel like this is something that demands answers to many questions, and there are not enough answers. I guess. It's time for me to do some more homework of my own.

Encounter 6
Submitted By: JM
Time: N/A
Location: Sheridan, Arkansas

MY NAME IS JM. I live in the small town of Sheridan, Arkansas. I was born in the Ozarks in Mountain Home, Arkansas. My dad was an outdoorsman and taught me early on to hunt and fish. I have always been interested in the Bigfoot phenomenon. I would listen to stories my father and uncles tell about their encounters. Bigfoot was a subject that I had always wanted to investigate. I have known of the Fouke Monster since I was a child. I have driven by the "Big Man" and heard the stories of the people who live in town. I have spent many hours in the woods of Arkansas, as well.

One day about three years ago, I was with a friend in the woods. We were shooting our guns, and I decided to practice my hunting skills. We were walking through the woods, and I had my weapon ready to shoot.

Suddenly, I heard a noise ahead of us in the woods. Whatever was making the noise was coming our way. It sounded like a huge man running. I could hear the earth shaking as it sounded like someone huge was running in our direction. My friend was scared and wanted to get out of there quickly. I said, "Just hold on; I will turn around and see what it is." As I looked in the direction of the noise, I could see a huge hairy figure running in the direction of my friend. I have never seen anything like it in my life.

I quickly told my friend to run, and we dove behind a large hickory tree. It was down a slight slope, so we were able to kind of duck down and watch. Right before our eyes, this huge running hairy man thing came barreling through the clearing in seconds and disappeared through the thick brush. My friend and I were pale and scared.

I don't know if that was a Bigfoot, but I can tell you that ain't no man. If I had to guess in under eight seconds, this thing cleared almost a hundred feet. That's unreal. And being out in this heat, humidity, and brush, there's no way. If that was a Bigfoot costume, their physical shape exceeds any living man's ability to do that.

We got back to my friend's house that night, and we couldn't stop talking about the fact we had seen a Bigfoot! We were in shock. I have never told anyone this story since I didn't want to cause problems, but I am sure many people in this area have seen it. I have heard many stories of Bigfoot sightings in the area, and I have an uncle who said he was chased by one. I am unsure if I want to see it again because of the skin-crawling feeling I had the first time I saw it. I wonder if the one I saw had somewhere to go because he was moving pretty quickly through the brush!

4

CREATURE ENCOUNTERS & SIGHTINGS

THERE HAVE BEEN many reports of cryptid sightings and encounters around the world. Some believe that these creatures are real, while others think they may be just myths or legends. However, there are many people who have claimed to have seen these creatures firsthand.

This section of the book is truly a Wild West of cryptid stories. I've purposely pulled accounts from various categories of cryptid sightings and compiled it here. While some lean more on the side of mysterious and unknown, others strongly hint at something more common. Say, a skinwalker or a dogman. Either way, these are all reports of real encounters with cryptids. So, sit back, relax, and enjoy some truly bizarre tales.

Encounter 1
Submitted By: Anonymous
Time: N/A
Location: Southwest, USA

THIS WAS YEARS AGO, and I am still terrified by what I experienced that night. This was from another world, and I've heard of skinwalkers and seen this coyote thing come onto our field multiple times, but never did I imagine I would encounter what my brother-in-law would refer to as a night spider.

Before I get more into that, there would be mornings where I would see this tall, upright walking coyote thing kind of just hanging around our field. Like it was always waiting and watching for the next opportunity to do something. It was very scary. It would always just crouch down in the tall grass and watch.

It tried to make moves on some of our small dogs and livestock a couple of times, and it did. They'd go missing. Our entire chicken coop was taken, along with all the chickens. (It was a small coop and not wired into the ground.)

Anyway, one morning, I look to the left, into the field. I did not see anything. When I looked off to the right I see this skinwalker creature that stares back at me. Off in the distance, I see it almost every couple of mornings. It is out there, and I want nothing to do with it. The same thing happens to my brother-in-law. He's very devout to the Navajo Way, and he doesn't believe in what we call skinwalkers. It's like he forced himself to confront this thing.

One morning he's out in the field, and the faceless skinwalker, sneaks up from behind my brother-in-law and comes up real close to him. How did it know my brother-in-law is Navajo? How did it know he's a spiritual man? It's like it puts thoughts in your mind, and you do what it wants. He didn't see that, but I captured what he saw. It's just powerful energy. It was about as hideous as you can imagine it being.

It grabs hold of my brother-in-law, and he's screaming prayers in

Navajo, and this thing takes complete hold of him and drags him back while subduing him. After it gets to about the edge of the field, it lets go of him and flees, and my brother-in-law continues to pray and shout in Navajo. I'm not sure what my brother-in-law said, but it worked. The skinwalker let go of him and fled into the nearby woods.

Right after he was freed, he went crazy, telling me to never encounter it. Never go looking for it. Although I don't go looking for it, I do my best to try not to encounter it. I try to keep my distance from these things, if you understand.

Being a traditional Navajo has a purpose, but many Christian religions are more open. Part of me understands because it's a validation for many Navajo Way practitioners to accept that it's there. There would be a lot of people who don't believe without visual proof. Do you know what I mean? Like when I first saw it in the morning, I would tell my father-in-law what I saw. They'd say they saw it two days prior in the same spot. Some people aren't really into the Navajo Way or just not into the religion for one reason or another, and they'd never seen anything like it, you know. So I respect that everyone has to make up their mind, but on that day, I don't know what could have happened. There's not much to say on that, I mean.

Now the following couple of nights, this thing comes back, but it's much scarier than before. The first few times we'd all seen it, and when it tried taking my brother-in-law, it was in its coyote form. I say coyote form because that's the only way I can accurately depict what this thing looked like. When it came back the following night, or a few nights later, it looked like a night spider.

If you don't know, night spiders are a branch of shape-shifters under the skinwalker umbrella, specializing in shape-shifting into these terrible beings. Instead of wearing animal skins, their skin is contorted and hideous. They usually have multiple arms with large claws on each hand and deeply sunken black eyes, with large black fangs protruding from their chest and mouth. They crawl more on all fours than they walk around upright. I'm not sure if you've ever heard of these night spiders, but that's what I've heard them be referred to as. I had no idea they were even a thing until I saw one the following night, as I discussed.

I was outside at night, pondering the day and having a small glass of whiskey I'd just poured for myself. I hadn't even taken more than one or two sips from the glass, and I saw this thing approaching from the field. The same spot where this creature had disappeared the day before with my brother-in-law. I immediately knew it was this creature, but I did not recognize the form it was in. I just knew deep down it wasn't a good thing.

As it came closer, even with how much light there was that night, I saw enough to horrify me. Immediately after its appearance, I went inside and woke up my wife. She had this big comforter over her, so I couldn't see her face. I asked her about it, and she was like, "No, there's nothing; you've just been drinking; it's the shadows from the leaves and stuff." But I pushed that aside, and I wanted to ensure that she saw it because I wanted assurance that I wasn't crazy. She just refused to budge, so I thought, *Okay, screw it*, and I went and grabbed my .44 out of my closet, and I stepped back out on the porch, and at that moment, I nearly soiled my britches right there.

Ten feet away from the porch, this thing was standing there like it was standing its ground on contested territory. I got a good look at this thing. It was like it came from the pits of hell itself. It was maybe slightly more than six feet tall. It looked like the night spider I mentioned. It was challenging me, so I slowly pulled out my .44 and aimed it right at this thing; I felt like I couldn't pull the trigger, like this thing was controlling my body. I felt myself tense up and had this paralysis feeling shooting through my body. This creature smirked at me slowly, and I felt myself losing control of my body. With the finger still on the trigger, my hand started to turn the .44 inwards toward my chest. I was frozen and couldn't fight off what was going on with my body, as this thing was practically controlling my muscles.

Just as I was putting the .44 right to my head against my own will, the loudest gunshot I'd ever heard went off, and this thing got shot right in the chest and let out this horrible scream like you wouldn't believe. I instantly felt my muscles relax, and I dropped my .44. This thing started screaming radically and began running off into the night as my brother-in-law came to me because he felt something was wrong, almost like some sort of crazy sixth sense or something.

He had shot this thing nearly point-blank right in the back and came rushing over to me to ensure I was okay. As I recall these events, I try to do my best not to make it sound like a fake story. I want to express how terrifying this thing was and how it almost got me to kill myself via mind control or something. That was when my brother-in-law, who, as I stated, is full Navajo, told me about the night spiders, what they are, and how they have this horrible ability to take possession of anyone they target to make them do their evil bidding. He refers to them as physical demons with a form and shape.

Anyway, there's not much else to add, but I wanted to say that I had never even really heard of a night spider before this. Whether it's that or a skinwalker, they're extremely dangerous beings that should always be kept at a distance as best you can.

Encounter 2
Submitted By: Emily
Time: May 2017
Location: N/A

I AM of high moral standard and personality with a deep understanding of the spiritual world. Too much to explain here. This is my eyewitness encounter with a creature. May 6, 2017. I was finishing my loop as I walked home from the market, doing errands. I saw something move in a tree from the corner of my eye. Upon looking, there was my first great sighting. The humanoid creature swung between the branches as if weightless, then dropped down very quickly and disappeared. The animal was at first crouched on the top of the tree limb, swaying side to side while staring at me. It appeared bubble-like as it moved. Once I saw it smoothly sit on the stem, it immediately leaped off and vanished. The drop was fascinating and quick. I don't know if it was followed or chased by something more significant, but there was no repeated sighting, so it is possible there were more of these creatures near.

Another exciting thing was another figure in my peripheral on my left as I was walking too. Once I looked over, it was then gone. I'm not sure how to describe such a strange creature. However, I do know that... it is something I will NEVER forget. I only saw it briefly and questioned myself, but it happened. This was my second encounter, when a few weeks ago, I experienced something brush past my legs in my sleep, and I felt its physical presence bruise me while in a deep trancelike state. I believe the frequent sightings I have had of this same type of being or beings are of high spiritual importance. Since I relocated to Mesa, Arizona, in February, I have been watching for what may be out there.

Encounter 3
Submitted By: Anonymous
Time: N/A
Location: N/A

I'LL START by saying this is my experience, not a story someone told me. I don't usually explore the woods at night during the summer because it gets dark around 10 p.m. The fact that I was out there late on a hot Friday night only means something must have compelled me to do so. Anyways, it happened around 10:30, and the temperature started dropping as soon as night came, but up until then, it was just one of those warm August nights.

I was listening to music, lying on my back, looking straight up, watching clouds pass by overhead, and thinking about life when suddenly I saw something move in the corner of my eye. I look over, and to my shock and amazement, there was a shape about five feet away from me. It was on all fours at first, but then it stood up like a man; however, when I say man, I mean that it looked humanlike but had no hair anywhere on its body, which caught me off guard considering how unnatural this was. Also, there were no distinguishing features such as a nose or ears, just a smooth surface where they should have been. Its head was bald and black, and its surface seemed soft. I immediately felt tremendous fear upon seeing this. Not just because it was the unknown, but because it was something I've never dealt with in my life before. I don't know how long I was staring at it, but eventually, it turned around and walked into the forest.

I stayed there for a few minutes, trying to figure out what just happened, looking for some logical explanation, maybe someone playing a prank on me, but there was no way that this could have been a person in any way, shape, or form.

I got up, ran home as soon as possible, and sat on my porch for a couple of hours, trying to calm down, smoking cigarettes, and going over what had just happened. It wasn't until I started writing this out that the things that happened next sank in.

As soon as I got home and sat down on my porch, I heard something moving quickly through the forest, still heading deeper into the woods. It sounded like just one animal, but it ran so fast that its feet were nearly silent even though they were hitting the wet mossy ground.

I know some animals could account for what I saw; however, up until now, none of them seem to fit my description. Nothing makes sense. I've tried to play it off many times, but nothing makes sense.

I've been scared for my life ever since that night; I sometimes feel like I'm being watched when I go outside. I can always feel something around me, even in bright daylight. I've never encountered anything like this before, and I don't know what to do anymore.

Encounter 4
Submitted By: Norman Tillman
Time: 2014
Location: Smokey Mountains

IT WAS a warm summer night in 2014, and we were camping in the Smokey Mountains. I had recently graduated from high school, and my friends and I were on a mission to go camping in the mountains for the night.

As we set up our campsite, one of my friends asked if I had heard anything strange. I hadn't. He said he had been up on the ridge earlier that day, and he saw something off in the distance that was walking upright, but he wasn't sure what it was because he knows bears walk upright but only for a short distance, and this did not look like a bear. I remember looking at him, puzzled, and thinking, *I'm not sure what you're hinting at*, but we both shrugged our shoulders and went on with the conversation.

A couple of hours passed, and we all retired to our tents for the night. I was in my tent, lying on my air mattress, looking up through the mesh of my tent toward the stars. For the most part, the night was very peaceful and quiet, although I distinctly remember not being able to hear any sounds, including crickets, which to me was very strange. To pass the time, because I'm a terrible insomniac, I pulled out a book and a small flashlight to try to get lost in the world of a good novel. There was just something about how quiet it was outside that I could not shake, which bothered me.

Maybe thirty minutes had passed or an hour, I cannot tell you because I was so lost in a novel, but I started hearing footsteps not too far away. This caught my attention for several reasons. My two other friends were asleep. I could hear them snoring in the tent next to my other friend and me. If he had had to pee, I would have heard him climb out of the tent, so that was already ruled out. And, of course, number two was we were far enough out that we didn't have to worry about competition with other campers or hikers. We were about six miles, roughly, off the trail. I mean, it was always possible but not likely.

The footsteps grew gradually closer, and this genuinely concerned me. I decided to peek through my tent's opening and see what was happening. As soon as I pulled up the entrance of my tent and peered out, I saw a humanlike creature about thirty yards from me, hunched over. What I saw was this dark hairy mass that moved very strangely. I was more alarmed at first than frightened, but I don't think I fully processed the thought that what I was looking at was not human.

It was completely bent over and appeared to be eating something. I almost felt like it was feeding until it raised its head and stared in my direction, and that was the first time I got a good look at its face. I had to hold my mouth because I almost screamed. The face was gross but very human and had blood all over its mouth. And I could see through the hole in the tent this thing had a dead rabbit that it was holding in its hands. It was carrying the animal in its hands like a human being would hold it. After maybe a second it went back down and took more chunks of flesh off this dead rabbit, and you could hear the flesh tearing off as it began eating this rabbit. It would look back over in this direction. This creature, whatever it was, seemed far more curious, and I think probably due in part to our small fire that was mostly dead by now, but there were still some glowing embers that were emitting light. I was hoping this was what its attention was being drawn to.

I pulled myself into my sleeping bag, wide-eyed and ready for this thing to come rummaging through our camp, where I know I would have to come face-to-face with this thing. Within minutes I could hear one of my friends shuffling inside the tent next to me. I started to yell his name in a whisper, but he did not respond, so I crouched over and looked through the hole again. The creature was gone, but I could see my friend half asleep, walking up to one of the trees and going to pee.

After he finished, he casually walked back to the tent and zipped up, snoring within a few moments. I sat there listening to every little sound around me, expecting this thing to pop out of nowhere. The rest of that night was eerily quiet. I thought this thing would come back, but I never heard it or saw it.

I barely got any sleep, if any, so the next couple of days of camping were exhausting, but I pulled through. I have no idea what this thing was; if anybody has any answers as to what it was, please let me know. I would like to know.

Encounter 5
Submitted By: Anonymous
Time: N/A
Location: N/A

WE HAVE a trail near our house that's known for being haunted. It used to be an old Indian burial ground, and then a cult was rumored to sacrifice women there during the devil-worshipping days of the '70s, so yeah, it has a bit of a scary reputation.

Anyways, I never really believed any of it because I'm not one to be afraid easily. But last night, my girlfriend and I were walking this trail at about 11 p.m. The moon was full and bright in the sky, so we didn't need our flashlights until we got to the part where you entered the woods. That was when she started saying she felt like something bad was going to happen and we should turn back. I didn't feel anything, so I kept walking up the trail, trying to ignore her pleas by explaining everything's going to be fine.

About two minutes later, I started feeling bad too—like pure terror in my chest, and my heart would not stop pounding. We were almost at the top of the hill where the dirt trail came out onto the road when we both experienced this panic so strongly that it forced us to sit down in the middle of the path until it subsided enough for us to stand up without wanting to collapse again. We both saw the same thing simultaneously, so I know it wasn't just me freaking out or her being weird.

Two glowing red eyes peered over the edge of the top of the hill. They were about thirty feet away from us and maybe seven to ten feet up in the air. We only caught a glimpse of them before they disappeared over the edge, but I can tell you that's not something you ever forget once you've seen it.

My girlfriend immediately grabbed my hand and dragged me back down to road level, where we ran as fast as we could out of there until we reached my house, where she was staying with me at the time. We locked all our doors, closed all the blinds, and just sat in my room together, talking about it and trying to figure out what we saw. I looked up pictures of big cats like mountain lions and stuff because that's what I think it was—a large cat or panther. After all, those eyes were terrifyingly huge; but there are no wild cats in Washington State or anywhere close to us, so I don't know what else could've been watching us from the darkness like that.

Anyways, now every time I walk down that trail at night, all I can picture is those eyes staring at me from over the edge of the hill. And I'm pretty sure my girlfriend feels the same way, too... so, yeah.

I think we'll go back there some time but probably not at night anymore.

Encounter 6
Submitted By: Anonymous
Time: 2015
Location: Northern California

RECENTLY, my friends and I started to do some paranormal exploring.

We found a spot on the side of the road and parked there; we all got out and started walking up the trail. We made it about halfway when I realized that I didn't have my phone on me. Jokingly, I was like, "Guys, I'll be back in two minutes."

Kaitlynn said, "Uh, less than that!" in a weird tone. I began to walk back down to the car, but our plan was for everyone to stay together, so I told them to wait for me at this rock formation near where we were going, so they did while I went back for my phone.

I kept hearing a whistling noise, so I looked behind me, and nothing was there; then I turned around, facing forward, thinking I didn't hear a thing. It started whistling again, only this time it was getting closer. I turned around, and there was nothing behind me like before.

The first night we went up there, we did a test run, started at 10:00, and got back to the car at 11:30. It was pretty scary, but nothing came out of it. We didn't find anything or see anything paranormal.

I had heard that if you go up farther in the canyon, there is a rock formation that looks like a table, and some weird lights tend to show up around it. So one night, I wanted to check it out with my friends Karlie, James, Jake, Stacy, Kaitlynn, and Josh.

We all have known each other since elementary school.

The second time we went up there was when we experienced some freaky stuff. Activity or something that I can't explain. Check it out.

It was about 10:05 p.m. We all loaded up in Jake's car and drove to the spot we wanted to go to.

We each got out and started walking the path. We planned for everyone to stay together, so I shouted, "Wait up, guys. I'm coming with you!" They stopped and waved me over. As we walked farther down this path, it seemed like we were somehow going deeper into the forest but not really far.

I looked back at them for a second, then faced forward on the path. That was when I saw it.

It was white in color and looked like a mass of moving shapes.

I stopped in my tracks, and they all turned around to see what was wrong. "What's up?"

"Do you see that too?!" I asked them, caught off guard by how much I saw coming towards us.

They started walking back towards me slowly, almost cautiously, until we were about six feet away from each other again. We all stood there silently watching this thing get closer for what seemed like forever; then suddenly it began to speed up even more! It was terrifying to watch that thing come at us like that...

It started whistling again, only this time it got so close to where we could feel its breath. We stood there frozen in fear, wondering what it was or what would happen next.

We all looked at each other, and I could see the fear in their eyes because I felt it too. It wasn't human at all!

I turned for a split second to tell them, "RUN!" but when I turned back, that thing had disappeared into thin air.

The whistling noise stopped, and we ran as fast as we could until we returned to the car. We jumped in Jake's car and drove home without saying what had happened until later...

To this day, I still think about that night, whatever it was. I can't explain it. Do you know what that was? It wasn't a bear, and it wasn't a mountain lion...

It didn't seem like any animal we have in this area or known to exist. Has anyone else ever had anything similar happen?

I'd love to hear your thoughts!

Encounter 7
Submitted By: Anonymous
Time: 2018
Location: N/A

MY FAMILY and I went camping years ago, and I had a creepy experience with a demon or strange creature that I simply can't explain. We had a cabin close by, but we were enjoying the solace of the night with tent camping at a secluded spot.

I went out one night to take a piss. It was pitch black, of course, and I am a pretty sober guy, so I had my flashlight on me and my knife. As I finished my business, I heard this sound that seriously made the hairs stand up on the back of my neck. It sounded like a distorted howling from a dog, but it felt much more sinister than anything an animal would make. The uneasy feeling was amplified by the fact that there was no light around us—nothing but darkness everywhere except our flashlights. You could cut through the tension with a machete at that point because everyone knew something wasn't right.

The howling became distorted and started sounding more like a demonic growl; then the sound stopped completely. I walked back to camp and told everyone about it, thinking that maybe we were not alone—an eerie feeling coming from the pitch-black darkness where you cannot see more than five feet in front of your face. Terror was pretty much on all of our faces at this point. My grandfather had also heard it and said he had some experience with hunting and knew good sounds versus bad sounds when it came to animals, and said this was NOT anything normal whatsoever.

I threw my empty beer can out into the distance while we were talking about it (don't judge me), but after hearing that noise, I did not want to be out in the forest's darkness. After throwing it into the blackness, we heard nothing—no sound aside from our voices for the next ten minutes. At this point, everyone was terrified and saw how serious I was about this.

As I wandered back over to my tent, which was on the other side of our group campsite, I saw something move out of the corner of my eye. I assumed it was just my eyes playing tricks on me (super common), so I kept walking. A minute later, it happened again but slightly farther away from us than before. Still assuming that it was shadows or some kind of insect crawling on the rock, we continued back toward our family friends' campsite until something caused me to stop dead in my tracks.

The thing I saw was hidden behind a big, log-shaped rock, and I jumped up on top of the rock to get a better look. It was humanoid in shape with dark fur all over its body. The area around the head was bare, with no hair whatsoever. Its face came to a sort of "point" on the forehead and cheeks, similar to a witch's hat or maybe a goblin's mask. It was crouching but still taller than me (I'm five feet three). I stood staring at it for about ten seconds before my brain could even register what I was looking at—which was probably why it wasn't more aggressive towards us.

Although the creature had furry skin, its fingers were very long and ended with sharp claws that didn't look like they were intended for climbing trees. They were more like the claws of a cat or lizard. It resembled an ape but walked upright. Its legs were very short and squat, while its arms were long. My brain could not comprehend this thing or why it looked at me the way it did.

The only sound I heard for the next few seconds was my heartbeat in my ears, but after about five seconds of standing still, it became even more aggressive. It had jumped off the rock and squatted on all fours—like an ape—while getting into a more aggressive stance where you could tell it was ready to pounce. At this point, I realized that whatever this creature was, it was not friendly. I screamed and ran as fast as possible back to the safety of the circle of fire with my entire family looking over at the commotion, unable to see what was going on because it was so dark.

The creature took off quickly, looking over its shoulder as it ran into the woods. I was hysterical at this point and was begging the family we had to leave and pack up now. We were not safe. My grandfather knew how serious I was and immediately jumped into action. Everyone returned to their tents in under a minute and packed everything in less than three minutes. We left the area to return to our cabin, about twenty minutes away.

This was no prank, and it's not even funny. This thing was REAL, and I'm terrified for my life every time I think about it because I know that there isn't an animal out there that can be so aggressive without good reason... I don't ever want to encounter something like this again, but right now, the only way to protect myself is by sharing this story with other people who might believe me instead of judging me like some kind of weirdo liar...

Encounter 8
Submitted By: Jordan Riener
Time: Summer 2014
Location: Klamath Falls, Oregon

LET me set up some backstory: It was a Saturday night, and I was at my friend's party with a few of our mutual friends. Everyone appeared bleary-eyed and mildly intoxicated from the previous night's celebration.

I don't remember how exactly we got into talking about this incident, but it started as most do—someone brought up a topic, someone else challenged it, and the challenge sparked a debate. In this case, everyone said you should never go into the woods at night for fear of encountering a cryptid or being abducted by extraterrestrials.

My friend's cousin then brought up something different, though. He said he'd had a very close encounter with a strange being in the woods not far from my house.

At first, I thought it was just another guy at a party trying to tell a spooky story. Let me preface by saying I don't think there's anything wrong with going into the woods at night so long as you have a group of people with you. I myself had a similar experience I haven't told anyone.

One night I was walking my dog by myself late at night, right past the woods next to our beach, and then I heard a crashing sound coming from within the forest. My dog, usually extremely quiet and docile, suddenly became a barking demon. It's one thing to have a stoned neighbor's dog go off on you, but it was a whole other sight when my deaf dog began going wild.

I tried to regain control of her, but she yanked free from the leash and charged into the forest. I took off after her, wondering what the hell she found that was more thrilling than a jolly stoner's baked Labrador retriever.

I had to use my phone as a flashlight because it was so dark, but finally, I saw what she'd been barking at—

A tall humanoid creature was lifting an elk carcass. My dog was going ballistic, but the thing did not move a single muscle.

This looked like a man standing about seven feet tall, clothed in leathery armor. It had two long horns protruding from its head, and its face was terrifying—it looked almost skeletal with large eyes that glowed blue in my flashlight's beam.

I thought my dog would surely die if she attacked it, and I was considering turning around to get my knife from home when the thing finally moved. It dropped the elk carcass with a thud and walked out of the light, taking several strides before I couldn't see it anymore.

My dog eventually came back to me with her tail between her legs, and that was when I heard the most terrifying sound in my life—

One that still haunts me to this day. It sounded like a deep, growling laugh coming from all around me. I cannot accurately describe what it sounded like other than to say that it was the sound of pure evil. When I finally got home, shaking with fear and my heart pounding in my chest, I grabbed a knife from the kitchen and sat awake all night in my bedroom.

The following morning I went back to see if it was still there, but the only sign of anything was the elk carcass, now fully devoured. I didn't want to stay there for too long, so I jogged home as fast as possible.

What do you think happened? If you're asking this question, it's because you don't believe me—which is understandable since most people are skeptics unless they've had their encounter. You think I'm just some crazy person, or this is some way to get attention, but the truth is that I'm not doing anything illegal, so there's no reason for me to lie about this.

If you don't believe it, then fine, but after hearing his story about this creepy humanoid creature with horns, I have to wonder if something lurks in the night. It doesn't matter if you're a cryptid enthusiast or just someone fearful of aliens abducting you.

There are other terrifying things lurking in the forest at night that are far more dangerous than any extraterrestrial being.

Encounter 9
Submitted By: Gunnar
Time: Fall 2016
Location: Idaho

MY WIFE and I were camping near the mountains on a very secluded dirt road. We found a spot called "the Circle," which has a perfect view of the sky and rocks surrounding us.

Without knowing it, we went into a restricted area for public use. There was an Air Force base not far from there, so it may have been some Military training ground; either way, no one could find us up there, so we would be safe from people or wild animals. We had water, food, flashlights, and everything you would need camping-wise. The only thing was that off in the distance over by where we came from must have been a homesteader because there was a green pasture full of horses. But it was at least half a mile away, so we couldn't see the people or even hear them.

It wasn't starting to get cold up there yet, but you could tell it would be soon. We went up there in mid-September and October. The night was pretty uneventful, except my wife kept having strange dreams, probably because she was pregnant though I never asked her about them when she woke.

I had stayed up until three o'clock in the morning, just looking at stars. We both got startled by this awful scream from somewhere in the mountains.

Neither of us knew what could have made that kind of sound, but it has stuck with me as I write these words months later. We were both scared over whatever was out there.

My wife said that she didn't quite even believe herself if it was a mountain lion or bear because of the tone in which it howled out there. But she could tell from me shaking so badly that whatever had made this noise was certainly something terrifying to behold. It wasn't until around seven o'clock in the morning before we finally got tired enough to fall asleep again, though this time, we slept next to each other, holding hands tightly the whole night through just in case one of us somehow fell asleep first.

My wife woke me up, asking me if I remembered her waking me up last night to tell me someone was outside the tent. I don't remember it, but according to her, I had been screamed at and told that someone was out there touching the side of our tent with their fingers. I'm not sure if there is a correlation between that dream and the howl. I wish we would have recorded this noise because it sounded like a human being making it, yet something was off about this sound. It's almost as if it were a poor-quality recording of a ghostly voice trying to be captured by technology. But one thing is for sure: this creature knew how to make an entrance and an exit before we ever even saw it coming or going from where we were.

We were safe, for now. But who knows when or where we will cross paths again? All I know is what has been going through my head every night I try to sleep is that scream. And it has gone through my mind so many times since writing this, though now I know what is happening whenever it happens again.

Encounter 10
Submitted By: Reagan
Time: June 25, 2015
Location: N/A

THIS WAS BACK IN 2015, but it still scares me when I think back on it. It was June 25, 2015, and I went out with a few friends to go and fish for the night. We took my truck and pulled up on this dirt road we've been down many times before, so we knew it was safe. We were watching where we were going, as any sane person would be because you can't see anything at all.We found our spot and made camp for the night, then walked down to the waters edge to drink some beer.

We popped open our beers and sat around talking when one of the buddies decided he wanted to head back to camp because he wanted another beer, I told him it was fine even though I wasn't that far into mine, but I didn't want to leave either. As he walked off, maybe fifty feet ahead of us, we heard a ruffling in some bushes and a snort-like "Hey." We immediately thought it was someone else trying to mess with us, and we all got really quiet and listened, then again the snort. What we saw next is something I will never forget until I die.

I swear this thing was no less than seven feet tall and all black, but it kept shifting colors between dark brown and black, almost like a shadow in the night when you take your eyes off what it's moving by. The hair on this thing was long and matted looking, like dreadlocks sticking out from its head. What struck us as odd was that there were no signs of eyes anywhere on its body, along with a nose or mouth, that we could see. It did have hands that looked human, except they had claws to them instead of fingers. Also, it had a tail about four feet long from what we could.

We were all terrified; none of us could move or talk for about ten minutes after it was gone. I tell you now, this wasn't your regular cryptid sighting, I've seen my fair share around here, but this thing had us locking eyes with something that knew exactly what we were-doing at all times during this encounter. We got in the truck and headed back to camp, where we packed up our stuff and left out of there as fast as possible.

I just hope nothing like that ever happens to anybody else again because it's not a feeling I would wish on anyone, no matter how many beers they have in them to calm them down.

Encounter 11
Submitted By: Anonymous
Time: N/A
Location: N/A

I WAS in the Army at the time, and my friend and I were in between deployments. It took place when we were home on leave before our next duty station.

We have no idea what it was, just that it wasn't human because of how it moved through the trees without ever touching them. It had a man's body and a goat's head and legs, but it was fast like no human could ever hope to be. I even got my scope on it when we found where it had come from and watched it fall back into the tree line. There were people and campsites all over the place, so we didn't want to take the chance of shooting it. I wish we did, though.

One of my buddies who was really into hunting claimed that a few years ago, he'd seen a similar creature in the woods while hunting, but it disappeared before he could get to where it was.

I've never seen anything like it since and haven't heard any other stories like ours. I don't care what this thing is because I know what we saw. After everything that has happened to me, I would have believed just about anything if it had explained this away, but it doesn't. This thing exists, and I don't think it's the only one of its kind.

I'm not sure what has happened to me; I still think about it a lot. But after seven years, I've finally told someone other than my wife. I don't know why it's taken me so long to tell anyone else, even my best friends.

Encounter 12
Submitted By: Glen Fulla
Time: N/A
Location: N/A

I WAS deer hunting years ago, and like any other hunting season, I was very persistent in getting a good buck. I have multiple stands set up throughout the central swamp that I hunt since the deer have been significantly populated over the last few years. I was out before dawn with my high-powered rifle and flashlight.

I was about to climb down the small ladder I had set up in one of my bait stands when something stopped me dead in my tracks. It was deathly silent; even the crickets stopped chirping, which gave me this ominous feeling like someone or something was watching me. I flashed my light around the central area of the swamp, looking for any movement, but nothing seemed to be there. The hair on the back of my neck stood up as goosebumps ran down my arms, so I decided it would be best to climb down from the stand and go home. Just before climbing down was when I saw it...

I looked over into a small den cavern formed by a large cypress tree that had fallen years ago and noticed something hunched over inside. I cautiously walked into the small cave with my rifle in hand to see what it was, even though I already knew. As soon as I shined my light on it, its eyes peered at me, followed by the rest of its body. It looked like a highly gaunt man standing there hunched and corrupted, and when it turned towards me, revealing its face, the creature that to this day haunts my dreams gave me chills down my spine. The head of this beast was abnormally large for its body and completely hairless; an animalistic sound bellowed from deep within its chest as drool spilled out of its mouth. The face was sunken with its bones protruding outward, and the creature's skin was a pale white color similar to a grub worm. I then noticed what appeared to be larvae growing underneath the creature's skin, making me nauseous as it stared into my eyes.

After a short time, I snapped back into reality and quickly exited the cave out of fear for my life. Once outside, I ran as fast as I could until I reached my truck on the other side of the property, where I drove straight home without looking back. When reporting this story, it dawned on me that as scared as I was at this moment, I was more terrified about not knowing what this creature was and why it was in a cave.

The following day I told my brothers and cousins about what happened, and to my surprise, they didn't laugh at me but believed every word. They went to the den cavern with me, where we found bones scattered around the entrance of this small hive-like cave along with game trails leading deeper into the swamp covered by heavy brush that would be impossible for a human or animal to traverse. There were also marks on the cypress trees nearby about eight to nine feet off the ground. It appeared to be large claw markings. After investigating and looking around these areas, we couldn't figure out what could live in such a place and still be able to sustain itself for that long.

I still go out to the same spot every year during hunting season, but I can't help myself from thinking about what this creature could be or where it came from. For all I know, people have seen some animal like this for years.

Now, I've reached out to places that will try to hear me out, and they recommend that maybe I should talk to some bigwigs of the government about this. I think that's a good idea because, more than likely, they'll think I'm nuts, but it doesn't hurt to try, right?

Encounter 13
Submitted By: Anonymous
Time: 2017
Location: N/A

IT WAS a beautiful Sunday morning after church when my wife and I decided to get lunch at one of our favorite taco truck spots and end the morning with a drive down by the marshlands to watch the wildlife. We never thought we'd see what we did that morning.

My wife and I have been married for eight years but have known each other since we were fifteen. We both love exploring outdoors, off the beaten path. So it was no surprise that after seeing all the posts of creepy humanoid encounters in Louisiana on /r/unexplainedmysteries, she thought it'd be fun to go down by the marshlands since our state is so rich with this particular type of folklore.

We turned onto Bayou Road and headed west towards San Leon. We drove about five miles into the middle of nowhere. The road looked like it went straight through what appeared to be a heavily wooded area (even though it's technically a marsh). We continued, and the farther we drove, the more I wanted to turn around. There was just something off about this place.

We crossed a small wooden bridge over some extensive swampland where cattails surrounded us. It looked as if it were abandoned by any stretch of the imagination—no people or cars for miles—except for a single house a few hundred feet away from us. The house had a white picket fence out front and an American flag hanging next to the front door, with two rocks on each side holding the posts in place. As my wife slowed down to drive past it, she commented on how she thought it would be cute to live there, that it seemed like a nice quiet area.

We continued; the farther we drove, the less I wanted to be there. We passed by two more houses before seeing anything else. We then spotted something in the distance between two places up ahead: a humanoid figure walking down the road towards us. As we got closer and closer, we realized this thing looked drastically out of place... and it wasn't human at all!

It stood about seven feet tall with mantis-like features yet humanoid characteristics as well... its torso had light green scales with four-fingered hands just like a humanoid. Its forearms were fully webbed, and it had large black eyes. Its entire body was humanoid except for its face, which consisted of an insect-like beak with two tusks coming down from the sides.

My wife immediately screamed as she slammed her foot on the brakes, trying to bring the car to a stop. I remember just sitting there puzzled, wondering what I was looking at... it wasn't human at all! But it quickly ran back into the woods before we reached where it was standing so abruptly. We both sat there paralyzed with fear as my wife slowly crept towards where it had disappeared. She wanted to keep driving but was hesitant because she didn't want us to lose sight of this thing.

I finally spoke up and said we should get out of here, that something was wrong with this place. She reluctantly turned around and drove back towards the highway, away from what I began to wonder if it was a demon of some sort. We both wondered for days afterward what in the world we had seen...

We both felt an intense dread for days afterward and have been reluctant to explore even closer to the swamps.

Encounter 14
Submitted By: Anonymous
Time: 2013
Location: Everglades, Florida

WHEN I WAS A TEENAGER, there was this large section of swamp and marsh I always enjoyed hiking into. I knew to be extremely careful because of snakes, water moccasins, and whatnot. One evening, my enjoyment of the swamp changed when I saw something that was not supposed to exist...

It was a late summer evening, and I had decided to go hiking through the swamp because it's what I loved doing. The sun was setting, so it must have been around 10 p.m. or so...

I got out of my truck and began walking through the woods towards the swamp. You take a trail of sorts, picking your way through fallen trees and old logs, which leads to a section of flooded cypresses called "the maze." It's supposed to be easy enough for anyone who knows how to walk on ground with not much of a slope, but if you don't know it—you're going to get lost even if you're an experienced hiker since there are two parts where it's difficult to tell up from down.

As I was making my way into the maze, all of a sudden, I heard something moving very quickly through the cypress trees towards me, which had an awful sound like leaves rustling real fast and tiny branches snapping. When I turned around to see what it was, I saw it...

It stood about eight to nine feet tall with glowing amber eyes. The first thing that came to mind was how demonic looking this creature looked. It was on two legs but hunched over.

I'm still confused about why I felt no fear as it approached. All I remember is how quickly everything was going and all the thoughts going through my head at once—but one feeling was prominent... It wasn't a feeling of being scared; it was more like knowing what this thing was and its intentions.

It didn't make any noise as it walked towards me almost in a hunched-over sprint or something just hidden within the swamp foliage's blind spot until you're right up on it. When I turned around to see what that rustling sound behind me was—that was when we made eye contact for about half a second before I turned to run.

Then everything slowed down because reflexes kicked in and told me I needed to run. It was either get eaten alive or get out of the maze. So that's what I did—I ran for my life through the forest, all covered in shadows from the trees, until I found myself back on the solid ground leading up towards my truck, which had an extra gas can in it because when you go off-roading as I do, it's good to have a spare if needed...

The path is mostly marshland with some dry areas in certain places where people camp, but there aren't many except one place near an old abandoned plantation house where most people park their cars.

After about thirty minutes of walking, I finally got to my truck and decided to take a different route through the marshlands until I found an area where the road started again, which took another hour or so...

I have not been back to those swamps since, nor do I plan to return anytime soon. What happened will stay with me forever. If anyone is thinking of heading out there—don't unless you plan on dying...

Encounter 15
Submitted By: Anonymous
Time: N/A
Location: Massachusetts

I WANT to share a story about an encounter my sister and her husband had while living in a small town of Massachusetts. I have heard about mysterious creature sightings and strange occurrences of UFOs in what is called the Bridgewater Triangle in eastern Massachusetts along the 495 corridor. The Bridgewater Triangle is a roughly two-hundred-square-mile area of southeastern Massachusetts that is said to be cursed or haunted and is the site of numerous paranormal activity reports.

In the fall of 2004, a group of teenagers in Massachusetts reported seeing a furry, apelike creature stalking through the woods. While they were camping near Freetown State Forest, the teens said they saw the monster standing on two legs, about six feet tall, and covered in dark hair. It made a loud screeching noise and then ran off into the woods. The creature, which they nicknamed "the Bridgewater Triangle monster," has never been caught or identified.

The Bridgewater Triangle monster is just one of many unidentified creatures that have been reported in the United States over the years. Others include the legendary Bigfoot, or Sasquatch, which is said to roam the forests of the Pacific Northwest, and the Jersey Devil, which is said to haunt the Pine Barrens of New Jersey.

While there is no scientific evidence to support the existence of these creatures, that has not stopped people from believing in them. For some, the idea of a mysterious creature lurking in the woods is part of the appeal of the outdoors. For others, it's a source of fear.

Which brings me to my sister's story. My sister, Mary, and her husband, Ron, lived in Dighton, Massachusetts, located in the south end of the Bridgewater Triangle. She owned an eleven-acre property with a farmhouse that is surrounded by deep woods. It had a corral with a stall for her two horses, which they would ride in the trails through the woods surrounding their home. Her husband, Ron, and my nephew, Jonah, would frequently go hunting for deer and occasionally even bears that roam the property and the woods surrounding them.

I remember spending the weekend there once, and while we were sitting in the kitchen having coffee at about four o'clock in the afternoon, we heard a loud crashing sound coming from outside close to the house. Looking out the kitchen window, we saw a black bear running through the yard. That was the closest I have ever been to a bear in the wild. I thought, wow, that was cool. But I was glad I was in the house instead of outside, if you know what I mean. My sister said, "Yeah, they come through the yard often." I asked, "How come Abby (her dog) didn't bark?" My sister just laughed and said, "Because the dog is getting old and probably didn't hear it."

Well, as the story goes, it was early in the fall season when one Friday night, she was awakened by a loud noise coming from outside her farmhouse. At first, she thought it was a racoon trying to get into the trash cans, but she knew they were locked closed and did not think any more about it and tried to go back to sleep.

But the noise continued. The sound got louder. It sounded like something was crashing through the woods. Then it sounded like it was on the porch on the side of the house. She could hear the loud stomping footsteps on the wood. Now she got out of bed and looked out the second-story window, down at the porch. She saw something. It was standing on two legs, and it was covered in dark hair. She said she knew it was not a bear, but she did not know what it was.

She noticed Ron was not in bed, and she called out for him, but he did not answer. So she went downstairs and into the kitchen, but he was not there either. Then she looked outside and noticed he was standing outside on their porch with his rifle in hand. She ran outside and asked him what he was doing. He told her he saw something, and it was not a bear. He said he wasn't sure what it was, but it definitely was not a bear. He told her it ran over to where the stable was; then he said he saw it go into the woods. And that he was going to shoot the thing if it got close to the house.

Even though it was late, around 12:30 a.m., he told her he was going to call Dave, his hunting buddy, to come over, and they would hunt this thing together. His friend Dave only lived a few miles away and was there in about twenty minutes. They each had a .30-06 hunting rifle, which they used to hunt deer and bear, plus each carried a .357 Magnum for extra firepower should they need it. Ron carried bear spray with him as well. So in the dark of night, they went off into the woods with guns and flashlights in hand to find this thing.

Dave had mentioned to Ron that he had seen what Ron had described to him a few weeks before while he was out hunting deer with his brother. He said it was about seven feet tall and covered in dark hair. And made loud screeching noises.

Ron and Dave spread out and began to look for the monster. They searched for hours, but they could not find it. They did find evidence that something large had been crashing through the woods though. There were broken branches and large footprints in the mud. They followed the tracks, but in the darkness, they eventually lost sight of them. Ron and Dave decided to go back to Ron's house and call it a night and get some sleep. They were both exhausted from their search.

My sister was still awake when they got back; she said she couldn't go back to sleep knowing they were out there looking for this thing. She asked them if they had found anything. They told her they had not seen or heard anything wandering in the woods. But they had found evidence that something large had been through the area. They told her they'd found twisted saplings and branches broken nine feet up off the trees. In addition were bizarre animal tracks that resembled a man's.

The next day being Saturday, they went back out into the woods to try to find this thing again. They searched until it got dark, but they still could not find it. Other than more broken branches and more footprints in the mud. Yet they did find a hair sample that later they sent to a lab to be analyzed. The lab said that the hair sample was from an unknown animal.

That same night at about ten o'clock as Ron and Mary were getting ready for bed, they heard the horses whinnying and neighing loudly from the stable. The horses are usually quiet during the night, so Ron knew something was up.

Grabbing a flashlight and his .357, he went out to the stable. As he approached, he could see one of the horses had gotten out of the stable and was in the corral. When he focused the flashlight at the horse, he saw some kind of tall beast trying to bring the horse down. It seemed to be clawing at the horse. Ron fired a shot in the air to scare the beast. He did not want to fire in the direction of the horse in case he would hit it. Yet the sound of the shot did not stop this beast from attacking the horse.

Ron then ran closer and, dropping to one knee, took aim at the beast and fired two quick rounds. Ron said both shots hit the beast in the back. The beast then let out a bloodcurdling screech and dropped to all fours and ran to the end of the stable. Ron said that the beast jumped the six-foot-high corral fence in one leap, landing on two legs, and ran off into the woods.

The horse was badly injured and had to be put down. The veterinarian said that the wounds were consistent with an animal attack. Ron and Mary were convinced that the monster was real and that it was responsible for the death of the horse.

Again, Ron called Dave and told him what had just happened. Dave called his brother, and both arrived at the house within a half hour. Now all three were armed and ready to hunt this thing. Dave also brought his hunting dogs this time. Two bloodhounds that he and Ron used often when hunting.

They all headed to the area at the end of the corral where the beast had jumped the fence so the dogs could get the scent of this thing. Then the dogs took off into the woods, following the scent. The three men followed the sound of the dogs. As they got deeper into the woods, the more they realized this thing was leading them in a big circle. It was toying with them.

After a few hours of this, the dogs and the men started to get tired, so the men decided to call it a night and headed back to the house. But as soon as they got close to the house, the dogs took off again into the woods. They were following the scent again, but this time they were not going in a circle. They were heading straight for something. And that something was the Bridgewater Triangle monster.

The dogs cornered it in a small clearing, and it was standing there on two legs. It was about seven feet tall and covered in dark hair. And it was making this loud screeching noise. Ron, being in front of his two friends, yelled to his friends that he could see this beast just in front of him. As he slowly approached the creature with his gun drawn, ready to shoot it, the creature charged at him and knocked Ron to the ground. Then it ran off into the woods again.

By the time Dave and his brother reached Ron, they could see he was covered in scratches and bruises. And he was really shaken up. They said they had never seen anything like it before in their lives. All three had seen the Bridgewater Triangle monster with their own eyes. And there was no denying that it was real.

Now they were more determined than ever to shoot this thing. After resting for a bit to make sure Ron was okay to continue, and the dogs had rested as well, the three set off again to hunt this beast.

The dogs went right after this thing, the scent was strong, and they ran after it. Dave said it sounded like the dogs went in different directions instead of staying together. This surprised Dave, because usually the dogs stayed together in pursuit.

He called out to them, but they did not come back. He then heard one of the dogs barking in the distance, but he could not tell which direction it was coming from. The three of them started to follow the sound of the barking, but then they heard the other dog barking too. The dogs were both barking from different directions. The men were confused and did not know which way to go. Dave led the way and decided to go towards the sound of the first dog barking.

As they got closer, they could hear the dog whimpering. They followed the sound until they came to a clearing in the woods. In the clearing, they found one of Dave's dogs. The dog was lying on the ground, whimpering in pain. It had been badly injured. Dave was in shock. These dogs were the love of his life, and here was one of his babies hurt. Dave said he was done hunting for this thing and decided that he needed to get his other dog and get to the vet as soon as possible. He picked up the dog and started to carry it back to Ron's house. As he was carrying the dog, they heard the other dog barking again. Dave called out to him as the three followed the sound until they came to another clearing.

In the clearing, they found the other dog. It was also lying on the ground, whimpering in pain. It too had been badly injured. Dave's brother picked up the other dog and began to carry it back to Ron's house. They hadn't got far when they heard the sound of something moving in the woods behind them. Turning around, they saw the monster standing in the shadows watching them. The monster had a strange evil look in its eyes. They all stared at the monster for a moment. Because two of them were carrying the dogs, they couldn't grab their guns and shoot at the beast. And Ron, being injured himself, wasn't quick enough to react. So instead of shooting at it this time, they all turned and ran the other way. They ran as fast as they could, but the monster was faster. It caught up to Dave and knocked him to the ground. Then it grabbed the dog and ran off into the woods.

Dave was devastated. That thing had just taken his beloved dog. Yet the three decided not to follow the beast. And Dave wanted to get his other dog to the vet as soon as possible.

Upon reaching Ron's house, they called the police. Dave and his brother left and took the dog to an emergency animal hospital in town. When the police came out to Ron's, it was decided to wait until morning to do a search for the dog. And Dave had said he would return the next morning as well. Early the next morning, the police and the three men searched the woods for Dave's dog and the monster. There was no trace of the beast that had attacked the men and taken Dave's dog. But sadly, they did find the body of the dog; it had the same claw marks as the horse. The wounds were consistent with an animal attack.

Ron never went hunting in the woods around his house again. And within a year sold the property and moved to Florida. He said they wanted to get as far away as possible from whatever creature that was that they call the Bridgewater Beast.

Encounter 16
Submitted By: Trevor
Time: 1990s
Location: New York

IN THE MID-'90S, I was a member of an occult group in New York City. It was a small offshoot of the Ordo Templi Orientis, one of the oldest existing occult groups in the world. We were a coven of about a dozen people who met weekly at each other's apartments to learn the fundamentals of ritual magic. We were taught how to evoke spirits and deities and work magic.

Everything was kept secret, and we were blindfolded when we were taken to the oratorio to be initiated. All I knew was that the head of our order was a man named Bill. He told us that we would learn a lifetime's magical knowledge in just a few years. He said that he was a direct descendant of Aleister Crowley. He told us he was the only one of his father's sons worthy of taking over the order. We were required to take a vow of secrecy and submit to a blood oath.

The ritual I saw was held deep in the woods of Northern New Jersey. It was taking place in a clearing that was surrounded by woods. There was a pentagram painted on the ground. The ritual was led by a man who called himself Osiris. He claimed to be the reincarnation of the Egyptian god Osiris. He was dressed in a white robe. There was a fire burning in the center of the pentagram.

There were about ten people in attendance, including myself. They were all wearing robes. At first, I thought the ritual was just for fun. I thought it was like a séance. I had been to a couple of those before. But when Osiris cut his arm with a ceremonial dagger and let his blood drip into the fire, I began to feel uneasy. Then he cut his other arm and let his blood drip into the fire. He was still chanting, and then he motioned with his hand, and the fire leaped into the air. The flames were burning so high that I thought they would set the trees on fire. He motioned again, and the fire went back down into the pit.

Next, he took a bottle of wine from one of the other people in the circle and drank from it. Then he poured some of the wine onto the ground in the circle. He began to chant in another language. He was repeating the same word over and over. I had heard him say that he was a magician and that magic was his language. He also said that magic was the only language certain spirits could understand. I had been told that the spirits we would evoke were powerful demons that would appear in the bodies of dead people. I had never seen or spoken to Osiris before this night. I did not know that he was capable of summoning such powerful spirits. I was scared. I was afraid that he might be summoning something that would be too strong for him to control.

Just then, some of our trances were broken by the sounds of something large moving in the woods around us. Then we heard growling; something was being summoned. Osiris continued to chant. Then he motioned with his hand, and a group of large black humanoid cats ran into the clearing. I had never seen anything like them before. I think they were part panther. They were walking on their hind legs. Osiris informed us not to be alarmed as they moved in the circle of light towards Osiris, and that these were the beings he had full control over. He waved his hands in a strange motion again over these things and began to speak in a different language again. They were growling and snarling, nasty evil things. He said what sounded like a shouting command, and they all departed from the light.

After this, Osiris motioned again, and the fire leaped into the air again. Then he did something that scared me. He picked up a dagger and began to draw a symbol in the air that I had never seen before. He spoke in that other language again. I heard one of the other people in the circle speak up and say that it was the symbol of a demon. Osiris then motioned as if he were pushing something away from him with his hands. Then he motioned as if he were pulling something towards him. He kept repeating this motion. He said that he was binding the spirit to the symbol. He spoke those other words again. He had a look of power and determination on his face. He was sweating and breathing heavily.

Suddenly, I heard a sound like some kind of animal growling in the woods. Then I heard something walking through the woods. I was sure that it was the demon. Osiris said that it was coming. He said that it was a very powerful demon. He said that it was the only one that was able to break through the barrier that had been placed around the ritual circle. I was sure that everything was going to turn out okay. I had no idea that the demon was going to be so powerful.

The demon came into the light. It was this huge black dog. It looked like a grotesque werewolf. It was growling and drooling. It had red eyes. I had never seen anything so terrifying in my life. Its eyes were so red that they looked like a pair of glowing red coals. It was coming towards Osiris obediently as if he had full control over it. He then motioned as if he were pushing it away from him again. He said that he was binding the demon to the symbol. He repeated those other words. Then he said something in the demon's language. The demon began to circle the fire. It was growling and snarling and drooling. It had this evil look on its face. It was so evil that it was beyond description. It was terrifying. I was shaking, and I felt so helpless.

Then Osiris made another motion, and the demon stopped

moving. It was still growling and drooling and staring at us with those red glowing eyes. It was looking at each of us, one by one. It was trying to intimidate us. Then it looked at Osiris, and he said something to it in its language. The demon responded with a deep growl. Osiris said something else to it. It responded again with the same growl.

Then Osiris made another gesture, and the demon began to move again. It was walking towards us. We were all in a trance, and we could not move. It began to circle the fire again. It then just dissipated into the darkness around the fire. Osiris spoke some more low-toned words and claimed the ritual was nearing the end. We were to go through one last part. Osiris then went around to each of us and placed his hand on the person's forehead. Then he would chant, and they would fall over unconscious. He went around and did this to each of us, including me. Before, he'd informed us that we would awake in our beds and the ritual would be sealed. We would now be a part of the night.

After I awoke in my bed, just as he had said, I felt different... I felt like something had been taken from inside me. Many things in my life after that started to go rapidly downhill. Lost my job, and family members died whom I was close to within just a few years, and I went through a few psychotic episodes and nearly committed suicide. I'm doing much better. I've never felt the same since. With 2020 seeming to never end I'm just like everyone else, trying to survive. Anyway, be careful what you involve yourself with.

Encounter 17
Submitted By: Delores Barker
Time: 1997
Location: Appalachian Mountains

I HAD JUST RETURNED from a camping trip in the Appalachian Mountains and decided to go back into the woods to find a few more mushrooms. I had been to the same place the year before. I had a general idea of where everything should be, but I decided to go with my gut feeling. The woods were thick and hard to walk through, and I was sweating pretty bad despite the cool temperature. I came to a small clearing and saw a small tree with a white trunk. I thought it was a birch, but it had white bark and a smooth trunk. I thought, *That's a strange tree for this area. There's nothing else like it around.* I also noted that the base of the tree had been charred black from a fire, and there were no other trees around it. I started walking past the tree when I noticed something white on the ground. I thought to myself, *That's weird. I didn't see that before.* I turned around to look at the tree again. I saw a white hand on the ground. I froze and started to panic. I looked at the tree. I looked at the hand on the ground. I looked back at the tree. I looked at the hand again. I realized that it was a human hand. I ran out of the woods as fast as I could. I took a few pictures on the way out. I went to the police, and they said they would send an officer to take a look, but I haven't heard anything since. I don't know what happened in those woods, but it was very scary. Also, there is a story I heard from a friend of a friend. A friend of a friend said that he was walking along a trail and saw a dead body hanging from a tree. He said he didn't look at it too closely and ran away. That area I was in was teeming with a different kind of energy. It felt dark. I've heard stories of occult rituals and sacrifice in and around that area. I almost wonder if that severed human hand was related to it. Is it possible that the white tree was some sort of ritualistic marker?

Encounter 18
Submitted By: Anonymous
Time: N/A
Location: N/A

WE WERE out camping one night. My family had been near a deeply wooded area for the past five hours. My father had just finished chopping wood and was walking to our tent. I was sitting by the fire and heard a loud "thump" from the woods. I looked at my dad and saw that he had frozen in place. He stood there as if he were frozen solid. It was a very creepy feeling. I looked at him and then looked into the woods. I was scared and tried to tell myself it was just a deer or another animal. I tried to convince myself that I was safe.

I walked over to my dad and tapped him on the shoulder. When I tapped him, he jumped and looked at me. I asked him what was wrong, and he said, "I thought I heard someone yell 'hey!'" I told him I didn't hear anything, and he sat on the log next to the fire. I turned around to sit down in my seat. I heard a noise, like someone stepping on a branch. I heard another noise, this time to my right.

I looked into the woods and saw a tall man walking toward me. As it turned out, it wasn't a man but some strange dark figure walking toward us. Now I was completely terrified, and this figure approached the trees. That was when I noticed that it had no face! It had a dark hood on and stood about six feet tall. I could not see its face and could not tell if it was a man or woman. I was too terrified to yell or tell my father. I was frozen solid. The figure stood about ten feet away from us. It just stood there watching my dad and me. Then it kind of just disappeared into the darkness. My dad looked at me and was just as panicked as I was. He stood up slowly and walked over to the tent. He told me to follow him. I had to fight every nerve in my body to be able to stand up and follow him.

I woke up the next morning feeling very tired and worn out. We packed up our tent and headed for home. We had encountered some sort of ghost. We didn't talk about it on the way home, but when we got home, we told my mother. I could tell she didn't believe us, but she never said it was a lie. She just didn't say anything. As for my dad and me, I have never been camping since.

Encounter 19
Submitted By: Anonymous
Time: Summer 1972
Location: N/A

IN THE SUMMER OF 1972, I was in my mid-teens. My family lived in a small town in the northern part of the country. It was a nice, rural area. There was a farmer across the street from us; sometimes, the grass would be mowed. There was a large field behind this house. To the right of the house was woods. To the left was a creek. Directly behind the house was a large hill that went up another hill, and on top of that was a small rock quarry.

I was sitting on my front porch when I saw something. It was gliding across the field. It was a gray-white color and looked like a huge sheet. I could see through it. It appeared to be moving very fast. I could see the grass moving as it passed over it, traveling in a straight line. It was just above the grass, about a foot or two off the ground. It looked like it would go behind the trees, about a hundred feet from the house. I called for my mother, and she came out on the porch. She watched it for a while and then went back inside. I went back to watching it, and it was still traveling in a straight line. It was almost to the edge of the woods when it suddenly stopped. It just stopped dead and hovered. I watched it for about a minute, and then it started moving again. It glided through the woods and over the creek. It was still moving in a straight line and still moving very fast. It disappeared behind the hill. This went on again for the next several years. The same thing happened just about every night.

I got married, and we moved away. I never forgot this, and I have always thought about it. I never told anyone about it until a few years ago. I told my wife and some of my friends. I have never been able to figure out what it was. It was very odd looking. I'm normally not a ghost believer or into any of that, but man, I certainly can't explain away what I saw that night in the field. Call it a trick of the eyes, but it freaked me out.

Encounter 20
Submitted By: Jock
Time: N/A
Location: South Carolina

I WAS deer hunting in the mountains of western South Carolina for the first time in about three years. I had been drawn to the area for several reasons I will not go into here. Suffice it to say that it was a very dark place.

I parked my truck on a gravel road leading to a small cabin and began walking toward the cabin. It was late, and it was getting dark. I was carrying a small backpack, and in that backpack was some food, a flashlight, matches, a knife, a bottle of bourbon, some cigars, and a gun. I had walked about a mile when I came to where the path entered the woods.

I knew this cabin people had talked about was deserted, so I should check it out. I'm all down for urban exploration-type stuff, so I thought, *Why not?* I was just a short distance from the woods on the left, but I also knew that the woods were thick and wild. I decided to walk around the perimeter of the woods and approach the cabin from the opposite direction.

As I walked the perimeter of the woods, I was startled by a huge raccoon. It was enormous, and it seemed angry that I had invaded its territory. As I walked away from the raccoon, it followed me for about fifty yards; then it turned and disappeared back into the woods. I kept walking. It was the strangest acting raccoon I'd ever seen. Whatever.

After a few moments, I noticed that I was no longer feeling the spooky feeling I had felt as I approached the cabin. It was a fairly large cabin, looked to be built a long time ago but had no door on it and looked a little ransacked. After walking into it, I immediately got this bad feeling and looked down. That was when I could see off on the left side of a large open room a giant pentagram spray-painted on the ground, a dagger covered in dried blood, and a huge pool of dried blood on the ground. Immediately my stomach sank, and I felt I needed to get out of there and now. There was no more time for exploring and having fun.

Initially, I was there to scout for good tree stand spots; this was just a detour. Now it was an escape. I walked out of the cabin and immediately headed back toward my truck. I was walking a little faster than normal, but I didn't want to run because I didn't want to draw attention. I knew that if I ran, I would be giving off the vibe that I was running because I was scared. And that was exactly what I was. I was scared.

Walking, I noticed a strange feeling that I was being watched. I would look behind me from time to time, but no one was there. I knew this was my imagination, but I could not shake the feeling. I kept walking faster and faster. I was breathing heavily now, almost running. I was increasingly panicked as I got farther and farther away from the cabin and closer to my truck.

I was about a hundred yards from the truck when I reached a section of the woods that was thicker than the rest. I was walking slower now. I was completely covered in sweat. My heart was racing. I could feel my pulse in my head. The hair on the back of my neck was standing up. I was looking around me, but I was not seeing anything. Then I started seeing these large shadows darting all around me, and I heard demonic laughing; man, was this too much for me? I finally got to my truck and left the area altogether. I don't even want to know what's been going on in that cabin.

Encounter 21
Submitted By: Conrad
Time: N/A
Location: N/A

I WAS out in the woods near my house and sitting down at the base of a tree. I was facing up the hill at about a forty-five-degree angle. I was facing the tree line. The sun had just set, so it was still pretty light out. The woods are so dense in that area that it is extremely hard to see into them, so I was just sitting there enjoying the darkening sky. Puffing on my tobacco pipe, like I tried to make a ritual out of every evening out here.

I had been there for about five minutes when I saw a black shape moving through the woods. I could not make out any details, but I could tell it was massive. It was far bigger than any man or any bear. It was moving fast, from left to right, as if it were following a trail. I had gotten to my feet by this time, and it was moving briskly. I stood up and turned around to face it. It was about fifty yards from me, but I could still only see the silhouette. I was not frightened, and I was intrigued. I wanted to see what it was. I was also a little scared, having never seen anything like that. I was not sure if it was going to attack me or just move through the woods. I decided to pursue it. I turned around and started to follow it.

I lost it in the woods, and I could not see it. I kept walking along the trail it was on and saw nothing. I came to a clearing about a hundred feet across, and I could tell something had gone through it. The only problem was with spring and everything, all the foliage and plants had grown back full force. The brush and briar bushes were so dense and thick that there was no way a man could just walk through this stuff. So I looked around for a while and kept walking. I was about to give up when I saw something in the woods, moving across the clearing. I crouched down and watched it more, but because the sun was setting, it was getting very dark, and I figured If I didn't turn back around now, I'd be stuck out alone.

I was about to turn back when I heard a cracking sound. I looked up in response to the noise and could see this large black shape up in the trees, jumping from tree to tree and then down to the ground below. I watched it for about ten seconds before it was off and out of sight. I have no idea what it was, but I will never forget that night. I returned to my house and stayed inside for the rest of the night.

5
DOGMAN ENCOUNTERS & SIGHTINGS

FOR ME, one of the most interesting aspects of a dogman is that it sounds almost like a literal werewolf. As a kid, I had a fascination with them. They were easily my favorite movie monster of all time. Then fast-forward to 2014 and I discovered the concept of a "dogman" through several YouTube videos. Shortly after this, I started on my several-year-long dogman binge to digest as many sightings and as much research as I possibly could, mainly due to my obsession with this particular cryptid.

Unlike Bigfoot, a dogman (generally speaking) appears to be the most vile, malicious and evil of any other cryptid in this book. Okay, well, compared to skinwalkers or mothman, etc. it might be the same scale, but I digress. Plain and simple: the idea that an eight-plus-foot-tall werewolf being is running around terrorizing the woods or eating people is downright terrifying. What's worse is that there appears to be an active coverup related to "Unknown Canine Attacks".This is the aspect of dogman that I find most interesting.

There are several stories in this book from eyewitnesses who claim they have seen a dogman, and their stories are absolutely chilling. I hope you enjoy.

Encounter 1
Submitted By: Dwight
Time: Circa 2011/2012
Location: Idaho

I WANTED to share a dogman sighting that occurred in Idaho. I've been checking out your site and others regarding these cryptids for the past few years. I can't say what year it was, but for sure, this happened sometime during the 2010s decade, maybe 2011 or 2012, if my memory serves me correctly. I was working night security for a business in Meridian, Idaho. My job was to patrol the grounds one hour before dusk till an hour after dawn and make sure no one was on-site who wasn't supposed to be there or causing trouble. The last thing you want when working graveyard shifts at businesses like this is homeless people sneaking into your lot because they see it as safe.

I patrolled around 6:30 p.m. to 6:300 a.m. in the winter, so it got pretty cold. The summer months were more difficult because of mosquitos and other insects, but I liked working at night; besides, you don't get many people messing with your business during this time frame, which is always a plus when they have expensive equipment on-site that shouldn't be messed with.

It was a clear night, so the moon provided enough light to see where I needed to go. Most of my time on this job was spent making sure no one sneaked in behind buildings or into areas we didn't often use, if that makes sense.

Anyway, as it got closer and closer toward midnight, things started getting pretty dead for me besides an occasional car driving past. I was walking around the back of the building when I heard a sound in front of me. A person running across my parking lot? That was what it reminded me of; I went to investigate. As I came around the front of my building, a sizeable wolflike creature was under the light. I could see it clearly because of the light above the entrance to my business; this thing was huge!

Easily over six feet tall and at least three hundred pounds, but that's just an estimate as far as height goes for sure. It had long skinny arms with pointed claws on its hands or paws, whatever you want to call them. The head was like a German shepherd's, just big and long. It also had the ear shape but was more prolonged than average; it didn't have any hair on its face or ears, though, which I thought was pretty strange. Its eyes were yellow with red around them, almost giving off an orange glow in color; the teeth looked more like a crocodile's. That was what they looked like to me. Its nose was flat, and its face was less pronounced and flat. It was hunched over, but it wasn't by much, though. Its demeanor seemed very docile and calm at the time, not aggressive in any way, shape, or form, but I had never been so scared. It seemed like it was looking for something and had not yet seen me.

I ducked back behind the building as swiftly and quietly as possible, which was hard because my heart felt like it had jumped into the back of my throat. As far as I knew, this thing might have heard me or seen me duck behind the corner, but nothing happened, so curiosity got ahold of me. I could hear it sniffing the air, so I peeked back around, and it was still there. It had turned its head toward my direction but didn't seem to pay much attention to me, which sounds weird. I think due to the lighting, it didn't see me.

Then from behind, there came another one! This time a smaller counterpart. The two seemed to what I would describe as intelligently communicate with one another—not talking but using body language and these strange clicking noises. The big one kept looking back in my direction, while the smaller one didn't. I didn't know if they knew I was there, but I started getting very nervous.

Every thought ran through my mind about being ripped apart by something that isn't supposed to exist. I needed to get out of there. I slowly backed away from the building with my gun in hand, ready at a moment's notice if they saw me and came after me, but it didn't happen, thankfully. They began moving back into an area surrounded by trees on the other side, away from the perimeter. You could faintly make out the outline of them in the moonlight.

Once they were entirely out of view, I ran back and looked at the camera feed to see if they could be spotted. Wouldn't you know it, where they were was just off camera. I felt ridiculous and ashamed at that moment. I realized that I'd have zero proof if I tried to tell anybody about this. Because of this, I've just not told a soul for the longest time. Even my family doesn't know about this, but I had to tell someone, so now you know. Hopefully, it will help in your research somehow.

Encounter 2
Submitted By: Rob Leighton
Time: N/A
Location: East Texas

I AM A HUNTER, outdoorsman, and survivalist. I live in East Texas on the border of Louisiana. The following account is 100% true: I was hunting deer with my hound dog at around 1 a.m. near our property line, which is about half a mile from our house. As we were walking along an old logging road parallel to Highway 59, something caught my eye in a clearing on our right-hand side, about 150 yards away from us and slightly farther than the highway. I immediately turned off my flashlight; plenty of moonlight shone down through the tree canopy above us and illuminated the nearby field. I slowly scanned the field with my eyes and noticed a large animal standing on two legs. Yes, I said standing on two legs. It was about seven feet tall, dark brown, and had long hair all over its body. It looked like it could be an old bear.

I watched this thing for at least five minutes as we stood directly under the tree canopy but never saw any movement from it except its head turning from side to side. I then noticed another standing behind a tree about twenty yards away and slightly obscured by brush. This one was also seven feet tall but had shorter hair all over its body. They seemed to conceal themselves, so we didn't see any movement initially. I then noticed a third one standing behind another tree about thirty yards away from the second and off in the brush. This one had longer, shaggier hair on its body but looked slightly smaller than the others.

At this point, I turned on my flashlight to better look at these things, which was when they immediately took notice of us. The first one I saw was the closest to us, and it immediately turned its head directly towards me, which was when I noticed that this thing had a face similar to that of a German shepherd. It then began making these loud vocalizations that sounded like an angry goose, waving its arms in my direction, but never moved from where it stood... I then noticed that the second one also made these same vocalizations but never moved from behind the tree.

The third one made no noise or motion toward me; my hound dog and I stood there for a moment to assess the danger. They didn't appear to be a threat but instead began retreating. I decided not to stick around any longer, so we turned back in the direction of home without incident. There was no smell, sounds of footsteps, or anything else.

I am a hunter and outdoorsman who has spent many hours in the woods but have never encountered such an animal before, nor do I know what it was. This sure spooked my dog. I find it odd that they waved their arms at me strangely as if trying to drive me out. They did not appear evil in any way but appeared cautious as if they were caught doing something. That's my take on it.

Encounter 3
Submitted By: Anonymous
Time: N/A
Location: N/A

I WAS WORKING the late shift at a meat processing plant. My friend Sean and I were smoking a cig outside on break at the time, just chatting away, when we heard something off in the trees right beside the parking lot. We both turned our attention to what we just heard. We could only see a rustling of leaves and hear some very faint breathing sounds. We looked at each other, puzzled, figuring someone was in the trees messing with us, but it was bizarre because no one could get in there because of the industrial barbed-wire fence blocking the trees from the parking lot. The surrounding area is just thick woods that connect to a national forest.

We started looking, but we didn't see anything, so we went back to chitchatting like we were, and the next thing you know, we heard the loud crunching of tree branches, followed by deep breathing. We looked up in the trees again, very slowly this time, and as we glanced towards the side of the tree line, we saw a thing. It was hunched over but then stood up to its full height. It was then that we both saw it, and Sean, my friend and coworker I was with, dropped his cig in shock. This thing was this large hairy creature; it was ugly looking. It had a snout and was covered in hair and had deep-set eyes. This thing was over six feet tall. The color of its fur was like a grayish black; it was hideous.

Imagine an orangutan crossed with a wolf to explain what it looked like. It had some traits like an orangutan, while others were more canine-like. I remember the two rows of large, pointed teeth the best. It, too, had a broad snout and was very strange around its mouth/jaw. It looked at us with contempt. It slowly walked towards us. I couldn't move; I was too scared. This thing was huge. This thing probably weighed four hundred pounds easily. It slowly bent down, looked at us, and stood upright against the fence, staring at us. After a couple more moments, this thing turned away from us and went back into the trees.

I looked at Sean, and he was terrified, as he saw that I saw it too. We used that as an opportunity to run back inside and end our break. We said nothing to our boss. We finished our shifts, terrified out of our minds that we had seen this thing. After work, Sean and I would only talk about it briefly, that we had never seen anything like it before, and no one would ever believe us. We talk to each other once in a while. We generally don't mention what we saw to anyone anymore because no one believes us. We still hang out on break, but as far as talking and being comfortable like we were, this sighting has changed us. I'm not sure what we saw that evening.

Encounter 4
Submitted By: Elma
Time: 1985
Location: N/A

MY DAUGHTER (twelve) had stayed overnight with me, and we had fallen asleep on the living room couch. We awoke around 7:15 a.m. to see this entity standing by the window. The first thing I noticed was hair hanging over the forehead and down the back of its neck, which was wet and soaked like it had just walked out of water. It was covered in nasty matted hair and looked like an ugly dog-looking thing. It was just staring at us. It felt like I was paralyzed and could not get up off the couch. I was petrified. We stared at it for what seemed like forever before I finally screamed, and it turned and walked away. My daughter was hysterical after seeing this creature. She ran up out off the couch and collapsed on me, crying.

I called the cops, but they told me there was nothing they could do about it. We had completely forgotten about the whole thing a couple of nights later. My daughter's father had come by to pick her up for the weekend, and as he was getting her into his truck, I heard him start yelling just as I got back in the house. I went back outside and saw this thing, the same thing we'd seen a couple of nights before, approaching my ex-husband and my daughter. I froze again and could not get my body in gear. I was so terrified I couldn't move. My ex-husband fired at it, hitting it in the chest, but the thing NEVER flinched; it just looked at him, turned, and started to walk off. He shot it in the back of the neck where there was no hair, but it didn't flinch again. It walked across the street and up over the hill. It never even stopped. The man always keeps a firearm on him, and I'm glad he did because who knows what would've happened had he not had a gun on him.

I couldn't believe he shot it, and the thing didn't even react. That thing was just evil. He was flipping out, asking me if I saw that, and I told him how we'd just seen it in the window the other night. I asked him to follow me up into the house so I could show him where the thing had been. I showed him, and we exited the house, and he went around and looked, and you could see, which I didn't see, but there were impressions in the ground where this thing had been standing. He seemed pretty shocked, but at the same time, he seemed like he knew what he had seen that night. There weren't any footprints, but you could see something big and heavy had been standing here right in front of our window. I shudder at the thought that this thing could've been there for a while, watching us sleep before we even woke up to see it.

For the next four to five months, we had weird sensations all around the house and property. Felt like we were either not alone or being watched. But to us, we never did see that thing again after that. My ex-husband always brought his .44 with him from that point every time he came to pick up and drop off our daughter. I never had an experience like that again for the remainder of my time in that house. I moved out of that house shortly after Thanksgiving.

Encounter 5
Submitted By: Anonymous
Time: 2009
Location: Michigan

I SAW the dogman in the summer of 2009. My two brothers and I were at my family's property in northern Michigan, near the towns of Vanderbilt and Mackinaw. My two brothers and I sat around the firepit, grilling burgers and hanging out. It was just starting to get dark. I saw a large, dark figure moving quickly across the sky. It was moving so fast that it looked like a blur. It was heading in a south-southwest direction. I noticed that it was not a bird because it had no wings. And it was not a plane because it was not moving like one. It was simply a vast black figure that was gliding across the sky. It was shallow in the sky, no higher than a few hundred feet off the ground. It was moving very fast. I had never seen anything like that before.

I pointed it out to my brothers, and we stood there watching this thing for a few minutes. Then I heard a strange noise coming from around my brother's tent. It was a strange kind of growling noise. A mixture between a dog and a wolf. It sounded like a dog with a deep growl. I ran to the tent, unzipped the door, and inside were my brother's two dogs, an Australian shepherd and a German shepherd. They were both growling and barking at something. I could hear something moving around near the tent, which sounded like a huge animal. I was scared, but I managed to get the dogs out of the tent.

My brothers and I stood in the dark when we heard a loud noise coming from near the woodpile. It sounded like a growl mixed with a roar from a gigantic animal. We turned on our flashlights and saw a creature standing behind the woodpile. We saw it very clearly. It was a giant, hairy creature that looked like a werewolf. I was terrified.

The creature was no more than thirty feet away from us. It had long black hair, and the hair on its face was dark brown. It was very muscular and very tall. It looked like it was a mixture between a dog and a man. It had pointed ears and a long, skinny tail. I could not see its eyes very well. The creature was growling at us.

We stood there looking at this thing for about two minutes before it turned around and walked off into the woods. It moved quickly, but it was also kind of hunched over. We never saw it again. I am not a hunter, have never killed anything, and am, in fact, very anti-hunting.

I've never owned a gun, but after that night, I bought one. And take it with me whenever I go camping. Just in case I see that creature again.

Encounter 6
Submitted By: Anonymous
Time: Spring 2019
Location: N/A

THIS WAS ALMOST A YEAR AGO. It happened in mid to late April of 2019. On my drive home after working a long day, I came across a sharp bend in the road where, out of nowhere, a deer jumped out in front of my Dodge Ram, and I collided with it. I don't know why, but its momentum must have propelled it a certain way because it shot off to the side of the road instead of over my truck. My truck did a little glitch thing. Everything turned off and back on within a split second as the car or engine malfunctioned. The impact was hard, and I felt like it damaged my front badly by the impact alone. "No, no, no," I told myself, quickly pulling over into the pullout right next to me.

I jumped out of my truck, eager to see if there was any damage. I had my nifty little utility flashlight with me. So even in the dead of night, I could thoroughly check my truck for any grave markings or damage; it looked pretty clean. Nothing too bad had been done to it. I was astonished, considering the impact itself had been immense. After taking a few quick moments to scan my vehicle, I turned to my left, and directly where my headlights were hitting was the doe I'd just hit. She was a big son of a gun. I must have hit her good because her head looked pretty smashed in.

Blood oozed out the side of her face and mouth. I had been doing a good fifty miles an hour around that curb. I know the roads well, so I guess I get a little lax sometimes when it comes to good driving. I was looking at this dead doe, just trying to take in that I didn't hurt my truck too bad. Before I got back in the truck, I figured it might be a good idea to pop my hood and just double-check to make sure everything was okay. Everything looked fine.

I reached up to close the hood and felt these dagger-like eyes on me. I felt the strongest feeling I've ever felt of somebody watching me. It didn't feel good. It felt terrible like someone was twenty feet behind me, coming at me with a knife. I've never felt such immediate fear in my life. I turned around, and keep in mind my headlights were fully illuminating everything in front of me. I saw the dead deer still. I heard this growl that had so much bass to it. I froze and tensed up, thinking I'd just angered a colossal bear or something.

Out of the trees popped this huge wolf-looking face but uglier. It took one look at me, then looked down at the dead doe. It looked back at me without even breaking a second of eye contact. This huge hairy black arm reached out below it, grabbed the doe by the neck, and pulled it back into the trees with it. Never once breaking eye contact. It disappeared altogether. I practically pissed myself; I was so terrified.

Without even turning around, I just got back in my truck. The hood did get closed, and I flew out of there so fast. For some reason, my mind went to a giant man-eating badger-looking thing, but it was a very wolflike, absolutely huge head. I'm talking huge.

Encounter 7
Submitted By: Sandy & Bob
Time: N/A
Location: N/A

WHEN I WAS MUCH YOUNGER, I was avid about hunting black bears. You could say it was a passion of mine. However, I had gone grizzly hunting a few times here and there with my cousins up in Alaska. I was on a crazy outdoor trek about a few years ago, fell off a slight thirty-foot incline, and shattered both of my legs. Had I fallen any other way? I would have been toast. Thank you, Lord, for that. But that's not why I'm writing to you.

When I used to bear hunt, I encountered all sorts of beasts out in the wild. I was born in the city and spent a lot of my time there in my life. And I did not have a hand in taming the wild till I was later in my teens and befriended those who made this their way of life. They taught me a lot in a concise amount of time, and I owe them a lot.

Not only have I encountered dogmen on multiple occasions, but Bigfoots as well. Both are beasts in their own right, and you want to respect them and be very careful; both can quickly kill you if you're not respectful.

I had an instance where I was tracking this big black bear once, and I came across these bigger, larger-than-life canine tracks in the soft dirt. This was after I had seen one already, so it didn't take long to figure out what these tracks belonged to. The stride on these tracks, though, had to have been five feet easily, massive prints bigger than my hand, went on for maybe forty yards and disappeared into the thick forest. The most haunting detail that gets me every time is that the prints looked bipedal, not quadrupedal. I knew what they belonged to, but I didn't want to acknowledge these things.

I've since come to terms with them and then lived around where I hunted later on. But at that time, it was a tough pill to swallow. Even more so than Bigfoot. At least Bigfoot, there's some introduction to its existence with the Patterson film and general knowledge of Bigfoot in modern-day pop culture. I had never heard of dogmen at the time I saw the first one. That's why I had a much harder time dealing with it.

My first encounter with these things was two years after that previous story; I was hunting black bears again. I had caught the tracks of this one black bear. These tracks led me a little farther in the direction of these mountains. I wasn't familiar with them. But I didn't overthink it. After a little way in, I had these two large, well, werewolf-looking creatures stalking me from farther back up in the trees scare the hell out of me. I wasn't going to keep following those bear tracks anymore. I got out of there quickly. I had no idea what kind of animals I was dealing with.

And I wasn't about to be ignorant at the time; you have to understand that these things were huge. At first, they looked like two wild dogs, the size of horses, darting back and forth between the trees. Then I saw both of them stand up on two legs—turned me whiter than a ghost; I would continue to run into the same dogmen in the years to come. That's for another day, though.

The subsequent encounter was about five months later when I was out hiking in that part of the woods again and felt the same feelings as last time, but much more intense. I checked my surroundings. And the scariest thing was that I remembered and recognized the feeling. I couldn't see them anywhere. That told me they were already almost upon me, so I got out of there, not waiting to find out. I had completely forgotten all about the last time until I felt that awful feeling again. The memories came flooding right back at the time. That's how I knew.

I had a couple of encounters with Bigfoot, two in the same area. But I never saw any of them at the same time. My Bigfoot encounters were similar but not aggressive in any way. Not like these things. I believe that Bigfoot is a much more docile, curious creature. Not anything like dogmen, though. I think they're all full of ill intent. And their auras are so much darker.

I believe they were trying to drive me out of their den or territory.

Whatever it was that I must have come into. It was always that same general area in the mountains every time I would encounter them. I had ventured off into that area of the mountains more often than not afterward and not always had those frightening experiences. I was always equipped with at least a machete and a .45 going back there, just in case anything happened.

There's a big river if you travel far enough; it's quite the scene. But I stopped going back in there after a while. Another time was going back to the mountain range. And I'm pretty sure I ended up sneaking up on one of those things—came across a large clearing with a large boulder, about the size of a small house, about two hundred yards away. Crouching on the top, clear as day, was one of those dark creatures I had seen previously. It was clear daytime, and there was no mistaking what it was by its shape. It was not a bear. It was canine by the head and upper body. It was fixated heavily on the trees that I couldn't see. It wasn't moving much either. So I sat there and watched it for a few moments before moving in the opposite direction.

Those are my stories, and I appreciate anyone out there who listens and is aware of what's out there. I'm not the best writer, but I've done my best to convey what I saw and experienced. Maybe sometime I can tell you about my Bigfoot encounters.

Encounter 8
Submitted By: Anonymous
Time: FALL 1981
Location: Outside Fayetteville

I WAS ONLY nineteen when this happened to me. It was back in the early fall of 1981. This was when I spent a lot of my time. I lived outside Fayetteville, not too far. About thirty or so miles away in a small town. My job would require me to pull later shifts since I would usually cover more than just my job. At the time, I had a good-for-nothing boss who insisted that it saved the company more money by throwing their employees more extensive tasks and workloads but no overtime pay. That's a story for another day.

One evening, I drove back home outside Fayetteville along Highway 68. I was probably on the road for a few minutes before my eyes caught movement. This tall figure was walking alongside the road about fifty feet away from the car. As I pulled closer, I saw that this looked like someone in an elaborate werewolf in London costume from way back. Why would they be wandering the side of the road out here? I thought the whole thing was strange.

But then I got closer. And what I thought was a person turned its head. I realized then that it wasn't just somebody having a convincing werewolf costume. If there was ever a living werewolf, this was it. I remember how scary its face looked. I think my headlights caught its attention because as it turned around, it also lifted its arm as if to shield its eyes from the light.

After standing there for a second, it quickly vanished off the road on the same side. Freaked me the hell out. I had seen enough to know that it was not a person. A person doesn't act like that in a costume and isn't capable of moving with agility like that. I could tell even in the poor lighting. Its fur was thick and matted, long, and stringy, as I said, a very convincing werewolf costume. I'd say it was Hollywood tier if it were fake. Think of a long-haired fluffy dog.

It had a longer snout. But the upper part of its face was what I thought was more fierce looking. It just had an angry expression. Do you know how dogs look when they're happy or even mad? It was the same kind of thing. He just seemed to have a scowl on his face.

I saw it for what felt like an eternity. But it did raise its arm fairly quickly to shield its eyes from my headlights. When I saw it, I came down almost to a stop to try to figure out what I was looking at. Never in all my years have I ever seen such a thing. I know about Bigfoots, but I don't know what I encountered that night.

Encounter 9
Submitted By: Peter Larris
Time: February 2016
Location: N/A

FOR THIS STORY, please use my first name only. Xavier. My story of The Dogman comes from Locust Bottom in Alexandria, VA. Please do not use my last name. I'm afraid it will have extreme negative consequences on my life.My encounter is not something I like to share but I feel I must. One night shortly after the full moon in June 2015, I was with a friend that I roll with on certain missions. We were on an operation. It was a simple one, collect a small quantity of high grade cannabis strains. We almost completed our objective and were heading back to my friends car. I should say here that at the time I wasn't a smoker but I sold it. I'm not proud of those days but it is what it is. Now, some important details real quick: There were two of us, me and my friend Adam. We were 20 at the time, and we room mated together. At that time and up to that night we were also dog lovers. This only makes our encounter that much more ironic. Okay so onto the encounter: That night me and Adam were out as we do most of our nights. It was well after midnight but not very late. We were heading to our car, which we parked beneath a light post along the dirt path. The path is near a large patch of forest on Locust Bottom park in Alexandria, VA. Our path had a small incline to it meaning near the edge by the parking lot near the tree there is a hill. Now we knew better to be there that late, but it's our neighborhood. We are safe up there. As we were walking up the pavement past the small hill, we heard the rustling of limbs in the bush. I looked over and saw what I thought was a dog. It was huge though Adam and I both took notice that it was bigger than any dog we had ever seen. It was darker and bigger. As we continue to walk past we notice that it starts to make its way towards us on the grass and began picking up speed. It was at this point the shape began to come into view more. My curiosity and confusion quickly turned into a fear I can't began to muster. I started to sprint towards the car, with Adam following closely behind me. Just as I looked behind me now as I am nearing the car. The creature running towards us. To put it simply, what I saw looked exactly like a werewolf. Plain and simple. It had hair all over its body, a pointed muzzle, and long fangs. Its eyes looked exactly like a dogs did only they were blood red. It looked exactly like a wolf but with everything else a dog has. Like a dog walking on its back legs As we got into the car, I screamed and began panicking. This thing quickly caught up to the car and began violently jerking on the car. Boom, the car engine goes on and without blinking I swiftly put it into drive and fly out of there. As soon as we drove away from it it quickly retreated as it did not want to be exposed out in the open for any longer than needed. For the next several minutes all I could do was cry. It had frightened the hell out of me. Adam agreed with my assessment. We both clearly saw the same thing with our own two eyes. I explained to him exactly what it was we saw. He agreed with me that we may have seen the Dogmen so many talk about up in the midwest. I have family up in Michigan that had told me stories of it but never in a million years could I have ever thought to encounter it myself. Now, I'm a believer.

Encounter 10
Submitted By: Taylor H.
Time: 1990s
Location: N/A

I SAW a dogman back in the early '90s. It was in the early morning hours, around 4:00 a.m. I was driving home on a back road in West Virginia and saw something running alongside my car. At first, I didn't know what it was, but as I slowed, this thing ran up alongside my car.

It was huge. It was twice the size of a normal man and had huge shoulders hunched over. It had long arms that were reaching out and running beside my car. It was all black, and it had a huge head. I could see its face, and it was all canine. It had a long snout like a German shepherd but was much larger. I could see its teeth, and they were huge. It was weird to see, and I was scared to death.

I was only about a mile from my house and drove as fast as possible. It followed me to my house, I pulled into the driveway, and it stopped at the edge of my yard. I sat in my car for about half an hour because I was scared to go into the house. I didn't know what it was, and I thought that it might come after me if I went into the house. It never came after me, but I was afraid that it would. I was young at the time and didn't know what it was.

I didn't tell anyone about it because I thought they would think I was crazy. I didn't know that these things existed. I had never heard of dogmen or anything else until I saw your night's show. I didn't know that there were other people out there who had seen these things. I never told my wife about it because she would think that I was crazy. I've never told anyone about it until now.

I'm not sure what it was, but I know the creature looked like a huge dog. I know it was real, and I can't believe other people have seen these things. This creature started coming around my house, and I was afraid it would get inside my house. I was young at the time and didn't have a gun or anything like that. Stupid, I know. I was a different person then. Anyway, this thing would always start to come around my house.

Later, my next-door neighbor gave me a couple of chickens. I don't know why he gave me a couple of chickens because I didn't have the coop completed yet, but once that was done, it was great. I had seven of them. Now, you talk about chickens and a dogman sighting—it's not a good thing. I shouldn't have brought chickens home after this sighting. I think it was even more of a reason for it to stick around.

Anyway, I came out one morning, and all my chickens were dead. They were scattered all around the yard, and a couple looked like they'd had their necks torn off or open. They were all ripped apart. I couldn't believe it, and I didn't know what to think. It was obvious that something had killed them. I was afraid to go into the woods behind my house because I was afraid that it would come after me. I knew this thing was behind it all.

One evening I was sitting out on my porch and heard a noise in the woods. It was like something large. I could hear it walking around in the woods,. It sounded like a huge man walking around in the woods. I was scared to death, and it came out of the woods. It was huge, and it looked like a huge dog. It walked out of the woods and looked at me with the most sinister expression I've ever seen. It almost smiled. It was like a "Haha, there's nothing you can do about me being here." It was as if it relished the very fact I was powerless against it. It blew me off and went back in the direction it was going.

The second encounter was like it was just letting me know who's in charge, and it wanted to terrify me, which it did a good job of. It was at this point I began having these severe hallucinations at home and even at work. I began emotionally breaking down for no reason. I feel like whatever this thing was affected my psychological state. It imprinted itself onto me like a demented handler.

This went on for months with it coming around my property. I wouldn't see it, but I knew he would be there. I could feel his presence.

Now, fast-forward to the early fall time, and my aunt, who's very religious, had come over in the evening. She and I were always close but hadn't seen each other in a while because she moved four hours from me. She just so happened to be in the area and wanted to stop by and catch up.

I don't know quite how it came to be, but she was reading her Bible aloud, and I began hearing this horrible screaming coming from out back near the tree line. She and I got up and rushed to the window, but we couldn't see anything. The screaming continued on and off all night and spooked my aunt badly. She left after a short time because she didn't know what it was. Here's the weird thing, this thing stopped showing up after that. I have no idea why or if my aunt reading out of the Bible had any part to play in this at all. Part of me believes that whatever being or creature this was had evil intentions. I would even go as far as saying demonic.

Encounter 11
Submitted By: Hutch
Time: early 1980s
Location: Outside Aberdeen, South Dakota

I HAD an encounter with a dogman in the early '80s. I was living in a trailer park outside Aberdeen, South Dakota. It was just before Halloween, and I was in the process of helping build a haunted house on the lot next to our trailer. I was up late at night, making the inside of the house. I was a teenager then and had an old German shepherd raised from a puppy. He was with me the whole time I was building.

It got close to midnight, and I decided to call it a night, so I took my dog inside with me. I decided to leave the outside light on to give me some light to see by when I went out to head back to the trailer. I was getting ready for bed, and my dog decided to go outside.

I went out to let him back in and heard something walking around the trailer. I thought it was a person, so I yelled to them to get off the property. I listened to a growl deeper than any dog I had ever heard. It sounded like something from a nightmare. It uttered a horrible, wretched growl. I just about fell over when it happened. My dog had come up to me and started barking, which I had never seen him do. I felt like something was coming over me because I was scared to death.

After several deep growls, I could hear it quickly moving towards the back side of our trailer. Sounded like it was taking off running on two feet. I had enough courage to run back into the trailer and lock our door. I grabbed my dad's shotgun, loaded it, and sat by the window, watching for anything coming our way. I was in fear for the rest of the night after that encounter. I didn't sleep at all.

In the morning, my neighbor came over to tell me that a few trailers down, they had found an animal carcass with its rib cage exposed. It was torn apart like no animal I had ever seen. He complained that I had been up early in the morning making a racket, but I explained that I'd shut down my haunted house around midnight. His face went white after he put two and two together.

After getting out of the military, I have been living in West Chicago, Illinois. My fiancée and I have been hearing strange noises near the back of the woods near where I live. I can't help but have my mind wonder about what that sound could have been all those years ago. My parents never paid attention, so I don't trust my family completely when it comes to something supernatural. I am more open-minded than they are, and at fifty-seven years of age, I fear what isn't known.

Is there any way you could look back at the dates and see if there were any disappearances around the time I encountered this thing outside Aberdeen? Hopefully, we both kept our eyes open!

Encounter 12
Submitted By: Tony Uzopa
Time: Fall 1998
Location: N/A

I AM WRITING as this is the first time I have ever told anyone about my experience. I have never told anyone in my family about this. My wife knows, but I have never told anyone else. It was so long ago, and

I have never had any other experiences, that it just seemed like a dream. I have been a hunter my entire life and know what a coyote and a wolf or dog look like. This was not any of those animals. I never told anyone because I was afraid they would think I was crazy. However, I have been listening to your show for a while now, and you seem like a very educated person, so I decided to send you an email. If you are interested, I will tell you what happened.

It was the fall of 1998. I was a senior in high school and had just gotten home from school. I had a paper route and delivered the newspaper before I went to school that day. It was a Friday, and it was around 3:30 in the afternoon. I had just gotten home and walked up the stairs to my bedroom.

My room had a window that looked out into the woods behind my house. I was walking up the stairs when I looked out my window and saw something move in the woods. I stopped and looked out the window to see what it was.

It was crouched down and looked like it was sniffing the ground. It was covered in brown fur, but it wasn't a bear because it was too large, and its shape was weird. It stood up, and I saw that it was far more gray than dark and taller than my dad, who's around six five. It was so big that it looked like a bear except for the shape and the gray color. Its head was huge, and it had a long snout. Its head looked like a dog, but bigger and longer. It had huge, long arms, and its hands looked large and flat. Its head looked like a timber wolf's, but longer and more snoutlike. It turned and looked off in the distance as if responding to a sound, then bolted off on all fours quicker than a flash. I remember standing there for a second, taken aback and just thinking... what... did... I... just... see.

I was old enough to know that werewolves and monsters didn't exist, but... how would I explain something like this? I made a conscious decision to forget about it and not tell anyone. I had no idea what it was and didn't want people to think I was crazy.

I still live in the same house since my parents sold it to me during college. It's sentimental to me. I even walk by those same woods from time to time, more so in the morning, and I swear that sometimes the woods goes completely silent. However, I never sense anything or "feel" anything out of the ordinary. I don't know how to explain what I saw. I'm not sure if it was a dogman, but I can tell you that it didn't look like any animal or creature I've ever seen.

Encounter 13
Submitted By: Erik
Time: N/A
Location: N/A

I WAS HUNTING in the woods with my dog, a boxer-pit mix. It is supposed to be legal, but I had not checked. I had not been in the woods long, maybe thirty minutes. I had let my dog off the leash. He was running around and tracking something. He came running towards me but did not stop. He ran right past me and kept going. I decided that he had something on the trail, and I would go after it.

As soon as I started going after him, I realized he was tracking something. He had been running along the trail and was now off to my left, weaving back and forth. I was a little ahead of him, but I was tracking him. All of a sudden, my dog disappeared. It was almost as if he had dropped into a hole, but there was no hole. I could not see anything, but my dog was gone.

I started yelling for him and then did what every hunter does, "Here, boy," but nothing. After a few minutes of yelling and whistling, I decided that he must have treed something, so I whistled for him to back up. I whistled, but he did not come, so I whistled again. No dog appeared, and no sound came back. I whistled a few more times and then walked back to the truck. I walked about two hundred yards and did not find him. I walked back to where we had been hunting and still did not see him. I called him and whistled for another hour with no sound or sign of my dog.

He did return about an hour after but was very timid and stayed about ten feet behind me for the rest of the day. I also noticed several huge gash marks along his abdomen and side that looked like a large dog had attacked him. My dog has gotten into pretty vicious fights before, and I know what a "dog" attack looks like. He was hurt. I did bring him to the vet, but she just assumed he had been attacked by a giant dog. I explained my situation, and she possibly chalked it up to a large coyote. Either way, the wounds looked to be made by a big animal.

I never thought about it until the day my dog was attacked; the woods had a different feel to them. I'm not just being paranoid, either. I can't say it was a dogman, but things point in that direction. It's been a while since this happened, and I did not think about the incident until your show was playing on YouTube. I heard one of your podcast stories about dogmen pop up in my playlist. I have had a few other strange things happen to me while in the woods, but that is another story I'll share later. God bless. Erik.

Encounter 14
Submitted By: Dillian
Time: Fall 2007
Location: Michigan

I LIVE in a rural part of Michigan. I have had two experiences with what I can only describe as a dogman.

The first one was in the late fall of 2007. I had just gotten off work and was going to the gas station. As I was driving on the road, I looked and saw what I thought was a deer. I stopped, as I thought it was going to cross the road. As I watched, it got up on its hind legs, which I didn't think was possible for a deer. As I watched, it continued to get closer and closer to me, almost as if it were stalking me. I then saw its fur, which was completely black. The only way I can describe its arms is that they were like a dog's, with long claws. It then started to walk like a man on two legs.

As it got closer, I could see its face. It looked like a wolf-dog-human mix. It had a long snout with huge teeth that looked like they could rip a full-grown man in half. I then realized it was coming towards my car, and I threw the truck in reverse, throwing it into third gear. As I looked back, it had a demonic look on its face. I then floored it and got out of there.

I looked in my rearview mirror; it was on all fours and had a more doglike face. This thing pursued my car for about a mile; stopping, it vanished into the woods. So I was scared out of my mind. It was about a hundred yards away from me when I initially saw it. It appeared to be about seven feet tall. Even at that distance I could see it's claws as they hung down. They were long and sharp and looked extremely deadly. Its fur was completely black, and its eyes were a deep, dark red. It was one of the most terrifying things I have ever seen.

The second time I had an encounter was in late 2008. I was in my room at about 3 a.m. and heard scratching on my window. I looked out the blinds and didn't see anything. The scratching persisted, and I finally got up to look out the window. As I looked, the creature was looking in the window. I nearly fell back in fear, as this thing's face was pressed against the glass, looking down at me. I then ran to my bed and hid under it. I could hear the creature outside the window, growling. I was shaking so bad, as it would not leave me alone. I waited until the sun came up to venture outside. I believe I saw the same creature as before, but I am not 100% sure.

I have not seen it since, but I know it is still out there. Every time I hear a noise outside, I get scared that it is coming for me. These creatures are real, and they are out there. I am unsure if there is more than one of them or if it is just the same one. But I do know that they are out there and are not human. I have kept this to myself, but I thought you'd be interested in my experiences.

Encounter 15
Submitted By: midnight_moses
Time: 2014
Location: N/A

I WAS RIDING with my brother and his friend. We decided to go into the woods and get drunk, as it was my brother's birthday. As we walked through the woods, I had my pocketknife out to cut branches in the way. It worked as pathetically as it sounds. I liked to pretend it was a machete. Walking through the woods, we had to go up a large hill. When we reached the top, my brother and his friend mentioned that we should venture into a small meadow right by the creek nearby and drink more. I was so down with this idea. We pushed onward and down the hill and found a place to sit on rocks next to the creek.

I wanted a cigarette bad, but I was broke, so I had to get creative. My brother and his friend were sitting on the other side of the creek, drinking beer and talking. It was dusk, and I had to pee; I found a nice spot behind a tree. After relieving myself, I noticed a deer with its head missing, probably about twenty feet away from me. It grossed me out. I ran back to my brother and his friend, and they had just pulled out a couple of joints and some more weed. We smoked a couple of joints in that spot, but I don't know... it wasn't doing anything for me. It was garbage weed. His friend went to light up a third one, and I declined when he passed it; it was just giving me a headache.

We decided to maybe walk and explore a little since we hadn't gone back there before. Maybe twenty minutes went by, and we found this small rock cave. It looked kind of like a den. Smelled bad. It was like a mixture of body odor, wet dog, and blood. We laughed and joked for a little while before my brother started seriously wigging out. I thought he was just high or paranoid, but he kept saying, "Guys, I think we need to go; I got a bad feeling." It wasn't until about close to dark that I noticed these things myself.

We were about halfway back, and I was in front of them. They had their phones out, filming themselves walking through the woods and talking. The light from their phones made a trail behind them, so I could see the shadows of the woods. It looked like people were walking behind them, but it was just shadows.

We kept walking, and I told them to shut up and listen. We stopped walking for a second, dead silence, but we were still walking back. Our footfalls were making the only noise in my ears. Then I heard or felt a vibration in the ground beneath my feet. The trees were moving, but I couldn't see anything. I stopped and had a really bad feeling, like what you get when you think someone is staring at you. I looked around but couldn't see anything. I told my brother and his friend to stop walking, but they ignored me. I turned around and saw what looked like a large dark shape crawling on the ground, on all fours. It was maybe twenty-five feet from me, and I turned around to run. It was following us.

I ran past my brother and his friend, who were so paranoid they were having a hard time comprehending what I was saying, and then I heard them both scream to run. As they were screaming, I looked over my shoulder and saw what was maybe ten feet behind us. It was a large shape, with long crooked legs. I pulled ahead of my brother and his friend, grabbing their hands as we ran. I didn't want to look behind us, but I could feel it following. I thought I could hear its footsteps, but my heart was pounding so hard in my ears I couldn't be sure. We ran for what felt like thirty minutes, but was probably more like five. The creek was right there, so we ran for it. When we got to the creek, I knew we were safe.

I kept looking back but didn't see anything, and we all sat there for a while, catching our breath. I should mention this creek goes back towards the way we came. That's how we got back; we followed the creek very loosely. My brother was FREAKED OUT. He kept saying it was a werewolf trailing us and that he saw its yellow eyes, etc. I wasn't about to tell him he's crazy because I saw it too. Or at least a big black shadow following us in the woods behind us. I never saw any definition in its shape as he did, but it was enough to scare the living hell out of us. We have never gone back there since this happened. This was in 2014.

Encounter 16
Submitted By: Charlotte Cross
Time: 1970s
Location: N/A

BEING the only child in my family, I spent a lot of time by myself outside; I spent a lot more time playing outdoors than most of my friends. Our home was on the outskirts of town and backed up to a vast forest. My parents were very strict about me being outside, I had to be within sight at all times, or they would come out looking for me.

I spent hours every day exploring this forest, which was my little world to get lost in. It was early in the fall, but it felt like late summer that day, not too hot or cold. There were leaves gathering everywhere; some had already turned brown and orange. It was about 7 p.m.; the sun was setting when I heard my parents start calling for me from inside the house. I knew that because it was dinnertime.

I started to walk out of the forest, picking up speed as I got closer to the fence line into our backyard. I stopped at the edge of a clearing just in front of our back patio, where I saw something strange in the neighbor's yard that made me stop dead in my tracks. It was standing next to their shed behind their home on four legs, hunched over like an ape with its forearms resting on its thighs. Then, at that exact moment, I heard something significant from behind me approaching...

The creature was doglike in appearance but had no fur. Its entire body was bare and appeared to be covered entirely with this gross mangy-looking skin. The whole thing looked wrong. I felt my stomach drop, and an adrenaline rush hit me as I heard the animal behind me start growling. I realized it was already too late to run past this creature in front of me, so I crouched down into a tense position, ready for whatever might come next.

This looked different from the other creature over by the shed, but they looked similar. This creature just looked at me like it was pleased I was going to be its next meal. I'm still shocked at how quietly it snuck up on me. My mother called out for me again, and as soon as the creature heard her voice, it stopped like it was surprised and looked in the direction of her voice. It then turned around and started jumping over fallen logs and running through trees at a speed I couldn't understand until it disappeared into the forest on the far side of our neighbor's yard.

I heard whatever the same strange creature was by the shed at my neighbor's house following it. I was so scared I remember I peed my pants. Of course, my mother kept laughing at me; she couldn't understand why I had peed and was so afraid. I just played it off and never told her because I knew she would never believe me.

This encounter was so terrifying. I've never explored the forest around my neighborhood since that day, and I never told or said anything to my neighbor. Come to think of it, after this, I don't recall seeing these strange animals again. I'm posting this here because it seems appropriate to share a weird experience I endured when I was younger. Stay safe.

Encounter 17
Submitted By: Edward Wozniak
Time: August 1, 2018
Location: North Carolina

IT WAS ABOUT 11 P.M., and I was walking home from work. It had gotten dark outside by this time, but there was a full moon that night, illuminating the surrounding area pretty well. I was walking down the side of the road, as there was no sidewalk, when I heard what sounded like loud panting from behind me.

I turned around to see what was breathing so hard and saw something running at me with its head low to the ground but up in my direction. It looked very tall and skinny from a distance, but its size must've been close to that of an average adult male human, if not more significant. Long arms were attached to its body, but they didn't appear to move as it ran toward me. The more this thing got closer, the louder it started breathing, which created a kind of a rhythmic tone.

It stopped and stared at me for several seconds before walking off. I could hear it moving through the woods in my direction. I realized it had walked into the forest next to me to stay concealed, and it was quickly approaching me from the trees. I began panicking, unsure what my next move should be or what exactly I was dealing with. I was convinced at that moment this was a demon.

I remained frozen where I stood, hearing it come closer and closer in the darkening woods. Once it got about twenty feet from me, I knew I had no choice but to flee, or I'd be a goner. I didn't think I could outrun it. So I quickly turned to my right and booked it back the way I came, towards my house.

I ran as hard as I could, looking over my shoulder every so often while expecting this thing to be not far behind me. It felt like an eternity until I passed the tree line for that side of the road and entered into a more open area again where there were houses with people living in them. There was still at least a quarter mile before reaching my street, which was when all sounds stopped behind me, and I started hearing a strange mechanical whirring noise coming from somewhere nearby but couldn't see where it was coming from.

The sound grew louder, moving closer, and this loud mechanical humming noise seemed to come from everywhere. I wasn't sure what was going on, so I continued pushing hard and running. That was when, with the full moon now behind me, I suddenly saw something moving beside my house, about fifty feet in front of me.

A tall black silhouette stood out against all the light around it. It was this translucent figure. It looked like something from another world. I knew at this point, whatever this thing was, it seemed to be targeting me specifically, and I watched its movement as best I could while darting between two houses nearby where large jagged piles of rocks blocked my path. The kind of rocks that people put in the front or side of their home for decoration. It's hard to explain. I quickly made it back into my house and locked everything. My parents were crashed out, so they didn't hear or see anything.

The rest of that night was so stressful. Even though I was on the second story, I would see these mysterious lights shining in my window. I would hear strange growling outside my house and these bizarre sounds. Mechanical noises, to humming, to heavy footsteps. I don't know if I had an alien encounter or what on earth I experienced.

Hands down the most frightening thing I've ever gone through to date.

Encounter 18
Submitted By: Anonymous
Time: N/A
Location: Maine

IT WAS 7 P.M., and a family was driving down a lonely road in the middle of Maine. It was a Friday night, and it looked like they would have the house all to themselves for the rest of the weekend, but what happened one hour later as they drove home changed their lives forever.

They saw something crossing the street ahead of them. At first, they thought it might be an injured dog or cat and stopped their car to see if it was okay.

As they got closer, it became apparent that this animal-looking creature had humanlike features but fur all over its body. This scared them, so they decided to step on the gas and get away from there as fast as possible.

One day after this incident, people started to report the same creature in other areas. Some people said it was a werewolf, and others said it looked like a bear with long legs.

There have been several reports of this creature, but no one has managed to get any clear pictures or videos of what is happening. All we know is that this thing is enormous and has been seen in many different locations.

We ask anyone who sees it... please look away fast!

This dogman creature was first seen in Michigan back in 1987 by two campers. They saw something chasing their dog, which led them to a prominent tall monster figure on its hind legs. It had a canine head, dark fur all over its body, strong arms, and a man's body type.

Since then, we have seen this creature more often in different parts of the world. In Winnipeg, Canada, people saw three creatures walking near one of the schools on their hind legs. When kids came outside to see what was happening, these dogmen started chasing them down before running away into nearby woods.

Witnesses in Virginia reported seeing a werewolf-like being five times between 2002 and 2005, where it tried to attack people living nearby but always ran off when someone spotted it.

This dogman creature can be seen as tall as seven feet and is very violent when it encounters humans. It has also been known to kill animals such as cattle and horses, so if you see it, stay away and call for help as soon as possible!

Encounter 19
Submitted By: Mikey Hoss
Time: Fall 2014
Location: Maine

I HAD A PRETTY horrific experience back in 2014 during the fall. I don't believe in werewolves or things like that, but I had an encounter with a strange being that resembled one. It looked like it came from Hollywood itself.

Here's my encounter:

I was walking down the street in Maine around 6:00 a.m. and on my way to work. It was drizzling, and I had my hood up over my head when a large shape caught the corner of my eye. I turned to look up into some trees by people's houses there and noticed something that didn't make sense. I saw what looked like a man covered in long hair that hung down all over his body, standing up, looking at me from one of the upper branches of an oak tree next door. The thing reeked, too; it smelled like rotting meat mixed with spoiled eggs. It stuck out to me at first because this thing looked so out of place, but due to the haze of the rain and how dark it was, I didn't register what exactly it was. Then, it stopped and looked over at me, and then I stopped dead in my tracks, as I could see its glowing eyes.

What's crazy is that I felt this jolt of fear when we made eye contact. Not a normal fear like what you think when you see something wrong, but I knew that an immense danger was in front of me, and if it wanted to, it could destroy me without even trying. Its eyes were so bright and glowing they lit up the early morning, and for reasons beyond my understanding, all I could think about as I looked at this thing was how much it reminded me of something straight out of a Hollywood movie.

It stood there staring at me with its yellow eyes for several seconds before slowly turning and walking to this small alleyway behind me like it realized it was out in the open and needed to conceal itself.

I was firmly planted in one spot, frozen as this thing disappeared from view.

This thing happens to your mind when you endure something like this. There are no words to explain it. This was genuine fear, a primal fear your body only experiences once. There are a few shortcomings to what I can accurately describe.

When you're in a situation like that, your mind isn't thinking about how you should be reacting, and it's not the kind of thing that can just be brushed off and forgotten.

I remember my legs feeling weak, and my body was entirely numb at first before this strange rush of energy hit me as if I had been ejected out of a slingshot. The second it happened, I took off. I ran home as fast as possible, without looking back until after I got inside when reality started to set in on what had occurred only minutes ago.

It's one of the strangest things that has ever happened to me, but for some reason, this is my most vivid memory.

I've never had any other encounters with anything like it since, but sometimes I think back to that night and wonder exactly what that was. I'm unsure how anyone could attribute what I saw that morning to anything other than a werewolf or mythical creature. It all sounds crazy when you say it out loud and doesn't fit the typical description of something simple like a big dog or regular wolf.

To this day, I've never heard someone tell me about seeing something similar before until recently when several friends on social media started posting stories about their own experiences with this strange canine beast in their hometowns, which has got me thinking again about my experience from long ago.

I'm not trying to sound like some kook or anything, but those eyes, that hair, and that smell will forever stick with me. I hope this isn't a sign of things to come. I hope this is just a fluke or something entirely separate from everything else in the world right now, but for some reason, I have this terrible feeling that it's only the start of something much worse...

Encounter 20
Submitted By: Tiffany Yu
Time: N/A
Location: Maine

MY BOYFRIEND and I were driving on a back road in northern Maine when we saw something terrible.

We were traveling along a deserted stretch of road, surrounded by trees as far as the eye could see, and white snow on the ground. On our right was a ravine, and on our left was where we saw it. It was hairy, had short ears, and walked like a man but stood like an ape. At first, I thought it was a bear or deer because we were deep in the woods, so seeing them isn't unusual here.

My boyfriend started driving faster after he looked at what pulled its head up from drinking water in a stream! He said, "Did you see that?!" I only got to catch a glimpse, but I can tell you this wasn't any animal any of us know. We were both so scared we didn't talk about it until a day later when we returned.

I have no idea what this creature is, but I don't care what people say; I know what I saw and now what my boyfriend saw too! It has to be investigated further! This wasn't some bear or coyote like everyone says it is.

Encounter 21
Submitted By: Jimmy
Time: N/A
Location: Pennsylvania

I'M a trucker and often make long trips across the country, sometimes lasting several days. I always sleep in the rig and have been doing this for a few years. While it isn't precisely five-star accommodation, and I'll never get used to relying on gas station restrooms to keep clean, it's a job that helps pay for my kid's college fees. It can get pretty lonely on those longer trips, but these days I got the advantage of podcasts and audiobooks to keep me from going mad. Usually, I drive until I can't anymore and then find a truck stop. Sometimes though, it just has to be the side of the road, so long as it is safe. And it was one of those times when this incident occurred.

I'd been on the road for hours, trying to find somewhere decent to pull over and stop for the night, but there was nothing for miles, just trees as far as the eye could see. I was in the Pacific Northwest, and there were huge Christmas tree farms and logging plants everywhere. You'd have thought they'd need plenty of amenities too, but the particular stretch of road I was on was strictly back to basics. Eventually, I found a safe spot where the road widened, and I could park safely, knowing that in the unlikely chance someone else needed to pass by, they could do so securely without crashing into me.

I shut my eyes, and I was out like a light. It was around 2 a.m. and very still outside. So I was pretty pissed when I woke up suddenly. Having been doing this for years, I have gotten used to sleeping through all sorts, and it usually takes a hell of a commotion to wake me after I have fallen into an exhausted slumber. What could be making all that noise in this empty stretch of road? It sounded like screaming, almost like a kid crying, but I have plenty of hunting buddies who would tell you that several animals out there make a noise akin to a woman being murdered. Therefore, I wasn't worried that I was witnessing some middle-of-nowhere serial killer, but I did want whatever the hell was out there to shut the hell up so I could go back to sleep.

I was staring out the window, thinking I could give a long blast on the air horn to scare off whatever was out there making a racket, when I saw movement from outside the vehicle. Whatever the creature was, it had come out of the trees and stood right next to the truck. Have you ever been in a country lane at night? There were no streetlights out there, so it was completely dark, yet I instinctively knew something was off. You see, although I could only make out the animal's outline, it was tall since I could see the head from the cab of my truck. That shouldn't have been possible. It didn't seem to be moving—whatever the hell it was, it just stood still in the road in front of me. So I carefully flicked on the engine just enough to turn the lights on, and then I got a full view of what was out there...

The lights blinded it for a second, and it let out another one of those damn scream/howls, and it was even worse with it being closer. But the sound I could account for. What made no sense at all was what the creature seemed to be. As I said, it was tall, around six and a half to seven feet at a guess, and stocky, almost the body of a pro footballer. And said body was very much like a guy's, a very stacked and hairy guy with all the torso and limbs in proportion, just the same as a human. But the head, oh god, the head. I'm not very good at identifying breeds of dogs, but when I got home, I looked it up and can confirm that this THING had the head of a Doberman pinscher, again totally in proportion to the size of the human-looking body, but 100% canine.

It was also grinning at me. At least that was what it looked like; try to imagine a dog's face manipulated into a very human-looking expression. If it hadn't already been something that had messed with my mind, and I'd never forget, that eerie and out-of-place grin cemented it. I honked the horn as hard as possible, giving it an excellent long blast. There was chaos around for a minute or two as birds took off out of trees; I heard other various critters sounding their displeasure. A deer made to cross the road, took one look at the creature still in front of me, and did a sort of backward leap back into the trees from where it came. The dogman gave another high-pitched howl and leaped after the deer. That leap shouldn't have been possible—it would be Olympic-worthy. I didn't even look at the clock. I slammed my foot on the gas and was out of there as fast as the rig would move. I drove for about another hour until I found a gas station, where I pulled in and slept fitfully for the rest of the night.

No one that I told afterward believed me, of course. They all asked what I'd been listening to (*Lord of the Rings* since the books are so long and the audio even longer, it keeps me entertained for hours), which is fantasy. Still, I'm pretty sure Tolkien didn't include werewolf/man dogs in his work. They also said I had been dreaming or was so tired that I just hallucinated the entire thing. My only counterpoint for that would be that until that night after I had gotten home and done some research, I had never even heard of the concept of dogmen. If I had ever supposed such a thing existed, not being that familiar with dog breeds, how could I have imagined the exact type of dog that these are partly made up of? I could have conjured up something like Lassie or even Scooby-Doo...

I know I didn't imagine that thing. It was as accurate as you or me. And it was nasty.

6
FLYING HUMANOID ENCOUNTERS & SIGHTINGS

IT SEEMS to be the thing in recent years more than ever people are reporting seeing flying humanoid beings. This includes Mothman, bat humanoids, gargoyle entities and much more. I've even heard reports of "bird men" and other winged beings. There are even those who say they have been abducted by flying humanoids.

What's even stranger is that these reports are coming in from all over the world and not just from one or two countries. People from the United States, Canada, Europe, Asia, South America and more have all reported seeing these strange beings.

Some say that these beings are extraterrestrial, while others believe they are interdimensional creatures or even time travelers. There are a lot of theories out there, but no one really knows for sure what these flying humanoids are. Perhaps they do hold some sort of supernatural power among many of the beings and creatures in this book.

Encounter 1
Submitted By: Anonymous
Time: N/A
Location: N/A

I KNOW people send you all sorts of crazy stories. Even as I recount it to you, it's still hard for me to believe this took place, even though I know it's common among the people who write to you. This was the fall of last year when I was gathering up firewood. There's a place up in the mountains that I go to where I'm able to cut up large felled trees. It's pretty desolate, so it's a good place for me to load up on cords of wood to haul back. I was by myself at this time, so there were no other witnesses.

I was loading the firewood into my truck when I heard a crashing sound behind me, about twenty-five yards away. From about fifty feet up in the trees, this creature came swooping down at my truck, flew back up into a nearby pine tree, and held onto the tree. I panicked and thought to myself, *What the hell is that thing?* It was black and had large bat-like wings, glowing red eyes, and huge teeth. It looked like a freaking gargoyle. I kid you not. I know I sound crazy, but I don't know what else to compare it to. Maybe a flying demon or something.

It set its sights right on me. Then it swooped down again at me from not even forty feet up in the tree, and I dove to the ground. It squawked this horrible cry. I was swearing up a storm and running for my truck to get the hell out of there even though the bed of my truck was wide open, and I got wood rounds in there that were going to fly out. I was being attacked by who knows what and was prepared to leave all my tools and chainsaw behind.

I jumped in my truck before this thing could make another dive, and I drove down this dirt road with this thing flying after me, hot on my tail. Wood rounds were flying out of the bed of my truck, landing all over the road. I lost all the wood I had back there. Being on a dirt road, you couldn't floor it at sixty miles an hour. This thing flew down, landed on my roof, and tried to stick its fingers in my window. I had to start swerving violently to shake it off my truck. It finally gave up before almost entirely tipping my truck over altogether. I was going way too fast on this mountainside, and I'm honestly surprised I didn't topple over down the sharp embankment going down this grade as fast as I did. I knew it was still above the truck, hovering, but as I got into the denser part of the trees down at the bottom of the grade, it couldn't keep up and zipped off into the sky.

I thought it was gone. But as I came around another curve in the road, it was there again. This time I had to slam on my brakes as hard as I could to avoid hitting it dead-on. The second I stopped, it attached itself onto my windshield and wouldn't budge no matter how fast I drove. At this point, I was driving completely blind except for a small sliver out the driver's side of the window where its body wasn't in the way. Desperate to see where I was going so that hopefully, whatever this thing was, it would detach and let me go. I tried honking my horn repeatedly as I drove, but it only seemed to make the thing angry.

The next thing I knew, its head started pushing through the glass of my windshield towards me. I was trying to hold it back with one hand while steering as best I could with the other, but then its teeth started gnashing and tearing at my arm. That was when I lost control of the truck and went careening off the road into a ditch. The impact knocked this thing off the truck. I was able to pull out of the ditch, thank God my truck is a 4x4, and I drove as fast as I could back into town.

I immediately went to the hospital. I got twenty-six stitches on my arm, plus a tetanus shot. And they even gave me a rabies shot, just in case.

The police came to the hospital, and I gave them my story. At first, they didn't believe me. But when I took them out to the parking lot and they saw the condition of my truck, they were stunned.

Before this, if you had told me anything remotely close to what had happened to me, I would have laughed in your face and told you that it made a nice fiction story. However, once I experienced it myself, I feel more traumatized than anything else.

There really isn't much else to add to the story other than I was attacked by some sort of flying creature that I could not identify. It looked like a demon or a gargoyle, and I don't know what else to call it. It was black and had wings like a bat. It was larger than me and had long claws that it used to try to break into my truck. I don't know what kind of animal or creature looks like that, but this did. I haven't seen it since, but now I always keep a gun in the truck just in case.

Encounter 2
Submitted By: Anonymous
Time: July
Location: Near Black Bear Lake

A VERY SCARY thing happened to me a month ago, right after the Fourth of July. I live not too far from the Black Bear Lake area. I was walking my dog one evening after dark (about 11:00 p.m.) when suddenly my dog started growling and acting really strange. Keep in mind that my dog is a year-old Labrador retriever who is very gentle with people. Even when I first got him to calm down, he seemed nervous about walking outside at night.

Anyway, I walked towards my house to head back, about thirty-five to forty minutes away. Suddenly my dog started growling and going psycho again and started taking off, pulling free of my leash. As soon as my dog got about ten to fifteen feet away from me (he was very fast indeed), he suddenly stopped growling and started looking back at me nervously.

He was just looking at something intently that I couldn't see. Suddenly my dog started whimpering and acting really strange, and that was when I began to feel this intense feeling like something was wrong. It was fear, and my dog felt it, too. And he was staring at whatever was causing this just beyond my vision in the dark. That was when I heard something growl. I had a small flashlight on me at the time that I was using to light my way. I began shining it all around but couldn't see a thing!

I was quickly and nervously scanning over the area where I heard the growling. Then my light shone onto the face of a creature that came out of a nightmare. Dark in color, reptilian-like eyes and a mouth full of razor teeth. It was grinning at me, opening its mouth like it was hissing. To be completely honest, the first thing that popped into my mind was the demon from the *Insidious* movies. That demon scared the hell out of me when I first saw it, and this thing I was looking at looked very close to it. Very identical-looking faces.

Then this thing screamed, jumped up, and flew into the air into the night, revealing an enormous wingspan. As it screamed and flew away, my dog and I took off, running back to the house in record speed. I don't even think it took us fifteen minutes to get back to the house when it should have normally taken thirty-plus minutes.

I contacted the police and reported this incident right away. I did not know what was growling or what this creature was. Still, I reported an unknown animal that appeared to be hostile.

They sent an officer out, and when he came to get a report of exactly what I saw, I was 100% honest and told them exactly down to a T what I saw and what had happened walking home. He asked me the typical police officer questions, where were you, why were you out so late, and what were you doing, you know, the usual BS. I answered everything honestly and truthfully.

The officer seemed to take me seriously and told me he was going to go take a look around. He spent about twenty minutes going in the direction I came from and came back and said a bunch of the trees had large claw marks where you could tell something had been resting on them up in the trees. He told me, "I don't know much about bears, but you may have seen a bear up in the tree that jumped off."

Before I could tell him off for writing my story off as it being a large brown bear that was perched up on a branch and then jumped away, he told me I was not the first person to report a similar sighting like I just had. This area has been full of weird things happening. And the officer even told me about some odd things that happened to him while he was out on duty that he shared with me personally. He's not sure what to make of it, and he's a firm skeptic regarding paranormal and strange things. But he told me to keep my eyes open in case anything weird does happen.

I'm part Native American, and I lived on a reservation for quite some time back in the '90s, so I know weird things happening is in my blood. I've even experienced bizarre things with a buddy of mine when we were hunting near our tribal burial ground, but that's for another time.

I have no words to accurately describe the creature I saw that night other than pure fear and terror. And dogs, dogs are very sensory-based creatures, and they know when something is afoot. I trusted my dog's gut instincts, and he led me right. He knew this creature was there long before I did, and I don't even know how long it was watching me from the dark. Had I not shone a light on it and heard it growl at me, I would have walked right by it. Had I not had my dog with me, it probably would have grabbed me, or who knows what else. Why was it resting there in the trees near me? I'm not exactly sure. Maybe it was looking for its next victim, or perhaps worse. Who knows.

I've had friends in this area who have had weird experiences, like seeing Bigfoot and other strange creatures they can't explain. So I guess I shouldn't be entirely surprised, but I saw what I did even though I've never seen a creature like that before. The world we live in just continues to get more and more bizarre.

Encounter 3
Submitted By: Anonymous
Time: July
Location: Near Black Bear Lake

A VERY SCARY thing happened to me a month ago, right after the Fourth of July. I live not too far from the Black Bear Lake area. I was walking my dog one evening after dark (about 11:00 p.m.) when suddenly my dog started growling and acting really strange. Keep in mind that my dog is a year-old Labrador retriever who is very gentle with people. Even when I first got him to calm down, he seemed nervous about walking outside at night.

Anyway, I walked towards my house to head back, about thirty-five to forty minutes away. Suddenly my dog started growling and going psycho again and started taking off, pulling free of my leash. As soon as my dog got about ten to fifteen feet away from me (he was very fast indeed), he suddenly stopped growling and started looking back at me nervously.

He was just looking at something intently that I couldn't see. Suddenly my dog started whimpering and acting really strange, and that was when I began to feel this intense feeling like something was wrong. It was fear, and my dog felt it, too. And he was staring at whatever was causing this just beyond my vision in the dark. That was when I heard something growl. I had a small flashlight on me at the time that I was using to light my way. I began shining it all around but couldn't see a thing!

I was quickly and nervously scanning over the area where I heard the growling. Then my light shone onto the face of a creature that came out of a nightmare. Dark in color, reptilian-like eyes and a mouth full of razor teeth. It was grinning at me, opening its mouth like it was hissing. To be completely honest, the first thing that popped into my mind was the demon from the *Insidious* movies. That demon scared the hell out of me when I first saw it, and this thing I was looking at looked very close to it. Very identical-looking faces.

Then this thing screamed, jumped up, and flew into the air into the night, revealing an enormous wingspan. As it screamed and flew away, my dog and I took off, running back to the house in record speed. I don't even think it took us fifteen minutes to get back to the house when it should have normally taken thirty-plus minutes.

I contacted the police and reported this incident right away. I did not know what was growling or what this creature was. Still, I reported an unknown animal that appeared to be hostile.

They sent an officer out, and when he came to get a report of exactly what I saw, I was 100% honest and told them exactly down to a T what I saw and what had happened walking home. He asked me the typical police officer questions, where were you, why were you out so late, and what were you doing, you know, the usual BS. I answered everything honestly and truthfully.

The officer seemed to take me seriously and told me he was going to go take a look around. He spent about twenty minutes going in the direction I came from and came back and said a bunch of the trees had large claw marks where you could tell something had been resting on them up in the trees. He told me, "I don't know much about bears, but you may have seen a bear up in the tree that jumped off."

Before I could tell him off for writing my story off as it being a large brown bear that was perched up on a branch and then jumped away, he told me I was not the first person to report a similar sighting like I just had. This area has been full of weird things happening. And the officer even told me about some odd things that happened to him while he was out on duty that he shared with me personally. He's not sure what to make of it, and he's a firm skeptic regarding paranormal and strange things. But he told me to keep my eyes open in case anything weird does happen.

I'm part Native American, and I lived on a reservation for quite some time back in the '90s, so I know weird things happening is in my blood. I've even experienced bizarre things with a buddy of mine when we were hunting near our tribal burial ground, but that's for another time.

I have no words to accurately describe the creature I saw that night other than pure fear and terror. And dogs, dogs are very sensory-based creatures, and they know when something is afoot. I trusted my dog's gut instincts, and he led me right. He knew this creature was there long before I did, and I don't even know how long it was watching me from the dark. Had I not shone a light on it and heard it growl at me, I would have walked right by it. Had I not had my dog with me, it probably would have grabbed me, or who knows what else. Why was it resting there in the trees near me? I'm not exactly sure. Maybe it was looking for its next victim, or perhaps worse. Who knows.

I've had friends in this area who have had weird experiences, like seeing Bigfoot and other strange creatures they can't explain. So I guess I shouldn't be entirely surprised, but I saw what I did even though I've never seen a creature like that before. The world we live in just continues to get more and more bizarre.

Encounter 4
Submitted By: Daniel Terrance
Time: N/A
Location: Nevada

I'M NOT QUITE sure if I saw something exactly, but I certainly cannot explain the phenomenon. Last year I was with my brothers and a friend of theirs on our way to Las Vegas for a one-week vacation where we planned binge drinking, some gambling, and debauchery. We decided to drive there. And if anybody has ever driven through Nevada or any of the southwestern United States, you would know that it is a vast wasteland of desert and nothingness. Because mistakenly seeing something being there and then not being there is pretty hard to do when your backdrop is just stale desert. On the drive there, I sat in the driver's side back seat.

We were about an hour away from Vegas and on a long stretch of I-15 North. To my left was kind of a rocky outcropping. Not quite a big mountain or a cliff but just a lot of rocky-like hills. I might be terrible at describing the landscape. Still, if you need a visual, simply Google Maps a random highway in Nevada so you understand what I'm talking about. The landscape really doesn't change anyway.

I was looking out the window when I saw what looked to be a large black shape sitting on a boulder a good distance away from the road. My first impression was that it was some large gargoyle or something. I remember thinking how weird it was because I was, like, who in their right mind would place a dark gargoyle here? I thought they belonged in Gothic-style buildings and things of that nature in downtown cities. It was pretty large, too. Even from far away, I could tell that the boulder and this thing were larger than the car. But I just assumed it was a statue of some sort. It wasn't moving at all and appeared to be perfectly still. I even nudged my brother to the right of me and said, "Look, I don't know why they need a gargoyle way out here." His reaction was to tease me a bit. He mentioned it to the others in the truck. He said, "Hey, everybody, look over there. There is a giant statue of a dragon." Even though everyone laughed, they did agree it looked weird. He then said, "Maybe the Natives out here built it for protection." The conversation probably lasted less than a minute.

I noticed the area we drove by had a section of specific houses in a row, maybe three or four, and a broken-down old blue Ford pickup in front. Not far away was the boulder in question with what I thought was a gargoyle statue on top of it. We continued our trip to Vegas and did our week-long vacation.

On the drive back from Vegas on the same road, I just happened to be on the passenger-side back seat this time, looking out in the same direction on the way home. We came across this same stretch of road, and without me even thinking, I just happened to be looking out to the same area. I knew it was because my mind immediately recognized the old beat-up Ford pickup truck, the blue one I had mentioned that I had seen a week prior.

Then I saw those few houses and realized this was the exact spot. However, the gargoyle-looking statue was gone when I glanced over at the large boulder. My stomach immediately knotted up, which was too strange for me. I want to clarify that this statue was at a distance; assuming that is what it was, it would be far too large for it to be randomly just taken down and away. It is possible, but why would there be a large gargoyle statue sitting on top of a boulder in the middle of the desert by a few old houses?

That might be exactly what it was. But if my memory serves me correctly, gargoyle statues are much more gray since they are made of stone. This was shaped like a gargoyle, or what my mind would depict as one based on figures on Gothic buildings. But it was very dark in color and not gray like stone. Its color was vastly different from the brown and tan rock it was perched on top of. Even though it was perfectly still, looking out in our direction, I never once would have thought it to be real or to be able to move. And no, I never once saw its eyes shine or anything weird. Just a big dark shape. Its wings were even folded up in the back just like a typical gargoyle would be, or should I say a statue.

To give more of a size comparison, even though we were far from the boulder, it was clearly larger than the Ford pickup truck I mentioned parked in that yard. And when we drove by the first time, this statue, or whatever it was that was perched on top of that boulder, was also larger than the boulder. Meaning that the statue had to have been huge, maybe twenty to thirty feet in height. I'm not trying to exaggerate details here; I'm trying to give you as accurate information as I can recall.

I didn't realize that I said it out loud, but I said, "Wow, they took the statue down." Everyone looked out the window and noticed it was gone too. My brother who had teased me about it on the way there now said, "Yeah, that's weird. Why would they knock it down?"

Suddenly, my brother who was driving slammed on the brakes.

He screamed, "Look up there!" as he pointed toward the top of the windshield at the sky. Sitting in the back seat, my other brother and I had to bend forward a little to see what he was pointing at in the sky. There it was; that gargoyle was flying. I'm not sure how far away it was from us. I guess maybe a half a mile and hundreds of feet above us. It looked like it had some kind of big animal in its mouth. And it was flying really slowly like it didn't want to be spotted. We watched it head in the direction of the desert. Not far from the boulder that it had been sitting on earlier.

My brother who was driving said, "We're getting out of here," and put the pedal to the metal as they say. I know he reached a hundred miles per hour as we drove away. He didn't slow down until we came to the city of Primm. That was when he pulled over at the truck stop. We all got out of the truck and just stood there. I think all four of us were in a state of unbelief. And I know I was still scared. I was glad I was with my brothers. We decided we would not tell anybody about what we saw except our parents.

But it has been a year since that happened, and I had to tell somebody. So I'm sharing this with you.

Encounter 5
Submitted By: Mason
Time: N/A
Location: Australia

MY FATHER recently shared some fascinating information with me when we sat down to watch a movie. The movie in question is *Army of Darkness*. I don't know if you've ever seen the movie, but it's great. But that's not why I'm writing to you. My father and I were watching this movie. There's a scene when a flying demon grabs a girl and flies off. As we were watching that scene, my dad started acting funny, and I looked at him and asked what was up. He literally got up and left the room, and I could tell he was visibly shaken.

I followed him outside and asked him what was wrong. He told me that he would tell me later. Anyway, I went back into the house to finish watching the movie. When it was over, I noticed he was still outside on the deck, smoking a cigarette. That was when I decided to pursue it and ask what that had been all about earlier. He told me, "Son, you probably won't believe me if I told you this." I told him I loved him and would believe whatever he wanted to say to me. Obviously, something about the movie bothered him, and I wanted to know.

My father spent a lot of time in Australia twenty years ago when he was married to his first wife of nine years. Unfortunately, she passed away from breast cancer over ten years ago. My father then moved to the east coast of the United States, where we live today. I don't know if he was a legal citizen, but he spent years there doing all sorts of stuff. I don't know what his line of work was, and I don't exactly know what he did. But he has told me about some of his adventures exploring the Australian Outback. And times when he'd almost been killed by some of the crazy wildlife out there. He even has a story about meeting some indigenous people after a five-day-long rendezvous in the Australian Outback and getting lost. I know the man has seen some things, but I wasn't expecting him to tell me what he did.

I bring up the Australian Outback because this was what he brought up. He told me that during one of his times of exploring out there and driving around, he came across a large pit in the earth, which he described to me. He said it looked man-made but was easily about thirty to fifty feet in diameter, quite literally a large hole that you could not see the bottom of. He said as he approached it, this flying demon flew out. And nearly grabbed onto and pulled him, almost dragging him down into the pit. He pushed it away in the nick of time and avoided falling into this hole. The demon flew off in the sky past the surrounding mountains.

He said the creature in that movie looked nearly identical to what he saw come out of that pit in size, stature, color, and everything. That scene immediately brought him back to that exact moment in his life and forced him to leave the room. (To give you a point of reference, Google "*Army of Darkness* flying demon," which should show you exactly what we saw in the movie and what my dad claims to have come out of the pit.) My dad's not usually like that, and he's not bothered by much. He's a firm and staunch believer in science and things that can be proven physically. So for him to tell me a tale like this was a little unnerving, to say the least.

I remember him shaking with his cigarette while explaining this to me. That will always have a lasting effect in my memory. The area where he found this pit was probably fifty-plus miles from any civilization. He was out there, and I mean it when I say out there. You have to understand that he would spend days, if not weeks at a time, just going back exploring and getting himself lost on several occasions. He's come into contact with all sorts of dangerous and poisonous animals. But this recollection of events really shook him more than anything else. I asked him if he thinks hell exists after he told me this story, and he said he doesn't know. I almost wonder if that pit was an entrance to hell or some sort of cavern system in which this thing lived, but even he didn't know.

My father never unveiled the province of Australia he was in when this encounter occurred. I am not too familiar with the geography of that country. Still, I know Australia is humongous, and the Outback stretches for miles in that area. I know there are stories from the indigenous people living in the Outback about strange and dangerous creatures. My father's story is only one. Indeed, there are other hair-raising stories like this one

---

Encounter 6
Submitted By: Tim L.
Time: N/A
Location: Northern California

I'VE SEEN my fair share of weird things in my life, but what my wife and I saw this day makes me question our reality. We were in Northern California at the time on our way to go see the Redwoods. We vacation around the United States often, so this was our first time driving through California. We were driving north along Highway 101, which runs along the coast. If you're going north, on your left-hand side, aka west, you could look out and see the beach and the ocean. I would frequently look over to my left, watching the beautiful waves crashing in. It's really a sight to see. If you ever find yourself on the west coast, it's genuinely worth the drive.

I remember it like it was yesterday, sunny clear skies, beautiful afternoon. But then I noticed something that didn't quite fit the scenery I was looking at. I was seeing this black shape up over the water. At first, I thought it was the shape of a seagull since there are tons of birds around coastal areas, but I noticed the shape didn't quite fit that of a typical bird. Plus, it was much larger.

It was flying at an angle, though, heading north by northeast. It was slowly coming in our direction while still aiming north. Meaning that eventually, this thing would fly directly overhead if it kept on its path.

The closer it got, the larger it became, and I soon realized that this was much larger than any bird I know of. It had large wings and was shaped just like a person. There was no coloring or any sort of light emanating from this animal, or what I would assume to be an animal, and it was just pitch black.

Then, as if on cue, my wife yelled, "What the heck is that!?" This thing had flown up from the ocean and the cliffs below and was almost level with the road.

I looked over just in time to catch a glimpse of what can only be described as a living pterodactyl flying above our car. Then it seemed to glide as it flew back toward the water. Then it dove into the water and came up with what looked like a small whale or shark in its beak. We were both shocked, as we had never seen anything like this before. We watched for a few seconds, not knowing what to do or say as it swallowed whatever was in its mouth, then dove again into the sea.

This time it went under the water and was no longer visible. It seemed to just vanish. We continued to stare out into the ocean when it suddenly came flying up out of the water again. It went straight up. I mean, this thing actually flew straight up like a rocket. We could see that it was holding something in its arms. Yes, it had arms. It must have gone several hundred feet in the air while holding on to whatever it had. Once again, we were both left speechless and in awe of what we had just seen.

Then it let go of what it was holding and dove at a fishing boat that had several people on it. They had obviously seen this thing too. Because as it got close to the boat, we could see the people in the boat trying to duck down away from this thing. It seemed to land right on the rear of the boat and grab a person. When it lifted off the boat, it was holding a person in its arms. We could see the person was flailing and trying to get away. But there was no escape. This thing flew off with the person in its arms. Then we heard a gunshot. Someone on the boat shot at this thing. When they did, the flying beast let go of the person it was holding. We saw the person fall into the water not far from the boat. Whoever he was started swimming toward the boat, and we watched as they brought him back on board the boat.

I feel terrible for admitting I should have spent more of my time looking at the road than I did, but it was such an anomaly that I couldn't help it. Of course, there was other traffic on the road, so I'm sure we were not the only ones to witness this that same day, and it was in plain view for anybody and everybody to see.

It just vanished at one point, and we never saw it again. We're not sure where it went or if it descended into the cliff basin below when it was shot at. With me driving, I couldn't keep my eyes on it a hundred percent of the time, so I would just keep quickly glancing over at it. In between the last glances, it was gone.

It sparked an hour's worth of conversation between my wife and me on what it could've been. Later on, with our laptop, we tried to look at anything that would resemble what we saw, and that's the first time we saw the Mothman picture. I don't know anything about the supposed Mothman. Still, I know that the silhouette of this enormous black thing with wings is almost identical to what we saw. Even with the sun shining and the broad daylight, there were still no distinct features. But the shape is exactly what I saw and remember it being. I don't know if there's any correlation, but my wife stumbled upon it and showed me and said that it is an interesting match.

My wife and I are pretty firm in our beliefs in science and being agnostics. But I try to keep an open mind if I am presented with new information that will change my beliefs. This has been one of those events in my life that makes me question what I know because there is certainly no explanation for what we saw. We have not talked to anybody else about our experience.

Encounter 7
Submitted By: Alfred S.
Time: N/A
Location: Mark Twain National Forest

I WANT to share a story of what happened two years ago with my best friend and me. In a nutshell, both my friend and I were being pursued by something, but I have no idea what it was. We were both in danger because of it, and I can tell you that it looked like a monstrous, hellish bat of enormous size. I count it as one of the most terrifying things that have ever happened to me in my entire life.

Due to my grandfather's passing, I was recently given some

money as an inheritance. And I decided to take a long road trip to the east coast.

My friend and I were interested in exploring different cities along the east coast, particularly New York and Boston, so we decided to visit, and any other place we thought would be cool to see.

I live in the Pacific Northwest just east of Vancouver, Washington, in a small town called Camas. In planning our trip, we knew it would probably take about a week to drive to New York. My friend suggested that, since we had the time and the money, let's extend the trip and do a scenic route of America. So we decided to go through Colorado and stop in Denver. Then continue east and go see the Arch in St. Louis. Then drive through the Blue Ridge Mountains in Kentucky and Virginia, and from there, drive up the east coast and stop at some historical sites along the way.

My favorite hobby is gaming. And I've made many friends via online gaming, so we planned to crash at people's houses that I had contact with instead of hoteling it or just sleeping in our car.

It took us two days of driving to get to Denver. But the drive was worth it because you went over the Rockies. I love the mountains in the Northwest, but the Rockies of Colorado can't be beaten. Denver was a bigger city than I thought. Lots of people. We walked downtown a little bit, but the altitude difference on our lungs was noticeable.

We spent the night there with one of my gaming friends. Unfortunately, we stayed up all night playing games. And when we left in the morning to continue our journey, we were both exhausted.

Our plan was to drive all the way to St. Louis and spend the night there.

But after driving all day through Kansas, which is as flat as a pancake and kind of boring in the scenery department, we realized we both were too tired to make the drive to St. Louis.

At this point in our trip, we were going through Missouri, and I want to say we were somewhere near the Mark Twain National Forest if I remember correctly.

I'm not exactly sure what happened because my friend put in the GPS coordinates to get us to a friend's house close by. Somehow the GPS must have rerouted us because we went in the opposite direction. We were wandering around the forest around ten o'clock at night, trying to find out where we should go.

Yes, the national forest is a beautiful place to be in, but when you're tired and stressed, it's not exactly fun. The GPS told us we were supposed to take this one road, we did, and it kept rerouting us. I was flustered, and so was my friend, so we were trying to make a loop around to see if we could get back to the way we came. Let me explain that we were the only people on the road at this time, as we did not see another pair of headlights for over an hour.

As we were driving along and he was fiddling with the GPS, trying to get it going, I had my brights on so I could see pretty much everything in front of me. But it was still dark all around us. Then I saw these two glowing dots in the dark up ahead, just beyond the reach of my lights. They were getting closer to us. I realized these dots were a pair of eyes. Then the beam of my headlights shined right on them, and I started to see the shape they were attached to, and I began screaming my head off.

For a split second, I thought it was a bat. Then I realized it was easily ten times larger than a typical bat, and its face was much more hideous. It looked like a demon bat. It flew right at our car and landed on top of the roof.

I could feel it land, crouch down and hold onto the roof. I began trying to swerve and knock it off our car while driving at about forty-five to fifty miles per hour. My friend and I were freaking out and screaming bloody murder. This thing stuck its nasty arm in the driver-side window, nearly grabbing my face. As I took a sharp swerve to the left into the oncoming lane, it pulled its arm out quickly to try to rebalance itself.

Thank goodness there was no other oncoming traffic during this. I was driving so erratically trying to get this thing off our roof that I'm surprised I didn't flip the car. I sped up to around sixty to seventy miles an hour and slammed on my brakes as hard as possible. I must have knocked it off the roof because I could feel the weight come off the car as soon as it left.

Yet within seconds it seemed to be on the roof again. Before I could even think, I put my foot down on the gas pedal as fast as I could. And then I thought if it worked once, maybe it would work again, and I slammed on the brakes again.

This time when it came off the roof, it landed on the road right in front of the car. My friend yelled, “Hit it. Run that thing over.” I floored it, and it lifted off the ground just as I hit it. But I know I made contact with it because we heard a loud piercing screech as it flew off.

My friend and I kept driving for hours, amped up on adrenalin and fear, not knowing what had just happened to us, and trying to process what that was.

We drove for a few more hours, stopping at a gas station just outside St. Louis, Because of the lateness of the hour, it was one in the morning. We decided not to stay at the planned house but to get a couple of Monster energy drinks each and push through until morning until we could find somewhere to crash.

We wanted to get as far away from that place as possible. We didn’t get to see the Arch in St. Louis. And I don’t plan on ever going back to that part of the country.

7

GOATMAN ENCOUNTERS & SIGHTINGS

THE GOATMAN IS A VERY interesting concept. I've collected reports new and old that offer a variety of descriptions. While the mainstream description is of a literal goat humanoid with horns, you'll notice among this large mass of stories that it does vary. Other times it can be described as a demonic being, while other times it's described as a satyr.

In general, the goatman is said to be a humanoid creature with the head of a goat. It's sometimes described as having fur, and other times it's said to be covered in flesh. The feet are usually hooves, but there are some reports of the creature having humanlike feet. The horns on the goatman's head vary in shape and size. A lot of "goat-man" activity does seem to heavily stem from the eastern/north-eastern section of the United States.

Personally, I'm not exactly sure why that is, but it is very interesting. There are even some reports of the goatman being spotted in other countries such as France, Romania, and Russia. There are a few famous cases of the goatman that have been pretty popular over the years.

Some have even reported that this creature is said to lure people to their deaths by hypnosis or supernatural powers. I'm not too sure about that, but this collection of stories will hopefully intrigue you and drive you to want to research more.

Encounter 1
Submitted By: Wild Turkey Joe
Time: N/A
Location: N/A

SO I THINK it all started in ninth grade when a friend came to school and told us about the goatman. He said he was driving home from his friend's to his dad's house late at night on River Road. It was very foggy because there had been a lot of rain lately. Out of the mist, he sees the goatman run across the road in front of them. He said that it looked like a man with horns.

He told me that he never believed in the goatman until that night. I did some research on the internet about it, and it didn't tell me much except that maybe there was a goatman somewhere in Waterford, Maryland. I forgot about it until I saw the story about the goatman attacking people in La Plata, Maryland.

During my senior year of high school, I was at a friend's house after the homecoming game. We were all chilling, and this kid decided to bring us some beers. We all got pretty drunk, and three of us decided to walk back home, maybe a mile away. By this point, though, we were all relatively sober.

We started walking, and the streets were empty because it was around 1:30 in the morning. We crossed a bridge and stopped to take a break. Suddenly, a friend of mine said he heard something in the bushes nearby. We all looked and heard this noise that sounded like heavy breathing or similar. I got the feeling we were being watched and that some crazy ax murderer would pop out and scare us at any moment.

We kept walking and started to hear this sound again. This time it was closer, though. We looked around but didn't see anything, so we assumed it was just some wild animal in the woods. It was incredibly tense, and every time we tried to sit down and take a break, the sound would pop right back up. It was the kind of noise that would make your skin crawl. The scariest part was the noise was following us.

We were past this farm field when my friend heard it again. This time the sound seemed like it was closer than before. We turned around, and a prominent black figure emerged from the trees and into the field towards us. It was hard to see at first, but it looked like a man covered in hair with horns. My buddy pointed it out to me, and we were all freaking out, saying, "What? What is that?" We all tried to say it was somebody in a costume, but you could tell by the shape and the size there was no way this could have been a costume unless the person spent thousands of dollars on an elaborate Hollywood-tier costume.

We all took off sprinting. What we all believed to be goatman started chasing us to the field. We went into the tree line on the other end of the area in just a little bit, and we tried to hide behind the trees in hopes we could lose it. We could hear this thing coming, and it sounded angry. My friend started to scream, and we were trying to get him to shut up in hopes this thing did not hear us. We listened to it stop in front of the tree line, and we could hear its breathing again.

I slowly peeked my head around and looked at it, but I couldn't see all the details because of how dark it was, but from the silhouette and the faint details I could see in that lighting, this was a demon. Plain and simple. I don't know if you could attribute this to a goatman, but assuming goatman is a demon, then it would make sense.

This thing was scary as hell, and it was now approaching us. All three of us were shaking at this point, and now we were pretty sure we'd die. It made this noise that was probably one of the scariest noises I've ever heard in my life—it kind of sounded like a deer but deeper.

This sounds crazy or unbelievable to some of you, but this

happened. Now we were terrified, and it sounded like this thing was coming toward us, so we decided to run for it. We all sprinted back to my friend's house. When we got there, and his mom asked what the hell was wrong with us. And we told her what happened. She scoffed at us and downplayed the entire thing because she could smell the alcohol on us from when we had been drinking beer earlier. We tried to explain that it had nothing to do with it, but she wouldn't take it. Looking back on this, I don't know what kind of fool would attribute drinking beer to seeing a flipping demon chase you. However, in her mind, it was all the excuse she needed for her to write us off as stupid teenagers.

We heard the noise again outside, not too far from the house; it sounded like a stag or the noise like a deer would make, as I explained. We were terrified the rest of that night, expecting this thing to have followed us back to the house, but thankfully, it did not seem to. However, we heard it making noises for hours after we got back.

The next day we went back to the field, once there was plenty of daylight, to see if there was any evidence that this could have been real. We only found one thing that might be evidence: footprints in the field. The tracks were not human by any means. They were too large and did not have any arch; they looked more like the hooves of a deer or goat. But they were not quite hooves either; they did not look like large deer prints. They looked... different somehow. None of us thought to take a picture. For some reason, I believe we were still just so scared that the whole experience happened, but I regret it now.

But other than that, we did not find any other evidence and haven't been back to this place since. The three of us have tried to move on with life, so we don't really talk about this much, if ever, but we're all still in contact. I know they've had their fair share of crazy experiences, so I didn't think much of it at first.

I'm here now because I just found out about this goatman thing and started looking for more info. Now that I'm reading through the posts, the goatman is the only thing that makes sense. I don't know what else to say about this experience other than it wasn't just terrifying, but this thing... it was a demon in its purest form.

Encounter 2
Submitted By: Trevor Paige
Time: N/A
Location: Geneseo, New York

I GREW up in the country on a farm. Growing up, I had many animal pets, from dogs to cats and even cows. I was a regular lurker on here for years until this happened. I don't know if I can handle knowing this thing is real and out there. I live in the city now, but I'll never forget this experience.

When I was about twelve years old, I lived in upstate New York in a town called Geneseo. It was the end of winter, and all the snow had finally melted after a couple of months. I was out playing in the woods behind my house with some friends. We were probably young and dumb, but we thought it would be fun to explore and try to find the goatman we had heard about.

I know what you're thinking: "Come on, kid, the goatman isn't real!"

I know; I didn't believe it either. We were all young and dumb kids who wanted to find something scary. We had heard that if you go out in the woods at night and call out to him, he'll come to see you. So we thought it would be fun to go out there and try. Off we went, my three friends and I, with a flashlight in the pitch-black woods.

We followed an old dirt path leading to a shack in the middle of nowhere. This thing looked like it would fall apart if you sneezed at it. It was old, run-down, and the windows were busted out or missing altogether. The roof had holes, which you could see the sky through.

It's funny what your brain thinks of when it perceives danger. Back then, I was an outcast and a loner. I was constantly picked on by the other students and teachers at my school, so in my mind, this place was perfect for the goatman. It was dirty, run-down, and isolated.

I felt like that's where he inhabited, this broken-down shack in the middle of nowhere.

Being the idiots they were, my friends dared me to go inside. I told them in no uncertain terms that I was not going in there. They kept pushing and telling me that the goatman was real and he would find me if I didn't go in. But at twelve years old, it all made sense. So in I went.

I walked through the broken door (it was already broken, to begin with), and it looked like nothing had been touched there for twenty years. It looked like an old broken woodshed with a few miscellaneous tools but nothing else. I stood there for a few moments, expecting something to happen, but it never did. My friends were whispering and laughing outside the door, but I said nothing to them. Instead, I exited the small building and walked around it, looking for something.

Being a twelve-year-old kid, I had no idea what I was doing. I walked to my friend's and told them the goatman wasn't there. They both busted up laughing in my face as if this was a big joke. They explained that goatman was not real and this was just an old shed that was probably used long ago. I was pretty upset that they would mock me like this, but a few days later, one of those friends explained we needed some offering for the goatman to show up. I was still hopeful about the idea of wanting to see a goatman.

My aunt at the time was heavily into witchcraft, so I took one of the crafts that she made. Forgive me, I do not know what they're called, but they are supposed to lure evil spirits or something, I don't remember. They are supposed to lure evil spirits so that you can burn them, but don't quote me on that. At this age, I thought it would make the perfect offering, so I met up with my friends again, and we made our trek to that old abandoned shed. I showed them what I had, and they agreed that it should work, even though just days before, they had been mocking me and laughing at me for goatman not existing, and now they were suddenly gung ho about this?

I walked in, placed this little craft right in the center of the shed, and stepped out. "Maybe we'll come to check on it tomorrow and see if you liked our gift," I told them.

We returned the following morning only to find the craft had gone and this eerie, ominous feeling all around. I was not the only one to notice; my friends were with me, and their demeanors changed as they noticed it too. It was like this draft of frigid air, almost as if there was just something different in the air. It was not just colder. It felt different. My friends were telling me that maybe we should go, and it wasn't a good idea to be here, but wanting to be brave and look like the hero to my friends, I insisted that we stay to make sure that our friend got his gift. So I started looking around the shed, and I did not see it anywhere. This is interesting because nobody else I knew went back there, not even bums. There was a complete lack of trash or graffiti anywhere, so to the best of my knowledge, nobody was going back there.

I went back outside, and I explained to my friends that I could not find it anywhere, but I knew I had left it there yesterday, and right at that moment, we started to hear something big moving towards us from the timber to our right. We did not stick around to find out what it was; we all just took off running faster than an Olympic runner. We probably made record time back to the house. Thinking about this critically, could it have been somebody? I don't think so because even at twelve years old, I remember hearing that crashing noise. There was something very, very big coming towards us in the woods. It was coming from deeper into the forest where there is nothing for miles and miles, and there was no way it could have been a man. No man is that heavy or big. This was a giant or something. I think we all just assumed it was a goatman.

Encounter 3
Submitted By: Ron wilder
Time: November
Location: N/A

I HAVE a bachelor's degree in anthropology and have been studying religions for a few years now. I'm interested in the paranormal, cryptids, and other strange phenomena. Enough about me, on with the story.

About two months ago, I was driving down a road in my town on a cold night in November, minding my own business and smoking a cigarette, so it was dark outside. Suddenly I saw some movement coming off the right side of the road. Thinking it was a deer, I began to slow down. As I came closer, I notice something walking like a man on two legs. It had long fur and was walking like a man does (hip movement forward as it takes each step).

The creature then looked at me, and our eyes locked. He looked right at me with his scary black eyes, hideous looking. I could see his fur ruffling in the wind. Without breaking his view, he slowly retracted his lips, revealing all his teeth. I felt all the color and blood drain from my face instantly. I knew I would be dead if I hung around any longer.

I looked away for a split second, and when I looked back, he was gone. I about slammed my foot on the gas pedal to zoom out of there, and I could see him in my rearview mirror sprinting toward the back of my car. I about pressed all my body weight onto my gas pedal to get my car to go faster, and this thing was catching right up to the back of my car. I heard loud banging from his hands as he slapped the trunk.

I was going about 90 mph in a matter of seconds, and this thing was still right behind me. He was so fast that it felt like my car would be totaled in a ditch if I made a slight miscalculation. I saw him in my rearview mirror leap off into one of the trees by the road, where I still kept going crazy fast.

Not even wanting to slow down one bit, I probably drove ninety-plus miles down that road for some time after. Afraid that if I slowed down, it would catch up to me.

I know it sounds crazy, but I'm not lying. To this day, I sometimes see that thing in my rearview mirror or headlights as I'm driving down that road at night. It's given me near PTSD symptoms from that sighting. It's horrible.

Encounter 4
Submitted By: Forest W.
Time: May 2013
Location: N/A

I HAVE BEEN WATCHING the show *Destination Truth* on Netflix for about two years now. I love to hike and canoe in the forest. I have been doing it my whole life with my father. He is no longer with us, but he showed me most of what I know about being outdoors and surviving.

Please understand that I am not a crazy person, and this is my 100% truthful account of what happened. It would be nice to know someone else believes me. I know you guys will probably say it's fake, but this is the most real thing in the world to me, and knowing there's someone else out there who knows what I know will make this easier to deal with.

If anyone wants more information, just ask. I know this can get pretty long, so I'm going to break it up into three parts: the background on myself and my experience, what happened that day in May, and then some extra information to debunk it.

As I said before, I am an avid hiker and camper who has been doing this my whole life. I often go out with friends, but sometimes I go by myself, mostly when looking for Bigfoot tracks or evidence since groups can be so loud.

MOST IMPORTANTLY, I do not believe in the goatman. I don't know why or how this happened to me, but I want answers. Some people might suggest that it was all a dream/coincidence/lie, but everything is accurate and will be backed up by statements from other people who were there. I am probably the least likely person to have this kind of experience since I don't believe in myths or folklore, but that's why this happened.

Here is what happened on that day back in May 2013: my friends and I drove out to go canoeing/camping near a lake. It was about 3:30 p.m., and we had just turned onto a road and were driving uphill when one of my friends saw something on the right side of the road. It looked like a dog but was too big to be an average dog.

We slowed down to get a closer look, and I rolled down my window, which was why this thing ran away. I can't go into much detail now, but I know what it was. At the time, all I could tell was that it wasn't a dog or deer. Hell, it didn't even look like an animal! It was just this lump of fur and flesh with a massive head. We were all dumbfounded, so we kept driving until we came to a bridge passing over the river.

After crossing the bridge, we saw it again. It was at the side of the road, and it stood up when we got close enough to see what it was: a goatman is the simplest way I can describe how it looked, standing about six feet five inches tall. His face looked like a wolf's, almost with the lower end like a goat's. It reminded me a lot of how modern artists depict satyrs but looked wild. Large black eyes too. Freaked all of us right out. It didn't do anything; it just stood there watching us as we drove on the right.

I have never seen anything that looked so out of place, even when I have seen other anomalies. This thing just stood there watching us as if nothing were wrong. Remember that it was about 3:30 p.m. on a hot day in May. Out in the open, no coverage or anything. Where the hell did this massive goatman come from? Why was it around there?

I've heard about the goatman, and it's the only thing I can

pinpoint it back to, but I can't be sure. I don't think it was a crawler or a demon or anything either, but these are just guesses.

Encounter 5
Submitted By: Corey Sullivan
Time: Around Christmas
Location: N/A

I'LL NEVER FORGET THIS; it was just days before Christmas. I was about eleven or twelve years old at the time. My parents had divorced due to domestic abuse; I guess he didn't like that I called the cops on him for beating up my mother. That's another story, though.

I was living with my mother in an apartment complex near the woods outside our home, along a busy street near a shopping mall. I woke up to use the restroom in the middle of the night, which was very common for me to do, as I have always been an early riser and always wake up incredibly thirsty, so I usually drank a large glass of water before going back to sleep. The moonlight was shining through my bedroom windows, so it wasn't pitch black inside the room, but it was still dark enough that I couldn't see anything.

As I walked towards the bathroom, I saw something very tall and large through my bedroom door's cracked-open sliver. Thinking that it may have been maybe my cat or something, I quickly dismissed it as anything. So I continued to the restroom.

When I returned to my room about two minutes later, I could hear something moving outside my bedroom window. Something big was moving towards the back of the house where our sliding glass doors are.

I felt like I was about to have a heart attack; my heart was beating so fast. I turned on my bedroom light, opened the door, and heard our dog Betty, a beagle mix, going crazy and barking up a storm. She's a very docile dog and pretty much never barks at anyone or anything. I was so scared to leave my room because her barking was just confirmation that something was outside our house.

I was too scared to even get up and close the door. I was afraid that whatever it was would see me if I did get near the door. After maybe a moment, I could hear a huge crashing sound out by our back fence. Something significant had hit it. All the commotion of Betty barking woke my parents up, and they went out to check on her. My step-dad was wondering what I was doing awake and with my light on. I told him I heard something huge in the back of the house and that my dog was barking up a storm. He came with me to look around, but nothing could be seen. We didn't go beyond the porch, but I felt safer with my step-dad. He has a lot of guns, so I knew he would bring out firepower if he needed to.

My step-dad found some hoofprints outside by the fence a few days later. They were large, and I wouldn't be surprised if they were over thirteen inches across. I'm not sure what it could have been, but this experience frightened me for years to come until I heard other people's encounters with this "goatman" to get a better idea of what it could have been.

Encounter 6
Submitted By: Alfredo Gonzalez
Time: June/July 1998
Location: New Mexico

THIS WAS at nighttime when I saw this thing. I was sixteen years old at the time. I grew up in rural New Mexico, right on the edge of a forest, which was where it happened. It was June or July of 1998 when this happened.

My family had our farm back then. We did traditional farming, meaning we sold cows and chickens for profit and raised goats because they were easy to take care of. My two brothers and I helped our parents with all the work like any other family would in these parts. It was late when this happened. We had all gathered together in our old house on the farm for dinner. The sun had already set, but it wasn't quite dark yet. My brothers and I were sent to do the evening chores, which included feeding all the goats. We didn't have a barn or a shed specifically for them, so we had to feed them in their pens outside.

After doing this for a while, my brothers said they would take a break and look around for some of the younger ones that hadn't fallen asleep yet. I had just finished feeding the last of them, so I decided to join in on the search. We didn't have a set area that we looked in, but if you were in our way, you wouldn't hear us coming because we would not say a word to each other during this time. My brothers and I had worked together a long time and knew how to communicate with our eyes.

After a few minutes of looking around, we didn't find anything, so my brothers headed off somewhere else while I went back to feeding the goats. It was getting dark quickly, but it wasn't pitch black yet. The sun was still bright enough for me to see what I was doing, but barely, but it also meant that I had to be careful when looking out in the distance because there wasn't much contrast between the sky and the earth. When I finished feeding them and heard a noise, I realized what was going on.

The noise came from inside one of the goat pens closest to me. The goats were freaking out; maybe a stupid coyote had gotten in there. I quickly ran over there to see what was going on. It was then that I saw it.

The thing that got into the pen with the goats had short black hair all over its body. It was holding one of the goats in its arms and quickly snapped its neck. Then it quickly bit into the goat's neck, suckling the blood that was coming out. This thing did not seem to notice me or even care that I was there; this all happened quickly. I ran out of there screaming for my dad. When I got my dad's attention and brought him to the goat pen, this thing was long gone, as was the goat it had been eating.

I thought I had been seeing things, but my brothers took it seriously when they returned and saw the goat was gone. We never found out what this thing was or anything about it. We all slept in the same room with the gun beside us just that night. My brothers found a dried-up goat carcass near our farm a few days later, but its fur color was different from the one taken, and it was smaller.

My dad said he had heard of things like this before but had never seen or heard about one. He said they were generally nocturnal and were good at hiding, so you'd never know they were there until it was too late.

My family sold off the farm a few years ago, as most people do around these parts. I don't think about this thing much anymore, but it has been a long time, so sometimes I wonder what it would be like if I could see it again.

Encounter 7
Submitted By: Miguel C.
Time: 1977
Location: Albuquerque, New Mexico

I WAS NEVER one for telling ghost stories. I never believed them, so why bother? But this one is different because it happened to my friends and me, and we all saw the same thing. As far as background goes:

I am now fifty years old and was seventeen at the time of the incident. My two best childhood buddies were Tom, who was sixteen, and John, who was thirteen. This happened in 1977 on the outskirts of Albuquerque, New Mexico.

It was Friday night, and I was with my friends Tom and John (the only ones who knew what had happened). We were like most normal young boys at the time; we loved horror movies, riding our bikes around the neighborhood, and acting "cool" around girls.

It was summer vacation, and there were many birthday parties at the neighborhood park because it was a holiday weekend. Well, we had been out cruising for a couple of hours that day until it got dark; then we stopped by the park to see what was going on with all the people and the colorful lights of the rides.

We heard that they were hiring teenagers to collect tickets at the lower end of the parking lot, so we decided to check it out since they paid $2.00 an hour.

A long line of people was waiting in front of two teenage girls who were handing out applications for this booth in the far corner of the parking lot near some trees. John felt brave (he was the youngest of our group and had never ridden a big-kid ride before), so he went first to fill out his application.

Afterward, we all walked up to the booth and handed our applications to one of the girls. She said she'd call us if they needed extra help that night, so we headed back toward the entrance.

One of my friends noticed a shadow figure slowly walking down the dirt road in the distance behind some parked cars at the edge of the lot. Tom had the best eyesight of the group; he was the one who spotted it first and seemed genuinely freaked out by seeing it. It was too dark to make out much detail, but it appeared to be a monster.

The hair stood on the back of my neck, which is why I believe in ghosts now. We all saw the figure, and none of us could describe what we saw other than it looked like a big scary monster. It headed in our direction at an abnormally quick pace in the darkness.

This was when things went crazy. John started to cry in fear, and Tom tried to yell at him to stop, but he couldn't even speak without sobbing hysterically. I got very angry with them because they were not behaving like men.

John kept yelling, "We've got to get out of here!" repeatedly. Tom finally shouted, "Use your bike, for Christ's sake. Let's go!"

We all hopped on our bikes and flew out of there as fast as possible; it felt like we were on those little bikes riding for our lives.

As we pedaled like crazy out of the parking lot to go home, Tom said he heard something running behind us, trying to catch up to us; but I didn't hear anything at all (he has much better hearing than me).

John kept repeatedly yelling how we saw the legendary goatman, etc. Even today, when we talk, and just before I wrote this, I talked to him on the phone about it. He still swears that what we saw then was the legendary goatman people talk about seeing.

Encounter 8
Submitted By: Anonymous
Time: 1950s
Location: Alaska

NOT MY STORY, but my great-uncle's actually.

He was in the military, stationed in Alaska in the '50s.

He was out with his friend, taking a piss on a tree nearby, when he said that about sixty yards out by the lake they were at, he saw this large satyr-looking creature watching him with glowing eyes. It frightened him badly.

My mother's side of the family is from Anchorage, Alaska. My great-grandfather was an old gold miner and had a site out in the woods where he'd leave supplies for his crew to pick up on their way home after weeks out. He said they started to find dead animals that looked like half-eaten carcasses with bite marks. This went on for weeks until one day, he saw what he described as satyr-like, with glowing eyes, standing over a deer carcass and eating it. It turned, saw him, and took off running at inhuman speeds into the woods. He said that thing ran faster than any animal could run, reminding him of a cross between a man and goat, and had long horns on its head. It also moved bipedally. Not on all fours as a normal goat would.

My great-uncle's military base moved in the '70s to the south, so that base no longer exists there, to my knowledge.

He didn't share that story with me until about ten or so years ago, right before he passed, and he wanted to ensure all his life accounts were spoken about. My grandfather, who passed away in 2002 (unaware of my great-uncle's account), also told me before he died. There's something not right up in the woods in Alaska.

Encounter 9
Submitted By: Anonymous
Time: Summer 1991
Location: Saddleback Mountain

I LIVED in Maine until about twelve or thirteen years ago when my family moved to New Jersey for a better life.

My friends and I used to go camping during the summer months up at this place called Saddleback Mountain. The mountain was an old ski resort that had been closed for years. The only thing that remains up there now is an old campground where you used to be able to stay overnight.

During the middle of summer, this guy named Roy Trudel built a wooden bridge across the river near the campground to provide easy access for fishermen and hunters. We all thought it was pretty cool until we heard about some strange things happening up there.

I remember hearing the first story from my uncle, a police officer at the time, and I just shook it off as a lame attempt to scare me. After a few more stories, I started to grow curious and decided to go see for myself.

During the summer of '91, a couple of friends and I went to check it out. We brought a few high-powered rifles and some night-vision goggles because we thought we'd be dealing with bears and coyotes.

As we approached the bridge that day, we could hear this unearthly howling from below the bridge. At first, I thought it was just a couple of stray dogs or maybe even coyotes, but that quickly changed once we got close enough.

As we approached the edge of the bridge, my friend Jeff dropped his flashlight into the water below, which sent ripples across the surface. And that was when this something jumped out at us from under the bridge.

Its face was something out of a nightmare, and if we were to ever forget it, my friends and I all agreed that we'd rather take our own lives than remember it. It looked like a deformed goat with humanlike eyes. We'll never know what exactly we saw that day, but that didn't stop us from leaving that place as soon as we could.

So there it is. That's my story. Can't say I believe in the whole goatman legend, but I'm sure you guys can see why some people think it's real after what we saw that day.

Encounter 10
Submitted By: Anonymous
Time: N/A
Location: N/A

I WAS sixteen when this happened to me. I wasn't much outdoorsy, so I didn't know anything about the outdoors. I went through school so fast and got stuck in grade 10 because I missed so much time after this incident that school just flew by.

I had to take summer classes, which were boring as hell. That was one of my first times doing drugs too. I was around 16 years old. My friends and I started smoking weed together. The first time my friend and I tried it, we took a few hits each to see what the effects would be like.

My dad smokes cigars, so he had an ashtray full of butts that were smoked down to almost nothing already, which we used to get high. After that, we just hung out every day.

One of our favorite things was climbing trees. It was springtime, and we could climb up to the top of the tree and hang out. It was fun. I don't know why we just didn't go to someone's house or something instead of wasting time climbing trees all day, but that's what we liked to do.

One day after school, I went home to my mom's apartment, which she shared with her boyfriend, now my stepdad. I got home, and I was hungry, so I asked her if we could go get something to eat. She said sure, and she put on some shoes, and we left for the nearest McDonald's, which was close by.

We drove down the road, eating crappy burgers and fries around five or six o'clock. The sun was setting, and it turned the sky pinkish orange. We finished our food and drove home on the road to my school.

It begins to get foggy here, but I'll try to explain everything as perfectly as possible because some things I remember vividly and others I don't.

We were driving down the road, and darkness came over the sky as we drove farther. We were in a very small town with not a lot of traffic at all, so it was usually pretty clear on this road. A wooded area stood out from everything else because there were no homes or anything near it. Everything else was clear, but this area was not.

This dark wooded area started to freak me out for some reason, and I'd always complain about how scared I felt when we drove past it. My mom's boyfriend told me that there were no such things as monsters and nothing to be scared of, and he would always joke about how he should know because he was a monster.

As we drove past this area, I felt relieved, but as soon as we got past the wooded area, the hair on my neck stood up, and I began to cry hysterically. I was just immediately so overcome with primal fear. I've never felt anything quite like that in my life. My mom asked what was wrong, and I didn't want to tell her because I thought she'd make fun of me for crying over nothing, but eventually, I told her.

She laughed and said that there was no such thing as monsters and asked why I would think there was. That was when I turned around in my seat to look at what was behind us. It was pitch black out, but the moon was bright and glowing. This shadow was like a black blob on top of the trees moving through them. I pointed at it and told my mom to look, but she immediately said that she couldn't see anything and asked why I would make such a big deal out of nothing.

I told her that wasn't what I saw, and we kept arguing. I was so confused because I knew for certain that I saw what looked like something moving across the trees, but my mom made it seem like she couldn't see anything at all, which seemed impossible.

She started saying I was just making it up and asked why I wanted to do that. I tried to explain what I saw, but she didn't believe me, so I asked why she couldn't see it. She said because she was looking at the road. After all, there was no way I could've seen what I thought I saw.

I turned around again, and this shape was now moving along with our car but now inside the woods, parallel to us. It was so fast. It moved so quickly, so fluidly and effortlessly through the trees. We were arguing over what I saw when I caught a glimpse of it in the faint moonlight, or whatever little light there was out there at night, and I saw this faintly lit face. It looked like a monster!

I started screaming, and my mom got mad at me for reacting that way and explained it was nothing. This was just nothing; there was something in these woods following our car. I begged her to stop or let me out of the car, and she just yelled at me to shut up and be quiet. She pulled into a small parking lot and started flipping out on me for some reason. I couldn't see the thing following us anymore, but we drove home after her yelling at me. That was the end of that. I still stand by that I didn't see a normal animal, and it was not someone running alongside our car either. It was big and hairy, whatever it was.

Encounter 11
Submitted By: Titus
Time: N/A
Location: Central Florida

I GREW up in a rural part of Central Florida, about five miles from a small town known as Sorrento. The area is heavily forested and has many lakes, ponds, and swamps. To the north, you have Disney World, which I know sounds weird considering what happened to me, but it attracts all kinds of people from around the world, so I guess I shouldn't be surprised.

My mother and father had me later in life, and I was an accident, if we're honest. My brother usually played the role of the "protector," but he moved out when I was about fifteen, which left me as pretty much an only child. My folks both worked during the week, and I ran around with my friends from school.

I was about sixteen years old at the time, and I had been out drinking with some buddies when we decided to try to get into a nearby club that was always hopping on the weekends. At the same time my two friends were trying to get in, I, being the stupid kid that I was, got cold feet and decided to sit outside.

I was sitting on the curb when I noticed something odd. A security guard outside the club was talking to this guy who looked pretty disheveled and wild-eyed. Some other people were standing around, so I tried to listen in on what they were saying, but it was really hard because of all the loud music coming from inside, plus they were talking low as if they didn't want anyone else to hear them. I think they were trying to convince this guy not to go into the club, and it sounded like a pretty heated argument.

The three guys beside me talked for a few minutes, then decided to take off, leaving me alone again. They got into an old pickup truck and drove away, making a lot of noise. I don't think it was intentional, but the guard and the guy standing nearby stared at them as they left.

I kept looking from one to the other, trying to listen in on their conversation, when suddenly, this guy who had been arguing with the security guard was telling him what he'd seen in the Everglades. Something about the goatman and how this thing was going to take his soul. He started crying and talking all crazy, saying something about "not wanting to die." The guard kept trying to calm him down, but the guy kept getting increasingly worked up, so much that I thought he would attack the guard. The conversation came to an ending point, and he eventually walked away. It was weird.

So my friends got out after getting kicked out, and we were now walking back. The entire time I couldn't shake what that guy was saying and how it was stuck in my head. I had never given the ghosts thing any mental energy in my life, but seeing someone so worked up over it, I don't know. He was coherent, too, and did not seem like some crackhead or someone out of his mind. It bothered me. And of course, right where we were walking by was all Everglades for miles.

I was just praying inside my head that nothing would happen. We kept walking while my friends made fun of me and how I didn't get to go in there with them. I reminded them that they were the ones who got kicked out. We were talking, and all heard this horrible scream in the Everglades. We all stopped and looked at each other with a "did you hear that?" look on our faces. We then went back to my house and have not talked about it since then.

Encounter 12
Submitted By: Anonymous
Time: Mid-August
Location: Outside Des Moines, Iowa

I WORK FOR A SMALL BUSINESS, so my hours are Monday to Friday, 9 a.m. to 5 p.m. I have always been outdoorsy, so I'd go out during lunchtime to go fishing or shoot the bow at the archery range near the cornfields whenever it was nice enough outside.

I was working at this job for several months, and this happened during my lunch break.

It was mid-August, and I was out on one of my usual lunch breaks at the archery range. It was a nice enough day outside (about 70 degrees or so). It wasn't raining or anything like that.

The parking lot for the pier next to this archery range was empty..

I had some fishing equipment and my bow and arrows with me.. I set up on a flat area on the pier and started fishing. No other people were around, and the only animals I had seen that day were birds; nothing was out of the ordinary. This is important because I don't want anyone thinking this was a simple misidentification.

After about twenty minutes of sitting there, something began moving and grabbed my attention (on the side facing the woods). I saw movement off towards the other side of the trees by the pier. I turned out of reaction, and whatever it was, it quickly retracted back into the woods around it. I tensed up a little bit because this wasn't natural for anyone. Either someone was planning on harming or mugging me, or things were about to get scary fast. I called out "Hello," but nothing. Everything got really quiet, so I figured it might just be a good time to pack everything up, head inside, and be done for the day.

I began walking back down the pier, and man, it was like whatever or whoever it was was just staring daggers into me. I refused to acknowledge or look in that direction. I could feel them watching me. I could feel their presence.

As soon as I was off the pier and back on firm ground (before reaching the grassy area), I began to walk faster, almost running towards my car.

I felt like they were chasing me, but I didn't dare look back until I got into my car, at which point whatever it was had disappeared. I felt like someone or something was behind me, but nothing was there when I looked.

It's really hard to describe the dread and fear I felt while walking back to my car (I can't explain why). It wasn't like anything you'd be able to experience here in your everyday life, not only because I have no idea how to describe what this entity was but also because it didn't feel real. You would never expect something like that could happen to you, but it did. I felt sick the whole drive back.

I told my work about it, and they said people who worked there had encountered some strange things before, but there wasn't much to be done.

A friend who will remain nameless told me he, too, had a very similar experience weeks ago. He told me that he saw this hairy, horned figure watching him by the tree line and that it scared him. Claims that it WAS NOT just someone in a mask. Could this be the same thing that was watching me?

Encounter 13
Submitted By: Brent
Time: N/A
Location: Northern Wisconsin

OKAY, so my sighting takes place in Northern Wisconsin. I grew up in the northwoods of Wisconsin and spent all my life here until I moved away for college.

It was a few years ago, so some specific details may be off. It was summer, and we were doing our annual thing where we'd rent cabins by a lake, go fishing, ride ATVs, etc.

My family rented a cabin at this lake that was on the smaller side, but it had three bedrooms and was nice for what we were paying. We had built up a nice little neighborhood of people who would frequently come every summer to vacation in their cabins. It contained about seven cabins in all.

On one of the nights of our vacation, we decided to go out and get some firewood so we could all sit around the fire later on. Nobody was willing to brave the dark woods by themselves, so I volunteered to team up and go with whoever wanted to come along.

One of my friends and I hopped into his pickup, and we drove up the side of the lake a ways and then parked and hopped out. We started walking through the woods, but we didn't get very far before we heard some pretty loud and inhuman screams.

At first, we just looked at each other with nervous laughter because we assumed it was somebody messing around. Then the cries kept getting closer until they were no longer distant enough to ignore. Now someone was close by.

Finally, we saw the source of the screams: a goat. A huge goat with large curved horns and an angry face. I grew up in this area and have seen plenty of goats. This was not a goat.

It might have been the lighting or the darkness of the woods, but when it caught our eyes, it took on an eerie appearance at that moment. The fur on its back looked black and matted, while the underside was pale white with thick, coarse hair and looked wet and slimy.

The first thing that came to my mind was that we were in some serious crap because I knew this wasn't a normal animal. I've seen a lot in the woods, but nothing like this.

I was frozen in fear, and I looked at my friend to see what he would do because if he ran, I planned on following him back to the truck. He had a look of pure terror on his face, and it looked like he was about ready to take off.

I mustered up some courage and told him we needed to run back to the truck as fast as possible because this wasn't normal. I don't think he could even hear me at that point because he was completely gone.

The next thing I knew, my friend sprinted through the woods with this... thing chasing after us. It wasn't a full-out sprint but faster than a regular person could run. I heard the snapping of branches and brushing leaves as whatever this thing rapidly closed the distance between us.

I didn't want to look back because I knew that if I did, I would freeze up again or be so panicked that I couldn't move. I focused on my friend in front of me and tried to stay close so that if he stopped running, I could stop with him.

It's kind of weird because even though there was this huge thing only a few feet behind us, the most frightening part was hearing it constantly changing directions as it chased us; I was constantly bracing myself for it to pounce on me.

Eventually, my friend realized what was behind us and started to outpace me until he was so far ahead that I couldn't see him anymore. I guess he was able to get his wits about him enough to figure out how to lead whatever this thing was away from me.

I kept running until I got back to the truck and jumped in. As I started the truck, this thing came into view from around a tree behind where we had left our stuff. It stood there, upright, and stared at me. I got a good look at this thing. If the goatman truly exists, this was it. It was some sort of demonic hybrid of a man and goat, but this thing... just looked so evil. There are no human words for this. There is nothing in this world that could explain what I saw.

I'll never forget that thing's eyes. They reminded me of a shark: just black and void. Like it was watching you, but you couldn't tell. Every bit of that thing screamed evil; nothing about that sighting was remotely normal.

I peeled out of there as fast as possible and sped back to the cabin.

We decided not to tell anybody about this because we were pretty sure they wouldn't believe us and would probably think we were crazy.

For the rest of the camping trip, we were both pretty paranoid about staying close together and not being outside more than we had to. We were always afraid that it was going to come back. Somehow though, that thing didn't catch us again the rest of the weekend. It was really weird, though, because there'd be a few nights we'd be out by the fire, and everything would suddenly go really quiet. I'm talking like the crickets just hushing suddenly, and everything would get tense. We'd always talk a little quieter and keep an eye out to see what was going on.

We ended up not returning to that area for about two years, and things seemed fine. I never did tell my family about my sighting. It's probably best they don't know.

There's not much else I can say about my experience, but let me leave you with a question.

What was that thing? I would very much like to know.

Encounter 14
Submitted By: Anonymous
Time: N/A
Location: Franklin County, Pennsylvania

MY BROTHER, sister, and I grew up in a rural house off a dead-end road in Franklin County, Pennsylvania.

Background: I was about eight years old, and it was the beginning of spring. The weather had been warmer but still cold enough to snow. One night after bedtime, my sister came into my room to tell me that she heard rustling out by our barn, about 150 feet from our back door. I, of course, was terrified and went to my parents' room to tell them, but they just laughed at me, thinking it was just a cat or some other animal. Right before Easter break, my brother and sister saw one of our cats out in the barn with something big. We all got a glimpse of it and assumed it was the goatman.

The following Tuesday, I woke up for school at 6:45 a.m. since we went to a small Christian private school. Being only eight years old, naturally, I was not a morning person. After getting my uniform on, I headed downstairs to eat breakfast and brush my teeth. While eating breakfast, I saw our back door open up. At the time, this was very odd because my mom always made sure to close it whenever she left for work. The door remained open, but I shrugged it off, gathered my book bag and suitcase, and headed out the front door for school. We were allowed to walk to school by ourselves then, and I always took the sidewalk that passed our house and circled into town. I would then turn and cut through the woods where I was supposed to meet my friends.

When I got near the end of our driveway, my mom's wish for me not to take the shortcut through the woods was fresh in my head, so as any eight-year-old would do, I ignored her.

As I passed the tree line of the forest and walked on the sidewalk next to some farmland, I heard a loud rustling in the trees across from me. Keep in mind this is probably about 7:05 a.m., so it's still pitch black outside since it's spring. The wind was also picking up, so I assumed it was just the wind making the trees shake.

As soon as I started to look back at where I heard the rustling, something large and brown bolted out of the woods and onto the sidewalk between me and the other side of the forest. Without seeing its face, I could only see the long hair covering its body; it was hunched over, had hands with long fingers/claws, and ran on two legs. It stopped in front of me so quickly that I could have reached out and touched it if I wanted to.

I stood there for what seemed like an eternity staring at the thing when suddenly, it bolted back into the forest on all fours and disappeared into the darkness. I was too afraid to move for a moment but started sprinting as fast as I could toward my school.

The entire time I ran, all I could think about was that goatman creature and if it would hurt me or not. When I finally made it to my school, I went inside and hid in the bathroom. Once school was over for the day, I ran straight home to tell my parents about what had happened, that this creature had crossed my path when it shouldn't have been near me.

My parents told me it was probably just a large dog or coyote, but since I was so young and it had happened less than twelve hours ago.

I had grown up hearing about the goatman for my entire life. I thought the thing that ran out in front of me had to have been a werewolf or something, but it was the long black horns sticking up out of its head like one of those goats or deer you see in Africa that bothered me. I'm 100% certain that what I had encountered was, in fact, a goatman creature. I know he exists.

Encounter 15
Submitted By: Stephanie Ortiz
Time: N/A
Location: Bend, Oregon

BEND, Oregon. A place that I hold dear to me, it has a very deep meaning for me. It's where I was married; it's where my children were born, and is the place that I call home. And this monster almost took that away from me.

This experience made me realize something important about myself. I realized I'm not quite the skeptic I thought I was. You see, the thing about skeptics is that we think we know everything, and we pride ourselves on it (and rightly so). But sometimes, we get caught up and refuse to believe something outside our way of thinking. And I did just that.

It was late spring in Bend, Oregon, and I was twenty-two years old. It was the early hours of the morning, around 10:15 a.m. I had just dropped off my girlfriend at her place.

I took one turn down one of the main roads that go through town, I was driving down this road, and I had this weird sensation come over me. It felt like pins and needles, except it was all over my body. It was almost this electrical rush or surge going through me. I also had a crick in my neck, which was uncomfortable.

I had to take another turn. I tried to relax and shake it off, thinking nothing of it, but then I saw something that freaked me out This thing was just sitting in the middle of the street. It looked like a man, but with horns like a goat, and not only that, it had these weird-looking eyes, if you can even call them eyes; they were solid black. It looked like something created in a lab, like something was just spliced together to create this thing.

It wasn't some little thing; this was probably around seven feet tall, if not more. I was freaked out at this point, almost shaking and trembling as I drove. I went right past it, but the figure was now gone. I thought that maybe I'd seen things that weren't real, but then something even weirder happened. I returned to my house after dropping my girlfriend off, and that same pins and needles feeling came back, and I felt very ill. Sick almost. Like this overwhelming dread just sitting down in the pit of my stomach. It was like being anxious constantly, with no peace. It was rough.

I kept expecting to see that thing outside my window that night; I'm thankful I didn't have to. Everything seemed to be calm the next day, but man, it was terrifying.

Over the next several years, I've heard about things and talked about things like goatman and not just Bigfoot. Because if you're in the Pacific Northwest, the only cryptid to exist out here for some reason is Bigfoot, but I had some friends share their own stories with me about a creature with horns that they claimed looked like it was half human, half goat or something.

I don't know what truly exists in central Oregon, but whatever this creature is, something is awry down here!

Encounter 16
Submitted By: Conrad Barker
Time: Various
Location: Various

I'VE GOT a collection of stories for you that I think you might enjoy. It's taken me some time to acquire them throughout my time investigating, as I have with past stories I've shared with you. These are all related to goatman sightings. If you don't know what goatman is, you can Google him. The reports I've collected of this cryptid are just as frightening as the dogman. It's a long email, so bear with me.

This email is from Sandra, her eyewitness account: "I had gotten married, and we were renting a house outside town. It was very secluded, and we didn't have to share it with anyone else, which was awesome. I would usually be up late at night watching TV or on my laptop. My husband worked nights, so he slept during the day and was gone every night while I stayed up.

"One night, I remember it was a weekday, and my husband had to work. I decided that since he hadto go to work, I would attempt to sleep. Around 3 a.m. or so, I woke up to the sound of someone walking around outside.

"I looked out the window, but there was no one in sight. The footsteps were loud, and they were coming from behind our house. I decided to ignore it, thinking it couldn't be the case.

"The footsteps got closer and closer until they stopped outside my window. There was a moment of silence before a low growl emitted from outside the window. I could hear heavy breathing as if something were running.

"I turned to look, and saw these teeth, red eyes, and hair looking in my window. I about screamed and fell out of my bed. I called 911 immediately, and when the officer showed up, he could see that the grass outside my window was trampled down, but no discernible trace of anyone having been around.

"I never got another glimpse of the creature after that experience, but I know it wasn't a bear because I've seen bears hundreds of times before, and this didn't look like any bear I'd ever seen."

I asked Sandra if she could elaborate more on what she saw that night. In her own words, she explained this thing looked like something out of a horror movie. That it was like this satanic goat-looking man. Sandra is a thirty-nine-year-old nurse with no reason to make this up or embellish her story. She was kind enough to share it with me after wanting some answers. She requested that her location remain anonymous, so I will honor that. She explained that after that, her husband purchased several firearms and kept them readily available by the bedside if this thing came back and spooked her. Still, she never had another sighting after that.

Sandra also made another point that I wanted to bring up. She said that this creature was hell-bent on scaring her. It could have broken into her house if it wanted to, but it just wanted her to know it was there and was watching her. The presence of this thing was overwhelming, she said.

At first, I didn't think much of the story, as some people seem to embellish their experiences, but after learning more about Sandra and her experience, it seems very credible. She wouldn't have any reason to lie or make up something like that. That's why I wanted you guys to know that a lot is happening in the world that we don't necessarily see or hear about at first glance. We, as investigators and seekers of truth, need to be unbiased.

Another email I have is from a gentleman who wants to remain anonymous. He told me he had seen this figure near his house in Portland, Oregon, for several days. The witness says he first encountered the creature on April 25, 2014, at approximately 11:30 p.m. He was outside having a cigarette before bed when he saw what appeared to be an "enormous" dog or goat coming around the corner of his house, screaming aggressively.

He described the beast as black with thick fur and catlike eyes that glowed yellow. The creature was only about twenty feet away from the witness. Still, it appeared extremely aggressive, prompting him to go inside immediately without another peep or glance back at the beast.

The next night his cat went missing. The witness believes the creature may have killed and eaten his cat based on evidence left in his yard and neighbors' yards, such as disemboweled and dismembered cats and other remains in the street. He also found what appeared to be huge footprints from an unknown species that were bigger than any normal goat or hoofed animal can make. He thought it was an exceptionally large cow, but there were no cows in the area, not to mention the tracks were completely bipedal.

I only spoke briefly with this man via email, and he claims that since April 26, 2014, he has not seen this creature again. He vehemently expressed to me that his anonymity was of the utmost importance because of his position in the private company where he worked. If anything got out that pointed to him being remotely crazy, he could lose his position overnight due to the company not wanting bad press.

I did some more research on the matter and found that there had been several other reported sightings of bipedal animals in the area recently. The witness was kind enough to send me links to news articles about these stories, but I cannot mention them directly because no one can be 100% sure it's legitimate.

This email I received is from an eyewitnesse who referred to himself as Kyle, and this is his eyewitness account:

"My summer of 2011. I had just moved into a new small town in Illinois with my dad and an older brother, who was seventeen at the time of all this, around July or August of that year. I am now twenty-one and wish I could forget it all.

"So we were unpacking and settling in and decided to take a

break and go out for dinner at around 7:00 p.m. There was this small general store we were frequenting because we were so far away from everything else. The building owner lived upstairs next to all the beer and cigarette machines; she was a nice old lady who always lent an ear if you needed to talk. Otherwise, she'd leave you alone.

"My dad and brother got a beer for the house while I got candy bars. When they returned (with the drinks), we started walking to the entrance when I saw something out of my peripheral vision, like a flash or streak of movement. But what stood out to me was the loud clanging noise it made.

"So that's when I looked straight-on at the thing, about twenty feet away from us, looking right at me. I couldn't identify any specific features because it all happened so fast, but I knew that what I saw wasn't human or natural. It moved like a blur, with long gangly, simian-like arms and legs, huge feet and covered in shaggy brown hair. And the smell it gave off was unforgettable... it smelled rancid, sort of like a wet dog mixed with garbage.

"It made eye contact with me for less than a fewseconds before it turned around and bolted into the trees.

"I stood there for what felt like forever, not knowing how to react, so I went along with my dad and brother, who were asking me if I was okay. After they started to walk inside, the old lady didn't say anything, but she looked terrified, and we never saw her again after that night.

"For a couple of months after this, I remember sleeping with the light on, freaked out by what I saw.

"I'm not trying to gain anything from telling you this story. So thank you for listening."

Kyle's case is very interesting, as he gave me a story from when he was only eleven years old that he still vividly remembers. I did not get the chance to Zoom call Kyle as I did with Sandra, but he was kind enough to speak with me over the phone, and you could tell his retelling the story made him nervous. I picked up on his demeanor change almost immediately in his tone of voice. Kyle seemed like a pretty quiet, reserved kid who was not seeking notoriety from his sighting. Just the opposite; he hoped that sharing it would get it off his shoulders, and he could move on with his life. He even told me over the phone that he would have these horrible vivid nightmares when he was a teenager for a few years in high school. I've seen this thing over and over. His brother and father were not looking when this thing revealed itself to him, so he was the only one who saw it.

Kyle had no idea what a goatman was; I don't think he knew what a Bigfoot was either, so I had to explain the physical differences and appearance between the different cryptids. He says that what he saw closely resembled what I was just describing for a goatman. Kyle also told me that before the sighting, he had spent a lot of time with his dad out hunting and tracking, so he knew well what various wildlife look like, and there is no way you can mistake what he saw for anything other than what it was.

Kyle also told me that there were a couple of other occasions when his family would find dead and mutilated deer and elk on their property; still, they never really suspected the goatman as the cause for those kills because his father knew firsthand how ruthless and cunning predators can be to one another. Hence, they always assumed another local predator like a cougar or bear was responsible.

Kyle was level-headed, and I got the impression that he wasn't embellishing his story. He seemed like an intelligent young man who wanted nothing more than to help his fellow cryptid enthusiasts or at least get this thing off his chest so he could move on with his life. I am very surprised some Bigfoot researcher has not picked up on this case yet, as it is fairly new, but we all know how hard it is getting people to come forward in these matters and keep their confidentiality agreements intact while still telling us what they've seen.

The next email is from a man who goes by the name Tony T.

"I was sixteen years old, on a Boy Scout camping trip with some friends and my father, uncles, and cousins in the mountains of West Virginia. We were camping in an area that wasn't heavily forested but was mostly an open field surrounded by woods. It was early October, so it had just rained; everything was damp and dark near the tree line, which made the typically bright moon appear even brighter.

"I walked out of my tent to use the outhouse around 2:30 a.m. and stopped about a hundred feet away to take a leak by some trees. After I was done, I began walking toward the tents when I noticed that everything beyond the tree line was very dark; not even moonlight could penetrate that far into the wooded area.

"My eyes slowly adjusted to the darkness, and I noticed that if I stared at any object for more than ten seconds, it would have a sort of 'vortex' effect—the object's color would drain out until there was nothing left except darkness.

"I shrugged it off and continued walking back to my tent when I noticed something moving in the woods. It looked like an emaciated wild dog covered in hair with bulging eyes, heading right towards me. I couldn't make out the size of the thing because it was still near the tree line, but it didn't seem larger than a medium-sized dog. I looked back just in time to see the thing open its jaws so wide I could see down its throat, revealing large, jagged teeth—not unlike a shark's. I was completely petrified, as if this thing was showing me its teeth to scare and intimidate me. At sixteen years old, I did not believe in monsters underneath the bed, but this was something real. Something that was flesh and blood that you could touch. I don't like using the term monster, but I'm afraid that's the only word that can describe what I saw that night.

"Instead of running back to my camp, I ran down a trail that led to another campground in hopes of trying to not have it follow me back to my tent. I remember crouching down on the trail, trying to listen for any little sound around me, expecting this thing to pop out of nowhere and grab me. I remember the woods being very quiet even though the crickets had been in a full-on chorus just a short time before, considering it was summer. I can recall the feeling in the air just being different, just so much tension. It felt like I was sitting there crouched for hours before I felt safe enough to return to my tent, hoping I was not being watched or followed. I can remember that night's sleep was pretty rough."

Oh, Tony, who is now a forty-six-year-old IT worker for a small security firm, detailed his account to me over a Zoom call back in July when we started exchanging emails and I brought up the alleged goatman. He was very kind and went into all the detail necessary to provide a full picture of his sighting. While his description of this cryptid is very canine-like, he described it as having large devil horns as a ram does, except they were black. When I asked him questions, specifics about its face, or any other details he can remember, he recalls it was just a blur. Due to the lighting and what he saw, he just remembers this thing having a longer snout and a mouth full of teeth as a shark would. He told me that, more than anything, that's what stuck out to him the most. He vividly recalls this thing having rows and rows of teeth. They were small and dagger-like, probably hundreds in its mouth. "If this thing wasn't designed to be a flat-out killing machine, then I don't know what its designed purpose was," he explained.

He didn't come forward with this account for so long because he feared getting mocked, and nobody would believe him. At his age, he had no concept of cryptozoology, so in his mind, he just had this freak sighting that cannot be explained by rational thinking or science. It wasn't until he was in his later twenties when he started watching some stuff on Bigfoot, which would eventually lead to his interest in cryptozoology., It made him think back to that sighting all those years ago. Now, when he gave me the description of this creature, I asked him if he was sure it wasn't a dogman. I even read him several sighting stories of people encountering werewolf-like creatures. Although his description was more canine-like, as I've said, he said the more he thinks back on it, and it looked more akin to that of a goat as far as the horns in the bone structure of the head are concerned. He explained that he couldn't remember much about the body shape, height, or structure, just the teeth.

I'll share with you this one last email that comes from a man named Joel.

"I'm not sure if I saw an unknown animal or a prankster in costume, but for whatever reason, it still has me terrified. I was around twelve years old, and my family had just moved out to the country in Oklahoma. My sister and I played outside at midday, probably waiting for my mom to get home from work. We saw this tall, bipedal creature walking through a field toward us. I don't recall it having fur, but the thing was huge and muscular with paws that were humanlike hands. From what I remember, it didn't look human; to me, it looked like a tall man in a costume. I called my sister inside, and we got in the house as fast as we could. As soon as we were inside, my mom came home and wondered why we weren't out playing. She noticed how scared we were. I asked her if she remembered the tall guy living down the street from us, and she said it couldn't have been him. I still think about what I saw all the time, which terrifies me."

Joel, a man who is almost sixty, is very credible. He's worked on and off in construction for years and even owned his own trucking business for a short period before selling it and retiring. He now spends his days hunting and enjoying time with his grandkids. I've known Joel personally for years, and he has no reason to make this story up, nor does he gain anything from it.

Although his sighting is very short, I find his story interesting because he says that this thing walking through the field didn't seem to pay any attention to him and his sister playing. After explaining that it was possibly a Bigfoot that he saw, he shook his head no and told me about a Bigfoot sighting he'd had while hunting when he was much older. Whatever he saw that day in Oklahoma, this creature looked much different than a Bigfoot. He described to me the Bigfoot that he saw when he was older was very broad; he thinks like a linebacker on a football team but on steroids. This first creature was very slender and lean but very tall and covered in long wispy hair. He recalls it having an elongated face and a snout similar to a deer but couldn't tell me much more about the specifics. When I asked him if he remembers it having horns, he couldn't remember, but the sighting alone scared him pretty badly, and he and his sister did not play out there for weeks afterward.

I'll get some more stories to you as soon as I have some, but to avoid making this email a mini novel, I'll end it here.

8
REPTILIAN ENCOUNTERS & SIGHTINGS

REPTILIAN BEINGS HAVE BEEN MAKING their way into pop culture in recent years. Everything from famous memes of "lizard people" to more tongue-in-cheek references like those signs found at the Denver airport. Either way, during my time as a narrator, I've come across a multitude of encounters that go so far beyond just "reptile" beings. I've come across alligator creatures that appear half human, half alligator. Dinosaur humanoids, or even a supposed sect of shape-shifters that live beneath the deserts of the southwest.

But what are these creatures? Are they aliens? Extraterrestrial beings of some sort? Or are they something that our ancient ancestors knew about and wrote about in their folklore? Reptilian beings have been seen all throughout history and across cultures. They are often described as being evil, cunning, and dangerous. But there are also stories of reptilian beings that are benevolent and helpful to humans. I think that the truth lies somewhere in the middle. Reptilian beings are certainly not human, but they may not be aliens either. Whatever they are, they are definitely something that we should be aware of.

Encounter 1
Submitted By: Ed
Time: 1980s
Location: Outside New Orleans, Louisiana

EVER SINCE I was a small boy, I would go hunting with my father in the swamps of New Orleans. One night we were out looking for game when an alligator started to appear. My dad shot at it and killed it right there on the spot. We went over to see if we could get some meat off it when suddenly, a human-sized lizard appeared from the bushes. It was dark brown and had big orange eyes like a cat's, but also reeked of decay.

My father started to shake as he slowly placed his shotgun on the ground. The pterodactyl-like reptile hissed at us and moved its way quickly towards the dead alligator my father had just shot. My father picked up his shotgun and aimed at it. He pulled the trigger, but the gun jammed.

Then suddenly I heard something behind me and realized that another reptilian creature was walking from a distance towards us! The one in front had picked up the dead alligator and started eating its flesh as we stood there in shock. The one behind leaped at us and knocked my father to the ground. I ran as fast as I could, hoping that it would give chase after me.

These things let my father go, and my dad came running up behind me while these things stole his kill and disappeared into the swamp.

I don't know what the hell they were, but I sure hope that no one ever has to experience such a thing. The weird thing is that this happened in the 1980s when a boy from Scape Ore Swamp saw a strange reptilian being run after him. I have no idea if they are the same thing or not.

Encounter 2
Submitted By: Kellen hodges
Time: October 12, 2003
Location: Denver, Colorado

I ENCOUNTERED a reptilian being during my junior year of high school in Denver, Colorado. It was October 12, 2003, and while going to catch the bus for school, something odd happened that would change my life forever.

While walking to the bus stop at around 7 a.m., this very tall being suddenly appeared out of the wood line. The thick brush from which this figure appeared was a kind of marshland beyond it. So I saw this figure, and I couldn't quite make out what it was at first, but then I realized this figure had scales! And it was walking upright just like a man would.

Curious and a little creeped out, I ignored it for a moment to pull my cell phone out of my pants pocket, only to discover that the battery was dead. This was in the days of the Nokia brick phones some of us had. My mother gave me one so she would know I was safe.

Upon putting my phone back in my pocket, I decided I would see what this being was, so I started walking towards it. As I got closer, this thing looked like someone's nightmare, as its skin was very scaly and covered with horns on the top of its head, it had no hair, but most impressive were these white eyes with slit pupils! I have never been afraid of anything before, but something told me to run!

I started running through the lot behind me, trying to get away from whatever this "thing" was, when suddenly a car passed by slowly. This thing didn't even seem to notice me but turned to get a better look at the car; when it did, I detected that its face was more humanlike in structure. I felt weird when I saw its face and began running faster back towards my house. Now I wasn't sure if this being was still there or not because by the time I reached my front door, it was gone.

Now, I'd heard of weird stuff happening in my neighborhood at the time. I went to school with other kids and always joked about what they called the green man. Supposedly a tall green lizard man who stalked the woods, but I thought it was ridiculous. I'm not saying that's what I saw, but I will tell you what I saw terrified me.

Encounter 3
Submitted By: Glen
Time: N/A
Location: Alabama

I'M a hobbyist and a paranormal investigator. I wanted to share an encounter story I've recently learned about in Alabama. A man had an encounter near his home with a reptilian that he said was about ten feet tall, and it left three claw marks on the hood of his truck in a fierce showdown. It tried to kill the man, but he was successful in getting away.

What made this the scariest of all possible encounters is that there were other witnesses to this weird event. The descriptions given by those who saw the same thing as the man were the same. The witnesses were his wife and older children. The man was terrified of what he saw that afternoon. He said this thing climbed right out of the swamp and went right for him. They had a huge fight that led to him getting away. The man admitted he was terrified of what he saw, and if the thing wanted him, it could have easily killed him in his home.

As described by the witnesses, the reptilian cryptid is between eight and ten feet tall, with grayish-green scaly skin and sharp teeth in its mouth; it has three claws on its hands, spikes all over its back, a long tail with what looked like barbs or thorns on the end. Its eyes are red and yellow with slit pupils and glow when mad. The thing can climb trees and walk on two legs and four if needed... I'm not saying this guy didn't run into something strange, but I think it was a reptilian-like creature that we usually refer to as the lizard man.

The witnesses say the thing blew a horrible, sickening smell in their direction as it came out of nowhere... They all smelled something terrible but couldn't place exactly what it was. They just kept saying how horrible it was, and they never wanted to have another encounter with whatever this was. The witnesses were so terrified that they moved away from the area after the incident.

The family now lives in northern Florida with their relatives to avoid that property.

When I spoke to the witness, he claimed a lot of swamp land surrounded that whole county. Lots of deer, lots of hunting. He said the surrounding county is very rural, and many people like to hunt. He says he's living in northern Florida because he doesn't want another reptilian encounter experience. He doesn't want to be that close to swamps and marshes after his family had their first encounter.

The man claims what he saw was not human but something else, something grayish green with scales all over its body; it had red eyes and yellow pupils, which were glowing on this dark evening when they were being attacked... he also admits he got a look at the creature for just a short time before it went into attack mode.

The man said his wife described precisely what he saw ... she hid behind a tree and watched as he fought back with whatever he had. The wife said a foul odor accompanied this being.; then she saw three claws that looked like retractable knives coming out of each hand. It made loud shrieking noises as it approached.

I don't suppose anyone else has had a sighting or an encounter story regarding this thing? In that case, I'd appreciate the information because what we have here is very strange, even if we don't have photographic evidence... at least not yet... If you have any knowledge of your own, I'd love it if you could share some with me.

Encounter 4
Submitted By: Marissa k.
Time: June 2002
Location: N/A

MY SIGHTING HAPPENED in June of 2002. My father was undergoing chemo, and I decided to bring him out in the canoe for an afternoon trip. We headed downriver to a secluded spot that we had been to once before. On our way there, my dog started acting funny, sniffing the air and barking...

That was when this large... lizard thing began coming out of the trees. I started screaming, pointing at this creature, wondering what we saw. My father grabbed our canoe paddles, I started screaming for him to paddle us away, and the beast kept coming toward us.

Now it was sifting through the water toward us like some giant snake or something, not swimming so much as flowing, until it was about ten feet from the canoe. Its head and body were above the waterline; my dad reached in his pocket for something.

Then I hear a gunshot go off, and a spray of blood shot out of this creature. The sight made me almost vomit. Then it just sank under the water.

The next thing I knew, we were at our destination, and my father asked if I was okay. I think I went into shock because the time from it being shot to us going on land was a blur of time. That was when he told me what had happened: him shooting this creature, then this thing disappearing underneath the water. I had fainted. I was so terrified. My dad explained that something significant had come at us through the water, and he wasn't sure what it was. My dad was so pale; I had never seen him like that.

Fast-forward fifteen years later, and my oldest son believes he's seen a similar creature when he was out in the forest with his friends. He was rounding up this group of kids when he saw something like a lizard. He said it stared at him for a moment, and when they all became aware of what he was seeing, the creature darted off into the forest...

My son is now twenty-one and has never told anyone about it until I mentioned my sighting to him, not knowing if it was the same. It was weird because his friend's parents had reported strange large three-toed tracks around their house at night. They would find these large feces piles with significant scratches on some of the trees. I can only suspect that it's this thing. It's hanging around this area. I don't know if we stumbled upon its territory or what we did, but I know it's hanging around here.

My son has seen it several more times since his initial sighting. The last time he saw it was a few months ago. He says this creature is getting violent, destroying people's property, and even attacking dogs. I am still in shock by what we saw all those years ago. I never believed in this kind of thing until that day. Now I know for sure it existed and will continue to exist.

I know I'm going to be attacked for what I am saying, but if anyone else out there has seen this thing, let me know. We need some answers!

Encounter 5
Submitted By: Anonymous
Time: 2014
Location: Texas

I USED to be a resident of Texas, and although I'm in Colorado currently, I still have family there in Dallas. That's not the part that concerns me, so let's go with it. My sister was studying at a university in Texas when she started telling me about some strange things going on out where she lived. She told me stories such as finding large clawed footprints in her yard, seeing strange lights on a wall outside her window when there wasn't supposed to be anything near their house, and other such weirdness.

I dismissed these claims as nothing more than paranoia or an overactive imagination until one night, while visiting my parents in Cedar Hill, Texas, this past summer (2014), I heard noises outside that sounded somewhat like growls at first. Still, as the night went on, I realized they were far too deep to be anything other than something like a bear, only more significant. The prints looked wrong too. My father grabbed his flashlight and headed out to see what was making these noises while my mother and I stayed inside.

I heard him go out there and yell at something for a minute or two before he came back in. He described the creature as between five feet eight and five feet ten tall and covered from head to toe in dark green scales that looked almost black in the moonlight. It had large muscular arms with three sharp claws on each hand and two sharp fangs sticking out of its mouth when it opened up and growled at my dad. The thing snarled at him and then retreated into the tree line. My dad was pale. I've never seen him so scared out of his mind before in my life. He told me he had no idea what that thing was and only remembered it making a horrible, high-pitched squeal before disappearing into the forest.

We came to find out the next day that this creature had been seen on their property in recent days by other neighbors, but we didn't find out about this until later. My dad still doesn't know what it was or why it would just up and visit his house like that out of nowhere. I looked up reptiles native to Texas, and nothing fit except giant lizards such as monitor lizards, which weren't supposed to be in Cedar Hill, so at least there's that much. Interestingly, my father described the strange lizard man/creature as having a "very human" face and that it looked strangely intelligent.

It gets stranger, though. My sister came across this story of a girl who saw some reptilian creature near her home in Copperas Cove, Texas, last year in 2013 one day on Facebook or something like that. She pointed out the story to show my father so he'd know she wasn't just making up stories. He brought this article over to me after I got back home and asked if I knew what was going on down there. My grandmother is also from Dallas, but she's moved away now, but even she told us she used to see unexplained lights outside her house when she lived in Garland, Texas. I know it's not exactly related but it's still strange.

I don't know much about these reptilian entities, but if they're real, I'd like to see why this is happening around Dallas. My grandmother told me she used to see lights outside her house late at night and that sometimes when she'd look out the window, there would be a large creature standing in the street, staring at her as if it wanted to come inside but wouldn't. At first, this terrified her until one day she realized that whatever the thing was, it wasn't anything harmful—it just stood there looking at her through its glowing yellow eyes with some interest-like expression on its face—and after a while, my grandmother began wondering what it was standing out there for. After a while, she was convinced it was a manifested spirit. One time she even called my grandfather, who was at work, about it, and he said there was nothing out there with her. She looked out the window again to see if it had gone away, but no—that thing was still standing in the street as if its feet were rooted to the ground while she watched. This continued for several years until she finally moved away from that house.

When I told my grandmother about what happened to us one night, she became pale and asked me not to tell anyone else because people might think we were crazy, we got those looks after telling a few friends what had happened.

Last week, I saw more news stories of these lizard men near Dallas when I did another search online where they described them as having green scaly skin, bulging green eyes, and whatnot. My sister even saw a YouTube video where some guy got footage of these reptilian creatures walking around on two legs in broad daylight out in California as well! If lizard men are genuine, then why is this happening? Is it just because of the increase in population around Dallas, or perhaps something more sinister...?

By the way, my father has never been interested in cryptozoology before that I know of, but he's terrified now as if whatever we saw was stalking his house specifically for him to see. He told me he wanted to move away from Cedar Hill ASAP if possible. He hasn't slept right since that night, over three weeks ago, and won't be sleeping any better tonight either...

Encounter 6
Submitted By: Ghost
Time: Circa 2015/2016
Location: Florida

FOUR OR FIVE YEARS BACK, I went through an experience with something that I can't precisely explain. I know many people go through different things in life, but this one stands out to me. There are so many who would have gone through what I've gone through with trauma and not being able to go back into the wilderness, but for me, it was more of a wake-up call to be open-minded and alert to all the things that we don't know about. I had no idea this would happen to me, and I ventured into this place not knowing exactly what I would get myself into.

Back in the late summer, I would usually hike and venture around in the swamps of Florida, Alabama, Mississippi and up into Louisiana. There's just something about the thick swampy humidity that just draws me in. I love the wildlife and the thrill and rush of being around so many poisonous and dangerous animals. I know many might call me crazy by saying that, but it puts you on edge and makes you have to be alert to the things and noises around you. I've camped alone by myself in the Everglades and all through the swamp for weeks at a time for years, and I feel like it's only made me a more complicated individual.

Doing what I do isn't for everybody, and it is undoubtedly a tricky feat at times. The scorching heat and high humidity levels make many novices and moderate explorers tap out. That also doesn't include water moccasins, poisonous insects and snakes, alligators, or thick terrain you could hardly get through. I think that's why it draws me in because it presents itself as a challenge that I want to conquer. I don't want to bore you with irrelevant details, and I just want listeners to know that many don't go trotting through this type of environment for long. I feel like that's the only reason I experienced what I did because I put myself in that environment for the time I did. How do I only go for a day or two? I don't believe I would be walking away the same person.

I want to say it happened in August of 2014 or 2015. I was deep in the swamps, right around the border of Louisiana and Florida. I can't precisely remember the spot, but I was in there. There were parts of the swamp that I traversed through that were so thick you needed a machete or some thick cutting tool to make your way in or around. The first significant component I encountered was what I believed to be the den or hole in which these things lived. After coming to an area where it was clear that man had not ventured because of the density of brush and swamplike conditions, I had to work hard to pave my way in. In the name of exploration, I put myself in harm's way, venturing into unknown dangerous waters with reptiles that could take me out. It's not like I wasn't vulnerable at all. Many would call me foolish for doing such a thing, but there's something about the thrill of it.

I lost track of how much time I put into cutting my way through this thick and overgrown swamp but came to a small patch of land that looked leveled out in the ground with what appeared to be a finely dug hole. This looked like a well-constructed entrance to a cave or something, but you could tell it wasn't naturally occurring. The problem is this hole was around seven feet tall, if I have to guess, but it was more narrow. I know it was taller than me, and I'm five feet eleven. No known animals in the swamp would make this hole the way it was, nor did any animals come close to the size.

This intrigued me, but I wasn't about to stick myself in a dug-out entrance or cave without light or equipment. The swamps are one thing, but that's venturing into a potential den of a dangerous animal. Boy, was I proven right. After being fascinated and spending a short time observing the entrance, curious about what would create it, I started getting this feeling. I began to get the feeling I shouldn't be there. It was as if my senses were screaming at me that a large predator would be coming out or possibly approaching. I'm no stranger to those feelings, having encountered multiple mountain lions and bears with cubs in the past. I wasn't about to blow off my gut instinct. I quickly continued and thought nothing of it. I made it about half the day to a spot in the denser wilderness where I could set up and make my camp.

The nighttime was when things got really out of hand and the following day. I made a camp spot in a little cutaway spot in the brush that suited where I'd sleep. It was already dusk, so I began setting up my one-person tent. Lay on my small cot with my small 9 mm by my side. My thoughts at the time were focused on where I was going the following day and what part of the swamp I would make my way through. I must have been intent on that because I fell asleep at some point or another, totally unaware of the day's exhaustion. I had forgotten all about finding the hole earlier and the feeling of doom following it.

I'm not sure if my senses woke me up or what happened, but my consciousness flickered on with my eyes still closed. I quickly was alerted that something heavy and oversized was approaching my tent. It was slow at first, but it became heavier closer to my tent. My mind was racing to find an answer to what this could be approaching from the thick swampy brush. I didn't feel fear, as I was perplexed by what I heard. That was when I was able to make out that what I was hearing was something bipedal and not four feet. I heard creeping up to my tent from the brush with one heavy footstep for each stride. I thought it to be a person at first, but then my thoughts quickly turned to fear as I realized no human was heavy enough to create loud footsteps. Whatever this was came in on my tent fast, and before I could even think, I could feel the presence of something right outside my tent. The air around me quickly grew incredibly tense, and I reached quickly for my handgun, which I'd cap-loaded for any given moment. As I got my weapon, I saw this claw, or what I believed to be a claw, begin to press itself so hard into the tent it ripped through.

Bursting through my tent wall was a giant black claw; my mind immediately went to the velociraptors' claws in the *Jurassic Park* movies. I grabbed hold of my gun and steadily flipped the safety off. As I was turning my arm towards this unknown intruder, this claw began to shred my tent to pieces, just dragging down, leaving a hole. I fired one good shot, and the scream I heard after that... was enough to tell me everything I needed to know. This thing wasn't a human, and it certainly wasn't any animal I'd ever come to know. I can't even begin to describe to you the sound of what this thing's scream sounded like. It was horrible. Whatever it was took off in the opposite direction, crashing through the brush rather quickly. Even faster than it had when it approached my tent the first time. It had torn such a long hole through my tent wall that I could jump out of my cot and step outside it to chase my assailant, but it was far too dark to see.

At that moment, I was just so pumped full of adrenaline that I wasn't even considering what it was that had even been trying to come into my tent because I feel most sane human beings wouldn't be chasing after whatever this thing was with a 9 mm pistol. I don't think I was standing outside, trying to let my eyes adjust to the darkness, for more than just a moment, when I started hearing more thudding coming in my direction. I jumped back into my tent, grabbed my flashlight, and shined it in the general direction. I listened to the thudding.

I assumed that whatever I shot or whoever it was was coming back. I was going to end it for good. I'm not a murderer by any means, but if it's a matter of you or me, sorry. I wasn't going to die out here all alone in the swamp. I shined my light. The first thing I saw were these deep red reptilian-looking eyes, followed by the body crashing through the brush, heading right for me. Now I realized a couple of things at that moment. Not only did I have a full view of whatever I was looking at, but I realized for the first time that there's more to this world than we could ever learn, whether we enjoy it or not. I don't think my brain took more than a couple of seconds to process what I was looking at because I never fully processed it. I started firing rounds like a madman into whatever was approaching me.

Let me give you some details real quick; this thing was taller than me, so probably seven to eight feet tall, maybe more, covered in dark green scales with lighter scales on the front of its body. This thing was walking bipedal and had a large reptilian-looking head. It, to me, looked very crocodilian, with large teeth protruding from its top and bottom jaws, and deep red reptilian eyes. I don't mean like those glowing fake red eyes in monster stories, they were just natural reptilian eyes, but they were a deep crimson. This was some sort of humanoid reptilian being that I must have pissed off somehow because it was coming right for me.

After I fired off a couple of shots, it disappeared into the dark. I realized then there were more than just one, and I jumped back in my tent with my gun clasped tightly, ready for war. I was so pumped full of adrenaline that I don't think I comprehended what was going on, just that I needed to survive and that some large swamp animal was attacking me. The swamp stayed dead silent around me, and I heard no more sounds for the next few hours as I sat up awake, alert, and was ready for anything.

The day started to break at some point, and I think I caught myself nodding off out of sheer exhaustion and being pumped full of adrenaline the night before. I didn't have a watch or any way to tell time on me, so I'm not exactly sure what time that little encounter occurred in the morning. All I know is as daylight came, I got my stuff together and tried to get out of there as quickly as possible. And don't worry, I kept my pistol ready.

I decided to keep going in the direction I was initially planning, which would take me out of the thicket of the swamp. I don't think it was more than an hour later that I encountered another clear area in the swamp with yet another giant hole like I'd found the day before. It looked the same with the same artificial-looking entrance that looked dug out. Even more disturbing was all around the hole in the soft mud were these enormous footprints from something that looked like a large bipedal reptile. These were massive prints far bigger than my hand, and the indent was at least an inch deep. Of course, I had nothing to cast these footprints with nor to take a picture with, but for the first time this trip, I felt spooked because what I'd dealt with the previous night was a reality.

And at that moment, I pieced it together that whatever I had encountered last night must have been whatever was traveling or living in these tunnels. Some sort of large swamp reptilian beings. This hole had a smell, too; it was a mixture of dead blood and swamp rot. I didn't spend any time hanging around other than to look at the tracks and reserve, but I tried to make my way farther away from this whole area that I regretted now going into.

It took me the rest of the day to get back to an area, well, not a location but a lone road where I was able to hitchhike back to civilization. I didn't tell anybody what happened to me or my story because I didn't think it would be appropriate. What happens in the swamp stays in the swamp, and I just figured that I had encountered some sort of creature that had been undiscovered in the swamp and had been left alone by man. I didn't know that there was such a thing as reptilian beings. These eight-to-nine-foot-tall bipedal reptilian carnivores. I speculate that maybe the first time I encountered one of their other tunnels, they were in the area or could smell me and didn't like that I discovered their hole, which is why they followed me and tracked me down to where I bedded down at.

As frightening as this experience was, I never let it stop me from exploring and going back into the swamp to the areas where I love to go. I just have to accept there's more there than meets the eye, and I need to be aware of my surroundings.

The area of the swamp that I traversed into was thick and difficult to navigate. As I cut my way into the thick brush, I could see why many had not traveled into it. This was miles and miles in and traversing through thick brush and questionable bogs and areas of water where there could be alligators and such. I don't think anybody would go so far back, which is why I was brave enough to do it. It makes sense now from an animal perspective why they would have some sort of den back there without the worry or fear of being disturbed by humans, but at the same time, I set myself up by being so vulnerable. For anybody out there who's an explorer like me and goes to the areas where nobody else goes, you need to be aware that there might be things that live there and that you might be encroaching on its territory. This is why respect for the wilderness and the things around you is vital, but take caution and heed. I would like to think that I share the swamp with every other animal.

Unfortunately, I don't share the swamp with friendly neighbors, and I guess some things wish to remain hidden.

Encounter 7
Submitted By: bloodman22
Time: 2012
Location: Arizona

MANY THINGS COME out of the desert that I don't quite understand, even if it's situations that I was put in. I'm half Navajo and know all about skinwalkers and the legends that part of my people have passed down for years and years. Because I am half Navajo, I always had many friends and family immersed in the Navajo culture and lifestyle, while a lot of my other family and friends were just regular white people. I consider myself extremely blessed to experience both walks of life and cultures.

I have even encountered such beings before, but that is for another time and place. What I'm talking to you about today is far beyond my understanding and something my people never discussed. I was out late at night. I had just been partying with a couple of friends, and we were doing a late-night drive. I should note that nobody in the vehicle, including in the driver's seat, was intoxicated at this time. This also includes me. We just needed some fresh air to get out, and there is nothing like the Arizona nighttime air.

We were driving down the road, the only ones we could see around us. If anybody has ever gone out here at night, you would know that it is pitch black except for the stars above you that only occasionally offer little light and the moon. My buddy was doing about seventy or seventy-five miles an hour when this lizard-like creature came flying out of the darkness over a ridge, passing by our vehicle. It began to run on all fours, but it looked strange, like it was forced. It would be like making a human run on all fours, it was awkward looking, and you can tell they don't usually run like that. This thing had protruding scales and what looked like small spikes or horns all down its back and shoulder blades, and it was scaly and almost a smokey charcoal color. It nearly collided with our car.

As it got close, it outstretched its arm and slashed at the tire, causing it to go flat, and we almost crashed off the road. All of us in the car were screaming and going crazy. Well, my friend was trying to floor it on a flat tire. Then we heard a loud crashing sound from his engine, and his transmission went out. Now he could no longer accelerate, and he was forced to slow down and pull over in the middle of the night on this road. We all sat there screaming, freaking out, and not knowing what to do.

After a minute, I think, we collected ourselves enough to have somebody try to make a phone call to get somebody to pick us up. My friend pulled out his phone and proceeded to call his father to get him to come to pick us up and let him know that our car broke down.

Purposefully not mentioning that we had just been attacked and chased off the road by some significant demon lizard thing.

He said he would be there in about twenty minutes and for us to sit tight. My friend, who is full-blooded Navajo, just started praying in Navajo while my other friends and I were freaking out, expecting this thing to show itself and kill us. It was incredibly eerie sitting there waiting for his dad to show up, knowing that this thing was just in the darkness surrounding us, waiting for the right moment to get us.

We saw some headlights show up over the horizon after some time, and lo and behold, it was his father to pick us up. I was never a massive fan of his father because he was an abusive alcoholic, but that was probably the only time I had ever been so happy to see him. We all piled in the car, and even though we never said anything about what we saw, I knew we couldn't be happier to be rescued.

For whatever reason, whatever it was we saw never tried to attack us once our car was on the side of the road, and I'm not exactly sure why. But I think the bigger question remains: what exactly did we see, and why did it attack our vehicle? This thing was huge and must have had immense force to use its claws to slash a tire open.

When his dad pulled up, since it was dark out, we didn't give him a chance to see what had happened and only told him. It wasn't until the following morning, when we all returned to retrieve the car and get it towed, that he saw the damage for the first time. I remember his expression and kneeling to look at the massive gash in the tire and sternly looking at my friend, asking him what had happened.

That was when my friend finally told him what had happened. His father had hugged him, something I hadn't seen him do in the years I've known them, and spoke something to him quietly in Navajo that I couldn't quite make out.

Apparently, not only had his transmission gone out randomly, but we had been attacked by something none of us even knew existed. At least with skinwalkers in our culture, we know about them. We know ways to protect ourselves from them and to stay away. There is no preparing any of us for this creature. I'm not sure if it was a creature of the desert or a creature of the night, but either way, it's just another nightmare to try to avoid now.

Maybe many of the older Navajo around here don't speak of other such things because it's true that if you talk about it, it will draw them to you. Could this be true for what we encountered, or were we simply marked and attacked by something more sinister and evil?

Encounter 8
Submitted By: Franklin
Time: 2007–2010
Location: East Africa

ABOUT TWELVE TO fifteen years ago, I used to do missionary work for a church that I was a part of, and I got to visit a lot of the world, and for that, I'm forever thankful. I learned a lot and grew a lot as a person, but what's even more remarkable is some of the stories I heard from some of these villages. I will tell you this particular story from a man from one of the villages in Eastern Africa; forgive me because I cannot remember the country. His English was pretty good for not being an English native speaker.

He would tell me things about creatures of the night attacking their village and taking their young children down into the rivers, drowning them and eating them. He explained these demons as crocodilian-looking creatures with long lizard-like heads and snouts and sometimes eating the children whole before taking them back to the river. He told me that even the river crocodiles in the hippopotamus would fear these beings and that they would only enter the village at night.

They had constructed several wards to try to rid these beings from entering the village, but it didn't work. Over the last year, more than a dozen of the village's children had been taken. Warriors and men of the village had put together hunting parties to travel into or as close to the river as possible to seek these beings out to hunt and kill them. They'd been able to kill a couple, but more men had died from fighting these things than they'd been able to kill, so there was a retreat. Some of these same men faced vicious repercussions of attacks with severed arms and chunks of flesh taken out of their bodies. These men looked like they'd been attacked by crocodiles but had only had fights with whatever these beings are.

I was even told that sometimes when these beings come to abduct young children, they will kill them right there on the spot, ripping them to shreds and biting off portions of the body, and leave them as a warning sign for other villagers.

When I asked him to clarify what these lizard-like beings were, he told me they were tall and skinny with very long arms. They had long claws and massive, serrated claws on the end of their fingers. When I asked about their face, he explained that their head sloped down and that the snout was extremely long, kind of like a caiman. Their eyes would glow a natural yellow, and they emanated evil from them. You hardly ever saw them on land; they only came out of the water at night. When they dragged children away, it was down into the river where they were.

So far, no one has been brave enough to try to swim down into the river to find them or to know where they're coming from. I never saw any of this myself since we were passing through the village shortly, but he and several other villagers I spoke to seemed terrified and only verified even more what he told me. I wish I could remember the word they used to call these things, but it meant crocodile people in his language.

That will always stick with me because it chilled me to the bone.

Encounter 9
Submitted By: Thomas Mueler
Time: N/A
Location: Idaho

THIS DIDN'T HAPPEN RECENTLY, but when I was a younger guy in my twenties. I had made the connection years earlier in a very odd way as a kid, so that wasn't the case when I encountered these entities. Instead, I had a sense of awareness—a sense where I knew these things were real and out to get me if I made the wrong move at any time. Things we don't know about exist out in the wild, something we think only belongs in our nightmares. That couldn't be further from the truth.

I went camping in the outback of the mountains in Idaho the night before I was attacked. I was sleeping under the stars with a group of six to seven other people, and we heard what sounded like a low-pitched hiss growl sound coming from behind us. It woke us all up, and we sat up and looked back at the sound. We had the impression that it was coming from behind us, and then we started to hear it all around us. Surrounding us. Then we realized it wasn't just a singular sound but a bunch of them. My roommate, whom I was camping with, started to reach for his revolver, but I was just scared because I didn't know what they were.

I had no idea what animals were out there. I was an outdoor newbie at the time. My other friend had a shotgun next to him, and he was ready for anything, so I looked over at his gun, and then he looked over at me and grabbed it. He gave it a cock, huddled there with it while we were all practically pooping bricks at this chorus of hissing and growling around us. It sounded like we were in a reptile zoo or something.

You can't even begin to describe the feeling I had. I was too scared to even leave my sleeping bag. Then, in the minimal light we had from the night, we saw these tall figures begin to step toward us from the thickness of the trees and leaves around us. Tall, hulking reptile-like figures stood on two legs. There were at least ten or twelve of them closing in on us. We were so terrified that my friends couldn't fire their weapons at the time.

And then this is where the story gets very strange, and I can't recall what happened because none of us know. One by one, we all seemed to black out and lose consciousness. Not fall asleep as you would think.

We were surrounded by large predatory animals closing in on us, and we didn't know what we were dealing with. The other four of us who hadn't come equipped with weapons just huddled and shook in their sleeping bags, as I did. As I said, though, we all blacked out and lost consciousness.

The next thing you know, all seven of us were waking up in unison on top of this rocky cliff, miles away from where we laid down our heads in our sleeping bags. No equipment, nothing. All of us were out of our sleeping bags. It was as if we had been dragged there. We were scared, confused, and had no idea what had happened or was happening. Both my friends, the one with the shotgun and the one with the revolver, noticed their weapons were gone. Our wallets were gone, everything. The only thing we had was the clothes on our backs. Our equipment and everything we had with us could be found nowhere. There was no indication of us being dragged, nor did we have cuts, scratches, or any footprints or marks to show we were taken. It was like we had been instantly knocked out and teleported to this tiny cliff.

Judging by the sun, it was close to midday, and in our panic and confusion, we had no choice but to try to hike down this cliff and find a way back to civilization. The brush was so thick that there was only one direction to travel down, and that was when we eventually ran into our camp from the night before. We had been taken about three miles in total from our spot. Our sleeping bags were still there, and all our equipment, but the weapons and wallets were gone. There were no footprints, no signs of a struggle or ripping anyone out of their sleeping bags. It was disturbing, to say the least. It's haunted me for many years not to know exactly what went down that previous night.

We gathered what we could and left the area. Everything was normal for the most part. We returned to civilization the next day, which ended my adventuring in the outback for years afterward. I don't know if we were abducted, if it was aliens, or what it could have been. I like to think those two-legged walking reptile things we saw in the faint light coming towards us had something to do with all of this, but I don't know.

Encounter 10
Submitted By: Anonymous
Time: N/A
Location: Sierra Nevada Mountains

I WAS with my climbing partner, high up in the Sierra Nevada Mountains. This was one of the most intense mountain climbing experiences I've ever had aside from this encounter. My partner sat on top of a large pile of rocks, pulled out his canteen of water, and took a five-minute break.

That was when over the rocks appeared these creatures. Monsters, I would say, because of how frightening they all looked. Three of them were of enormous size. They were about eight to ten feet tall and had scales all over their bodies from head to toe. The lighter green was on the front of their torsos and bodies; darker was on the back. They had these spines protruding from their backs and their necks. Their faces were very reptile-ish but also very humanoid. They had large yellow reptilian eyes with slits and mouths full of little knives for teeth. Each one carried a dead deer in one hand, dragging it by the neck.

As they immediately noticed us stepping over the rocks, they dropped their kill and began charging us. Because of their large size, their stride was enormous, and they reached us in such little time. Next to us, the pile of small rocks we were on, was this tiny drop-off of maybe twenty feet that my partner and I both jumped out from and landed on the heavy brush to break our fall. These things charged us so fast we didn't even think. The fear that came over us drove us to jump off this tiny drop-off, and when we landed, yes, it hurt like a mother. We just pulled ourselves up and ran down the way we came.

I've never seen creatures like those before in my life, and it terrified us to our cores. The last few days, I brought this incident up with my old hiking partner, who remembers it all too vividly. We're very careful about where we go hiking now.

Encounter 11
Submitted By: Anonymous
Time: 2008
Location: N/A

THIS WAS BACK in 2008 when I was just twelve years old. I'm twenty-four now. What happened has left me with severe PTSD due to what I saw that day. Even now, it's hard for me to talk about it, actually.

My family has a large creek that runs down in this ravine through the back side of their property. It feeds off one of the main rivers that flow through the area here, so you must be careful with powerful currents pulling you under. Not so much the creek, but as you get closer to where the river feeds into the creek, it can be really easy to slip and fall. I was swimming back here because it was a hot August day, and the temperature outside was probably 102, I'm guessing. Where I was at in the creek, I was perhaps about thigh deep, and I had just come out of the water from submerging myself as much as possible, trying to cool down my core. The water was cold since the river was mountain run-off water. I heard a noise behind me, and that was when my heart dropped in my body.

Coming down the creek, walking in my direction, looking right at me, was this creature, this monster. It was large with a slim body and was arched over slightly. It looked like a cross between a snake and Smeagol from *Lord of the Rings* and had huge canine fangs just like a snake does. It was jet black and covered in scales. The fangs were comparable to that of a saber-tooth tiger. They were exaggerated and extremely large and long. I had a powerful feeling of death, and I knew my time was up at that moment.

The second I made eye contact with this creature, it reached its hand out to me as it kept walking in my direction. Not like it was reaching its hand out to help, but to try to get to me. It had long, sharp black claws at the end of each of its fingers. I screamed so loud I hurt my lungs, ran out of that creek, tripped on a rock, and fractured part of my leg from the impact. I had so much adrenaline pumping through me I didn't notice right away, and this creature pursued me and chased me out of the backwoods up the ravine I was running up.

It's weird because I felt like it was strong and fast enough it could have gotten me if it wanted to, but it kept a short distance between us as if to terrorize me and chase me out of there. This is still hard for me to talk about, so I'm sorry if I'm not making much sense, but that's what happened to me.

I ran back to my house, crying. My leg was swollen, and I needed medical attention. I told my mom what happened, and my mom called 911. My leg got treated, but my dad thought it was a bear chasing me, and went back there with a rifle but came back a half hour later saying he didn't see anything like what I described. I didn't care if he or my mother believed me or not. It's a trauma I'll have to live through now, and I still have frequent and vivid reoccurring nightmares.

Encounter 12
Submitted By: Anonymous
Time: Summer 2013
Location: Eastern Texas

THIS SIGHTING OCCURRED in the summer of 2013, when I first had my experience with the unknown. Let me preface and say I can confidently say that I'm not exactly sure what "this" thing was. I'll do my best to describe it to you, and maybe you can figure out what I saw that day. I've never seen any animal like it and never knew it even existed. I live around a vast swampy plot of land, hundreds of acres of undeveloped marsh and swamp.

I was walking home from school when I noticed something in the trees moving nearby. I thought it was maybe a dog at first, but as it began moving around, it turned out to be a giant lizard with a long tail. This thing was standing completely upright like a grown man, taller than I was. I never in my life could imagine or had seen a full two-legged lizard until this day. I was in shock when I saw it. I had no idea what this thing was. It was like a partial man and partial lizard hybrid. I could see its clawed feet and hands as well as the lizard-like head and body.

This thing was brownish in color and had the most humanlike eyes I've ever seen on a reptile. It did not have any hair on it at all. I believe it was looking for food by the way it was walking and sniffing in the air. I saw it for a few seconds before it realized I was looking at it, and it then ran off into the trees. I didn't know what to do or think. It was like I was in a trance, shocked and scared. I couldn't even move to call out for help. I just stood there in shock and disbelief.

I thought, "Did I just see a giant lizard?" I kept thinking about it for the next few days. I kept telling myself it was a trick of the eye, my mind playing tricks on me. I thought I was going crazy. I kept trying to rationalize what I saw. I knew I saw something, but I was confused about what it was.

I told my friends about this thing I saw in the woods, but they had no idea what it was. It was a whole week later when I saw it again. Also, the area where I first saw it has very thick brush, trees, and a swamp. It was around early June, just before school got out, and everything was so thick and lush. It would be tough to get back there, let alone in a giant lizard suit, so I never thought it could be someone in a suit playing a prank.

The second time I saw it, it was moving slowly back towards the swamp in an area that was a little clearer but still littered with marshes and trees. Just more open so you can see farther back, and I caught movement out of the corner of my eye. I turned to look, and for a second, I saw the same creature darting through the trees way back in there. It honestly made me shudder. I could feel my heart pounding in my chest. I was a little more prepared this time because I saw it before it saw me.

This time I was able to get a better look at it. I could also see its body and hands more clearly from this angle. It looked very muscular, like a bodybuilder. It was standing in a wide-legged stance and was watching me. I couldn't see its facial features very well because it was still far away, but I could see the shape of its head and eyes. I also saw its tail, again much longer than an ordinary lizard's tail. It was brownish with a lot of green in it. I didn't see any hair on it this time either. It wasn't until this second time that I realized I was looking at a living, breathing creature. I started to think about it more and more. I thought it was a mutant, but I didn't know of any radiation in the area. I know that's probably a stretch to assume such a thing, but from what I saw, I have no idea how to explain it away.

Can giant human lizards possibly live down here in the swamps of Eastern Texas?

9

SEA/LAKE ENCOUNTERS & SIGHTINGS

THE OCEAN IS NEVER safe like we think it is; there are always some dangerous sea creatures lurking in the deep. Even though we may not see them often, they're still out there. Every now and then, these creatures make their way to the surface, and we get a glimpse of them. There are legends and folklore enriched with beings and creatures from the deep. Mermaids, leviathans, etc. It's clear that the sea holds deep mysteries and even stranger creatures than we could ever imagine. While this section is a bit shorter than others due to not having as many stories on hand, I thought I would share a batch that offer variety and are equally interesting.

Encounter 1
Submitted By: George O'Sullivan
Time: 1952
Location: Cornwall Coast, England

I USED to enjoy watching my father fish when I was a young boy, and I suppose it was inevitable that I would follow in my father's footsteps when I got older. And that I did. I worked as a fisherman for forty years, and I suppose the years drifted by quickly. And it's only now, at eighty-seven, that I pause to reflect on the past, and I feel now's the right time to come forward about an experience that I had at age nineteen.

During the summer of 1952, two of my colleagues and I were on our boat off the Cornwall coast. We were looking to cast our rods to catch red salmon, as we were getting a handsome check for providing a local butcher with fish. It was a hot summer day, and we had a few beers on the boat. Our T-shirts were off, and we were enjoying waving at a group of young ladies who were having a picnic on the coast.

We didn't know the girls, but they beckoned us to come and join them for their picnic. It was certainly enticing for a nineteen-year-old. I'd been working as a fisherman apprentice for around five years at the time, and it was very rare that I ever encountered the opposite sex. The ladies continued beckoning us; the smell of their vanilla perfume seemed to gather and cluster on our boat. Their soft, feminine overtones were almost hypnotic and filled me with youthful desire. I can remember it like it was yesterday.

Well, what occurred on that day was nothing but sheer madness, sheer terror. As I was waving to the girls, the others on board decided to jump overboard and swim towards the shoreline and walk up to meet the girls. I told them that it seemed like a good idea and encouraged them to go. No sooner had they jumped overboard than the sky became very gray, and it started to rain heavily. I watched as they struggled to swim against increasingly erratic waves.

I caught a glimpse of the girls, and I could see them jumping up and running away. I started to wonder if I was missing something or if it was some kind of trick girls' play, because it seemed like it was too good to be true. Maybe they were afraid of the impending rainstorm, or perhaps they were hesitant to actually meet the guys.

The skies continued to pour, and I noticed that my friends were struggling heavily. Then I witnessed a horror that made my hands shake with fright. A large serpentine creature shot up out from the ocean, long, over fifteen feet long, with a huge body, green and slimy, like a sea snake. It had fangs that looked to be a foot long, and the size of its head that was protruding from its body was larger than a human's head.

It was a disturbing sight. And just the memory alone terrifies me. The guys in the water noticed the serpent too. And I noticed that it seemed to be hunting them. After it had lunged at one of my friends, I saw signs of blood in the water. I grabbed something nearby and threw it out in the direction in which the serpent was now thrashing around, jumping in and out of the ocean like a dolphin, but viciously and with clear intent to wound.

The creature then turned around and noticed me and bolted towards me through the water. As soon as it was close enough, its enormous tail shot up out of the water and attempted to cut me in the face. But I managed to block it with an oar in the boat. It seemed like it was intent on striking at me. It sprang about, thrashing and hungry for human flesh. I was absolutely petrified beyond belief. I had never witnessed such a creature before.

And at only nineteen years old, I was still a virgin of the sea. Even my own father had never heard of anything remotely similar to this or come across anything of the sort.

The creature that resembled a serpent was able to climb aboard the boat, and it was now facing me head-on. The boat capsized slightly, seawater started pouring in, and both of my feet quickly became soaked. I felt like I was going to die, but I knew I would not give up without a fight against the beast. I couldn't shake the feeling that I was about to lose. I continued kicking frantically at the beast, hoping that if I made contact with it, it would retreat in fear. But this beast looked just as vicious as it did hungry. I managed to hit it slightly with the oar.

The problem was that the boat was now almost completely submerged. Instantaneously. The storm that had been raging overhead ended all of a sudden, and this serpentlike creature dove back down into the water.

The sea became calm and still. And I now felt safe to swim to shore. By the time I got to the shore, my friends were nowhere to be seen. I found them later, and they were still bleeding from the deep wounds and cuts from where this creature had attacked them. When we told other people about our experience, nobody believed us; however, some biologists said it was possible that it could have been a mysterious underwater creature that had not been discovered by scientists at the time.

Whatever it was, it was terrifying. And I was glad to have never encountered it again in all the years I spent fishing. Look, I know it might sound outlandish, but this is a story that happened to me when I was younger. And I haven't experienced anything like it since. I know there are crazy tales of sea experiences out there. And well, this is mine. Just remember that almost every fisherman out there has his or her own story to tell.

Encounter 2
Submitted By: David L.
Time: 2018
Location: Northern Ireland

LET ME INTRODUCE MYSELF. I'll go by the name David. I am a primary school teacher from Northern Ireland. I came across your channel recently and would like to share an experience that has been disturbing and wreaking havoc on my mental health.

I've taken a leave of absence from teaching for the past year. I have concluded that I don't believe I'll be able to return to work anytime soon, and it's not just because of COVID. It is about an encounter during the summer of 2018 with something in the ocean that, to this day, I still can't explain.

At the end of each school year, the teachers of the seventh grade at the primary school take their students on a field trip to a coastal resort. It's all to wish them a farewell before they enter secondary school. The weekend is always memorable because it is packed with many activities and fun. The children, mostly eleven years old, really enjoy doing it. And so do the teachers. Over the past decade, I have looked forward to the annual trip, and I have done so with great pleasure. Yet in 2018 that all changed.

I was the designated teacher for a group of five kids. And it was my job to take them out in the ocean for a short canoeing excursion. This was just off the coast of Cork. And to say it was picturesque would be a complete understatement. I remember thinking how lucky I was to be Irish and how blessed I was to have a job that allowed me to explore such beautiful spots and get paid for it all at the same time.

We all went out on the water in our canoes, everyone wearing life jackets for safety. In addition, we all carried whistles with us just in case of any difficulty. Canoeing was not a new experience for most children; some had a natural talent for it.

But one kid on the autism spectrum was high functioning but had poor hand-eye coordination and struggled to use his oar. I had to help him and spent a little extra time showing him the technique. But he eventually got the hang of it. He was just a little slower. So we all adjusted our speed to accommodate him.

There was a small sandbar about one-quarter mile from the shore, which was the destination we had in mind for our planned pit stop for a snack before heading back to the beach. I had some fruit, biscuits, and juice with me, all of which were stored in the backpack I had brought along. To guarantee that the children would have adequate energy and be physically prepared to row the canoe trip back to shore.

Reaching the sandbar at low tide allowed the children to explore and collect seashells. After having the snacks, it was time to head back to the beach before high tide came in. Once in the water though, the currents became strong, and the waves started to make the canoes shaky, and some kids said they were struggling to row.

It was a bit worrying. But I could see that they weren't far from reaching the shore. Dennis, the child with autism, began to really struggle. First, his oar fell into the water and sank; then he started to panic. He kept trying to stand up in the canoe, which caused it to rock back and forth. I could see the kids in the other canoes becoming scared.

I told the others to go ahead and row to shore, as I was going to tie a rope onto Dennis's canoe and pull him with me. When I reached him, I noticed something large and green, like the shape of a cobweb, just under the water. I squinted to see better from the sun's reflection off the water; looking downwards, I brushed it off as some weird type of seaweed or something. As soon as I tied the bow around Dennis's boat, I saw this thing circling. It also seemed to pulsate, getting bigger and then smaller again. I just hoped it wasn't a jellyfish or some dangerous sea animal.

At that moment, the motion of the water abruptly ceased, and I turned around to check on the other children and ensure they were all safely on land. As I turned my attention back to Dennis, a snake that looked like a serpent leaped out of the water and bit the top of my head.

Blood ran down my face due to the large sharp fangs cutting into my head. I felt like I was going to die, and I yelled at Dennis to get in my boat. But he was panicking even more now. This creature kept exploding out of the water as quickly as lightning, each time trying to attack my head in an attempt to bite me. It was the most frightening experience of my life.

I was being attacked while on the water with a very vulnerable child. On top of that, I had never before encountered a marine creature that was so hostile. After being bitten, I could feel the skin on my forehead spreading out. Without a doubt, as a result of a reaction to the venom that was released from this bite. This snake, or whatever it was, was not very big; it was probably about the size of a typical rattlesnake. It was enough to, nevertheless, act aggressive and hostile. In addition, I had no idea how poisonous it might have been. I've read that sea snakes have a particularly potent venom. I let out a sigh and a curse. I got Dennis's boat's bow and started paddling like hell.

This creature shot up again. Its eyes were like slits, yellow and soulless. Clearly intent on killing me. I did the best I could to try to avoid it. But to no avail. Bit again, the canoe boat shook and almost nearly capsized with the impact. Eventually, we reached the shore; the beast now abandoned its endeavor.

As I lifted Dennis out of the canoe, he was dripping in a cold sweat. The remaining children came running over to us and gave us hugs.

They had seen it all and were traumatized and scared. All the children were pale from shock and required immediate assistance obtaining water and food.

We called an ambulance and explained the situation to the dispatcher. I received initial medical attention and had my wounds dressed. The venom, fortunately, did not prove to be fatal. But I must confess that the memory of that event has remained in my consciousness ever since it occurred. It seems like every instant of every day, I am reminded of the anxiety and fear I experienced while in that canoe.

I fought for my life, not just mine, but for the little kids entrusted to my care. I sincerely feel I will never go back in that canoe again. And I'm reluctant to even go near the water.

The last I heard of the kids, their parents had taken them out of public school, and they were being homeschooled for the time being. And poor Dennis had completely retreated into himself.

Obviously, what we saw had a scary effect on all of us. In sharing this experience on your program, I hope you can enlighten me and inform me if other such creatures exist and have been sighted by others in the sea. I know it was some sort of sea serpent. Nothing crazy, like Leviathan or anything. But I've never run into a sea serpent so aggressive before. I mean, this thing was intent on bringing me down. So much so that I almost capsized our canoe. Anyway, I would like to thank you all for your hard work. It is genuinely appreciated.

Encounter 3
Submitted By: Anonymous
Time: 2002
Location: Coast of Mexico

I'M sure you're no stranger to terrifying, large and harrowing fish found out at sea by fishermen. Just like many of the details you describe in your accounts listed on your channel. Well, I too have an interesting story about a very large, what I'll call an unknown fish.

While I was cage diving with great white sharks off the coast of Mexico, many years back around 2002. To be exact, I'll spare you all the boring details about going out there on the boat, whom I was with getting suited up, and getting into the cage, because that's pretty redundant.

But anyway, great white shark diving is something that's amazing. And if you ever get the chance to do it, it's quite an adrenaline thrill. In fact, I was loving it and having the time of my life. I'm not really what you'd call an adrenaline junkie or even a thrill seeker. But this was something that I had to cross off my bucket list at least once; anyway, here's where things become crazy.

I'm in the cage, watching these beautiful and large, majestic fish swim all around me, knowing I'm literally within twenty feet of a man-eating predator, as Hollywood portrays them to be; there's about three of them swimming around me. And that's when I noticed their sudden disinterest in swimming around me, if that makes any sense. They kind of start to trail off towards the other directions out into the open sea. And as I sat there confused, wondering why they're no longer swimming around me, I began to see that deep below me, underneath me, a very, very large shape was beginning to emerge closer to the surface.

Now at first, I thought this might be a whale. But this shape, whatever it was, never fully surfaced enough that I could really make out vivid details; all I can really tell you is that it was a very, very large, dark shadow of something. And it seemed to be moving. Maybe it was a craft of some kind. It's hard to say. It looked very long. Like if you were to take a sperm whale and enlarge it even more. And I'm terrible at describing things. But the best way I can describe it is, it was some large marine animal or fish or something that was much, much larger than any great white that I've ever seen.

But again, I can't give you great details. Because it never fully surfaced enough even in the water that I could make out what it was. What I can only assume looking back on the event is that this thing approaching us made the great white sharks flee. Now you tell me, what lurks beneath, what's out there in the ocean, that the sheer presence of a fish makes even great white sharks flee?

So that's something that's left for another day of mystery. And I'm not kidding when I say that the shape of this thing was massive. It engulfed the entire underneath of my cage. And again, it was just a black mass. I couldn't tell what it was. But it seemed to go in front of me below me and behind me for maybe only a moment or two before submerging back down to the depths to where I couldn't see it anymore. After that the sharks stayed gone. And once I went back up to the boat, I didn't tell them what had happened. I only mentioned how the sharks just seem to lose interest. And that was it. It didn't really scare me as much as it makes me think about all the mysteries the ocean holds.

Encounter 4
Submitted By: Dante
Time: Summer 2019
Location: Louisiana

I FEEL foolish for saying this. But I think I saw something that might have been out of place. Whatever that means. I was at my grandfather's lake house out in the woodland area of Louisiana last summer when I had an encounter with some kind of creature, or I guess it would be a lake creature. I know that sounds crazy, like some sort of Hollywood movie plot. But I promise you the truth is stranger than fiction. I couldn't fully understand or describe what it was. I'm hoping somebody can help me identify what it might be.

And after doing some researching, I found your channel and saw you did a series about lake and sea creatures. Maybe one of your followers might be my ticket to getting a resolution to what I am about to explain.

My dad and I go fishing a few times during the summer every year at the lake where my grandfather's house is situated. This particular year was no different. It was just like any other trip this time. We got our gear together, did our traditional cola pop chug (downing a can of soda in one big gulp) and rowed out into the lake.

Normally, I will row around till Dad is satisfied we have found the right spot. Because Dad is a more experienced fisherman, he lets me go first hooking my bait onto the hook and casting it into the water. I set it and wait. When Dad cast his pole, he got a bite almost immediately. He pulled out a little three-inch trout, which would explain how he caught it so fast. You see, baby adolescent fish aren't smart enough to stay away from your bait, even though they know what it is, so they're easier to catch.

We don't take our phones out on the boat, so I can't ever accurately judge what time it is other than looking up at the sun and guessing by its location. I would say maybe forty-five minutes went by after he caught his fish that I finally had a bite. It definitely was a fighter.

After a lot of persistent pulling and leading, I finally started reeling it in; just as I was about to take it out of the water, a larger fish grabbed it from me, hook and all, and took it away. I rehooked my line and threw it back into the water. I don't know why, but larger fish always love taking my smaller bites.

Luckily, I had another bite a little while later, and I was determined not to let this one get away from me. I let it lead around for a little while before starting to reel it in hard. I waited long enough to see if it caught the fish off guard. Then yanking hard, I started to reel it in. And as I was lifting it out of the water, I saw another fish trying to snag it from me. I yanked it out of the water quickly. But that didn't stop the other fish from jumping out of the water to bite it as I pulled it away. It wasn't much larger than the fish I pulled out of the water. Yet it definitely was a predator. When it landed back in the water, oddly enough, it stared at me for a minute before swimming under the water.

It was a pale blue fish with weird yellow and brown eyes. It didn't look like it had scales but almost looked like it had skin. Thinking about it, I'm not quite sure it was a fish at all. Its head resembled a fish. But it didn't look like a fish that I had ever seen before. I told Dad that I had to use the restroom. I rowed back to shore and thought to myself, *I am done for the day*. I didn't tell my dad what I had seen. But I think the lake and the heat were messing with my head. It was quite hot out. And I think I just needed to lie down to get rid of the ominous headache that I had.

We went out again the next day. I chose a different spot in the lake for us. Just in case whatever I'd seen yesterday happened to still be there. It took a while for either of us to get a bite on our lines. And whatever happened to the fish must have happened overnight. I told my dad that we must have caught all the fish yesterday and that the lake was up for the summer. He laughed at me and said we should find another spot because after being in the spot for the same two hours and not finding anything, it was considered bad luck.

So I rowed over to a spot near the edge of the lake on the farther side of the lake that face the woodlands. Not much activity was happening until my father got a fish. I don't know what he caught, but it was very large. He was losing his grip on the pole. When I helped him hold on to the pole and the fish came out of the water, it must have been a sixteen-inch fish. Something like that was enormous. But that wasn't what surprised me. What did surprise me was the gigantic bite that was taken out of the side of it. The reason it was so hard to reel in and felt so heavy was because we were fighting with something that was already eating it. We looked around in the water and could see those faint glowing yellow brown eyes. Then I realized it was the same thing from the other day. My dad got kind of spooked after that, and he decided to call it a day. We rowed back to shore.

We had to go to the store to buy something for dinner since we hadn't caught any fish that day except that half-eaten one that we pulled out of the lake. Dad said he wasn't getting as much excitement out of fishing this year. And I told him if tomorrow didn't go any better, then I would be okay with heading home early.

The next morning, I woke up early and went out to the lake to sit on the dock. I watched the water as the sun rose. I couldn't see any fish in the water from where I was. Normally, when you come out there that early, it looks like the whole lake is moving, as the fish are swimming, creating an orchestra of watercolors. Not today though. The lake full of fish was still, as if the fish were all gone. I looked across the water to the spot where we'd struggled to catch the fish yesterday. I then saw a fawn coming out of the woods towards the edge of the water. I watched it as a stumbled across the ground and dipped its head to the water to drink from it. It was so peaceful until something long and pale came out of the water and bit onto its neck, pulling it down into the water.

I stood up, frantically looking around to see if the fawn got out of the water. But after about ten minutes, I could only assume what had happened. I just sighed and went back inside. I walked into the kitchen to find Dad drinking his coffee. I didn't tell him what I saw happen to the fawn. I did tell him about the stillness of the lake and that there were no fish. And there wasn't any reason for staying for another day of fishing. He was disappointed, but he knew I was right.

When we had packed up all of our stuff and loaded it onto our truck, I turned to look back at the lake one last time. And I swear, just like out of some sort of nightmare, I swore I could see faintly glowing eyes staring at me from underneath the water just offshore. And then something far more horrifying happened in that very moment. We both heard some swishing around like something heavy was under the dock.

And that was when we saw the body, or should I say half-eaten body, of the dead fawn from earlier come floating out from underneath the dock into view. There really wasn't much left of it. Other than a massive heap of torn-up eaten flesh and a leg or two, which was the only real way you could even discern it was still a fawn or had been a fawn. And it's safe to say that my father and I don't go fishing out there anymore.

Encounter 5
Submitted By: Florence
Time: 2021
Location: Florida Everglades

I WANT to share an experience I had in the Florida Everglades in 2021. It was early summer, and I was preparing my airboat to race in the yearly speed contest. I had just completed several test runs for speed along the Tamiami Trail, reaching speeds of about one hundred miles per hour, but I knew I could go faster. As a result, I came to a stop with the boat so that I could work on the engine and make sure that I had the proper mixture of fuel to achieve my maximum speed.

That was when I heard it. The sound of an alligator coming from the swamp. The sound was so loud and menacing that it made the hair on the back of my neck stand up. In all my time spent in the Everglades, I have seen and heard a great number of alligators, but I have never heard a bellow quite like this one. I could tell it was a large alligator just by the sound it made.

I saw it coming out from the tall grass; it was about a hundred feet away. It was unlike any gator I had ever seen before. It was massive, easily over twenty feet long. Its body rose above the surface of the water. After that, it did something that was far more terrifying than anything I could have ever imagined: it stood up on its hind legs. It towered over the water at a height of more than ten feet and was as tall as the pilot chair on my boat.

I'm not sure how to fully describe it. It had a head that resembled an alligator, only smaller. Its snout was not exceptionally long, yet its mouth was full of teeth. The eyes were set back and large, with large pupils, black as coal. The front legs more closely resembled the arms of a gorilla; they hung down, were full of muscles, and had hands with fingers; in addition, they had long claws that extended approximately four inches. I couldn't tell what the legs looked like because they were below the water, but I could see they were thick and muscular.

This thing started to walk towards the boat. I knew I had to get out of there fast. But my engine would not start, and I became trapped. It turned to one side, as if turning away from me, and I could see its back was like an alligator's except it had huge spikes sticking out.

As it turned back towards me, it brought both hands together and smacked the water, creating a wave that came at the boat and almost knocked it over. I thought about jumping overboard and swimming, but then I realized I couldn't outswim this thing. So I just sat there frozen in fear, not knowing what to do.

I tried starting the engine again. This time it started. I revved it up and took off as fast as it would go. It only took me several seconds to reach sixty miles an hour. The beast swam through the water close behind. It wasn't until I reached the speed of about eighty miles per hour that the beast started to fall behind. Yet I could see it was still following me. I wondered what beast could travel at that speed.

It took several minutes to get back to the launch ramp. As soon as I arrived, I immediately jumped from the boat, ran to my truck, and grabbed my rifle. Looking back into the swamp, I could see the beast just lying offshore. I fired two shots directly at it. I know I hit it. But it didn't move. I was about to shoot again, but it slowly went under the water. I couldn't see it anymore.

I have since sold my boat, and I will never again go back into the Everglades.

10

SKINWALKER ENCOUNTERS & SIGHTINGS

WHAT'S REALLY interesting about skinwalkers is the fact that it's become a catchall phrase for practitioners of dark magic who can shape-shift. Skinwalking—something that's very specific to Navajo culture—has caught on in the creepypasta/scary stories realm and kind of bled into every other tribe to describe beings like this. The truth is that while almost every tribe has evil magic practitioners who can and do shape-shift, they're not skinwalkers. There are certain qualities that make skinwalking unique and proprietary to the Navajo. These include rituals and other various practices that are only known to the Navajo.

I could go into further details on this, but since that's not what this book is intended for, let's jump right into the encounters!

Encounter 1
Submitted By: Kris Wight
Time: Summer 1973
Location: West Kansas

I AM a retired police officer in Kansas.

I was born in a small town in western Kansas. Growing up, I had a close encounter with a creature I believe was a skinwalker.

I have been studying the skinwalker phenomenon for about twenty years now. I have concluded that a skinwalker is a shape-shifter from another dimension that can take the form of anything it wants.

The incident I am about to tell you about happened in the summer of 1973. The strange creature I saw was about seven feet tall, hairless, and with glowing red eyes.

I lived in a farmhouse where the front part of the house was a single story, and the back part was two stories. My bedroom window faced the front part of the house.

One night while I was in my bed asleep, I was awakened to what sounded like a helicopter landing on the roof of our house. I went to the window and looked out. I saw a huge figure standing on the front part of the house. It had long arms and a long thin neck. And a face that was long and pointed. It looked a little bit like an ape. It had a shuffling kind of walk, like a gorilla. But it was not a human. I couldn't believe what I was seeing. I yelled for my dad. When he got to my room and looked out the window, he didn't see anything. So then we both ran outside. When we got out, the creature had disappeared. It was gone. But this creature left a very strange smell. There was a strong sulfur smell like you would smell in a chemical factory. I also sensed a strong manure smell. It was a very unpleasant smell.

The next day, I told all my friends about it, and they thought I was making it up.

That night my father and I pulled up to the house, and as we got out of his truck, my dad gasped. He saw this thing on our roof and pointed. I saw it now too. The creature was there again. It was about seven feet tall with red glowing eyes. I was so scared. This thing jumped up into the air and behind the house; we both ran into the house and slammed the door.

Later there would be times at night when we could hear this thing walking around the back side of the house as if waiting for the right opportunity to do something.

I tell you this story with 100 percent certainty. You can believe it or not. I know what I saw. I'm confident that it wasn't a human in any way, shape or form. This thing was terrifying! I don't know what this creature was. It was not a human, and it was not a demon. I have been trying to figure it out for twenty years. Was it a skinwalker?

Encounter 2
Submitted By: Anonymous
Time: Summer 1995
Location: Lakota Pine Ridge Reservation

LET me start by saying that I am a Christian, and things like the skinwalkers and shape-shifting humans remind me of what the Bible calls demons. The only thing that I knew about demons was from movies. I remember seeing the movie *The Exorcist* and thinking, *I don't believe that stuff really happens today*. Well, that all changed with the encounter I am going to share with you.

I first heard the term skinwalker in the Val Kilmer movie *Thunderheart*. The Indians call them "yee naadlooshii," which means, literally, "with it, he goes on all fours." The Navajos say, "May you walk in beauty." They are the shape-shifting, man-eating monsters of Native American legend, and they are real. Chiye-Tanka in the Sioux language means "big elder brother."

It was during the summer of 1995. I was a youth group leader and brought a youth team from Boulder, Colorado, to work at the mission on the Lakota Pine Ridge reservation for a two-week missionary experience. And man, what an experience it turned out to be.

The mission compound has a well that the local Indians who live close by use daily. The mission would lock its main gate in the evening, and no one was allowed in during the night.

So, early every morning, the local natives would come and line up outside the main gate, waiting for the gate to be unlocked to bathe and fill containers of water. Apparently, they didn't have running water in their houses. We were told that some Indians had torn out the plumbing pipes in their homes and sold them for money.

Our first week at the mission went by without any major incidents. We went around and did vacation Bible school at the local schools. Some of the youth volunteered to be candy stripers at the local hospital. Others helped at the mission, doing needed repairs.

During this week, I befriended one of the elders of the tribe, who happened to also be a Christian. We seemed to hit it off. He liked the fact that I had read a book on the life of Chief Sitting Bull, as well as the book *Bury My Heart at Wounded Knee*. I expressed to him how appalled I was that the army had massacred all those innocent Indians. I even took the youth group to the Wounded Knee site and prayed for our nation's repentance.

Because of this, the elder asked me if I wanted to go see the initiation of the braves doing the pole dance. A sacred ritual that no white man was allowed to see. Of course I said yes to this.

On the day of the dance, we drove out to the meeting place in his old station wagon, and just before we arrived, he had me hide in the back under some blankets and told me to stay hidden.

When we arrived, I could see about fifty vehicles parked around this small area. He parked toward the back of the parking area at an angle that allowed me to see the pole and a small area of the circle between the parked vehicles. There seemed to be well over a hundred people there. He exited the car and reminded me to stay low and hidden. I was able to see out the side window of the station wagon with the blankets over my head so no one would see me. I watched from the back of the car for what seemed to be an hour or so.

I watched as the braves did the dance around the pole. Some had their chests pierced with an animal bone tied to rawhide thongs attached to the center pole. They began to walk backwards from the pole to rip the bone out from their chests. I could hear the sounds of the chants and the whistles the braves were blowing.

It got sweltering under the blankets, and I had to raise them from time to time to get fresh air flowing. Then I saw the elder running toward the car. The look on his face told me something was not good. He quickly got in and yelled at me to stay down as he started the car and said we had to get out of there, fast. It wasn't safe. Someone had seen me and reported it to the others.

If caught, they probably would beat me up if not kill me for violating this sacred rite. It seemed like he floored it because I could see the dust flying into clouds behind us as we left the area. He went even faster once we got onto the blacktop road, speeding back to the mission.

A few nights after the ceremony, I was awakened by a noise outside the bunkhouse. I got up to see what it was, and when I looked out the window, I saw a man standing there. He was completely naked, and his skin was as black as coal. His eyes were glowing red, and he had sharp teeth. I ran to wake up the missionary and did not want to scare the kids. When I told him what I saw, he said I described what the Indians call a skinwalker.

It was right after this event that things started to get weird. Our group was staying in the bunkhouse at the mission, and every night, we would have a bonfire, roast marshmallows, and sing songs. On this particular night, about fifteen of us sat around the fire when we heard what sounded like a woman screaming. It seemed to come from the area outside the mission compound. We all turned and looked at each other, and then someone said, "It's just the wind." But then we heard it again, and it sounded like it was coming from the direction of an old cemetery.

Now, the cemetery is maybe a hundred yards from the bunkhouse, but outside the compound; there is only one way in and one way out. So, grabbing our flashlights, we all decided to go check it out.

As we got closer to the cemetery, the screaming got louder, and it sounded like someone was being tortured. When we pointed our flashlights in that direction, we could not see anything. As we approached the entrance of the cemetery, the screaming stopped. We all just stood there for a few seconds, not knowing what to do, and then we heard something running towards us from the other side of the cemetery. We all turned and ran back to the mission compound as fast as we could.

When we got back, we told the missionaries what had happened, and they said that we were probably just hearing things because it was late at night. But the next night, it happened again. And the night after that.

Finally, one of the missionaries said he would check it out. So he took a flashlight and a Bible and walked over to the cemetery. He was gone for maybe ten minutes when we heard him screaming.

We all ran toward the cemetery. When we got there, the missionary was lying on the ground just outside the cemetery entrance. His eyes were wide open, and he was shaking and sweating. We asked him what had happened, and he said he'd seen something in the cemetery that he couldn't explain. He said it was a man, but he was unlike any man he had ever seen.

He said the man was naked, and his skin was as black as coal. He said the man's eyes were glowing red, and he had sharp teeth. Then looking right at me, he said, "That must have been what you saw, too." I nodded my head in agreement.

The missionary said that the man started to chase him out of the cemetery, and he thought he saw it turn into a wolfman. He thought it was going to catch him. However, as soon as he got outside the cemetery, he turned back to see if it was still chasing him; that was when it disappeared. He had collapsed on the ground where we had found him. He had been so petrified he literally collapsed and could not get back up.

We all stayed up that night, praying and trying to make sense of what had happened. The next day, we went out to the cemetery to see if there was any evidence of what the missionary had seen. There were footprints in the soft ground, but they were unlike any human footprints we had ever seen, and they were more like animal prints. We also found some strange handprints on the ground and on some of the tombstones. We had no idea what to make of it, but I knew that whatever the missionary and I had seen was real, and it was something evil.

After that incident, we all became more aware of our surroundings, and we started to notice that strange things were happening on the reservation. We would see people walking in the woods, but they would disappear when we got too close. We would hear strange noises at night and see lights in the distance that would move and change shape. We started feeling like we were being watched and were all very scared.

A few days later, we went into town to get some supplies. When we came back, the missionary told us he had talked to some elders, and they said there had been sightings of skinwalkers on the reservation.

We ended up leaving the reservation early because we were all too scared to stay any longer. I don't know what we would have done if we had stayed any longer, and I'm not sure what we would have seen or what would have happened to us. I will never forget that summer, and I will never forget what I saw on the Lakota reservation. I know that what I saw was real, and it was something evil. I pray that I never see anything like that again.

Encounter 3
Submitted By: Hartley
Time: N/A
Location: N/A

I BELIEVE skinwalkers still exist among the Navajo down in the rez. I'm a third-generation Navajo, so I've heard about these types of creatures from my great-grandparents. They used to sit around the fire and tell us skinwalker stories when we were little. They always said it was vital that we learn about them because they're still around as far as the reservation is concerned.

My first encounter with one took place at night. I was sleeping in my room with the shades wide open, and it was pitch black outside due to a new moon. I had just gone to bed not too long before when suddenly I could hear this scream from somewhere far off in the distance that made me feel chills up my spine. It sounded like someone being tortured, and what was more terrifying was it sounded like the scream was coming from right outside my bedroom window. I felt paralyzed with fear because I couldn't move a muscle. It wasn't until that moment did I realize how dark the room was, even though streetlights were shining into my room from outside through the shades. That was when I could hear the movement of something coming towards my house. I could feel the fear growing inside me as something approached.

The movement stopped, and that was when I could hear the loud thumping sound of something walking up my porch stairs onto my front porch. I heard this big "BANG" against my front door as it knocked over a small table where we kept our keys and mail, which was located right outside my room. I still couldn't move and felt that whatever this thing was, it wanted me to know it was there. The thumping sound started coming towards my bedroom door, across from my bed, and suddenly stopped again. Then I heard a deafening bang on the door right behind me on the wall, but when I looked back, nothing was there. I was terrified at this point.

The thumping started walking back towards the front door right behind my bed, and that was when I heard the movement towards my bedroom window begin again. I couldn't move the whole time even though I wanted to get out of there so bad. It felt like an eternity before the knocking started. Right then, I felt like whatever this thing was, it wanted me to feel the fear of not being able to move while it was walking towards my window. Then I heard a loud bang on the window as though something or someone had jumped up against it. While all this was happening outside my room, I was terrified and still couldn't move. It wasn't until I heard the thumping sound start walking away from my bedroom again that I felt like I could finally move again. Then the moment it left, I felt incredible relief as though nothing bad was there anymore.

I got up out of bed and turned on my bedroom light. I was expecting to see something in the room, but nothing was there. I felt this relief, like whatever it was, it finally left. But suddenly, I heard loud scratching noises from outside the window right behind me, where it had just been standing before I could move again. I turned towards my window, seeing the curtains moving as though they were being pulled. The window was opening and closing by itself like someone was trying to open it from outside but wasn't strong enough to lift it. That was when I heard this voice calling my name in a low whisper coming from behind me. It sounded like a man's voice, but the tone was very raspy. I couldn't tell where exactly it was coming from because it sounded like the one in my room and behind me at the same time. I just remember getting up from bed and running out of my room into the living room to wake my roommate up because I thought she could see what was happening in my room.

While running toward my roommate's bedroom, Itsounded like something was pounding its fists against the wall next to her door and right outside it as I ran through the hallway towards her bedroom.

I was expecting to see something when I entered the room, but nothing was there. The sound stopped as soon as I entered the room. I could hear this thing walking along the outside of our trailer. As I looked out the screen, I could see this thing walking along right outside our window while it was still pounding its fists against the wall next to my roommate's door. After that night, we never heard or saw anything like that again.

Nothing happened until a year later when I had just gotten married and moved in with my husband. We had just bought our first place and were settling in when we heard strange noises from the other side of the walls that we thought were coming from upstairs or downstairs. It sounded like footsteps, moving furniture, and things being knocked over regularly. My husband is an atheist, so he didn't believe anything supernatural could happen and thought I was just hearing things.

One day, as we were both sitting and talking in the living, there was a loud banging noise from upstairs. It sounded like someone was beating on our ceiling with their fists.

I went up to see what it was while my husband stayed downstairs in the living room. I got up to the top of my stairs, and nothing was there. I turned around to go back down, and as I did, a loud crash occurred outside our home. My husband and I ran down, and we looked outside but didn't see anything.

The next night, my husband was talking on the phone in our living room while I was upstairs cleaning up the bathroom when there was a knock at the door. The only problem was that no one had knocked or rung our bell. My husband heard it too and walked over to the door, expecting someone to be standing there, but there was nothing.

Another night, my husband went upstairs to take a nap while I stayed downstairs to watch TV. As he was going up the stairs, he looked back at me before disappearing out of view and said, "I love you." Then he went upstairs into our bedroom and lay down to nap. After that, I heard him calling my name in an urgent tone. He said that while he was lying relaxing, he looked over and saw me standing at the foot of the bed, black eyes and face distorted. That was when he started screaming urgently for me, and this fake me vanished in the air. We didn't know what to make of these experiences, so we ignored them and tried not to think about them anymore.

After a while, we were used to those strange sounds coming from walls and our stuff being knocked over for no reason, but I don't know. I'm beginning to think that there's an angry skinwalker spirit that is following me around. What's your take on all of this?

Even though I grew up Navajo, I never participated in much of our culture's rituals and religions. I've always done my own thing, but now I feel like I've somehow made myself a target of this thing. Do you know how to get rid of something like this without hurting someone? I have a baby now and don't want anything messing with her. Thank you for your time. I apologize if the details in this story can be hard to follow at times. This is my best recounting of the events that happened. Take care.

Encounter 4
Submitted By: anonymous
Time: N/A
Location: N/A

SKINWALKERS HAVE BEEN on this earth, in one form or another, for thousands of years. Skinwalkers are evil beings that take the form of a man or an animal and are believed to be able to shape-shift into other creatures such as wolves and coyotes. They possess powers beyond normal men and animals. Skinwalkers are believed to cause mischief, sickness, and death amongst their victims.

To become a skinwalker, one must undergo an initiation ritual that requires great strength and determination. The first test is to kill the person who taught you how to perform the ritual. The next test is to kill your close family members, including parents and siblings.

I firmly suspect that my grandfather, now passed, was a Navajo witch. A skinwalker.

My grandmother would tell me all sorts of terrifying stories about him. Fortunately for me, he passed of an unknown illness before I was born, but I heard from my family and grandmother he was a wicked man. Very abusive, cruel, and sadistic.

My grandmother explained that he ultimately loved pain, giving and taking it. She believes that's probably one of the big factors why he got so involved in magic and shape-shifting.

He would often leave at night and be gone for days. Coming back wearing pelts, covered in dirt and animal blood. Doing crazy things.

My grandmother once told me he had killed off several livestock and eaten them. He had been shot at by farmers and even nearly killed. The man was reckless, dangerous, and a threat to our family.

I can't help but wonder if the way he died was as mysterious as everyone says or if the black magic he practiced ended up killing him.

Encounter 5
Submitted By: Anonymous
Time: N/A
Location: Navajo Reservation, Arizona

MY SKINWALKER encounter story happened on the Navajo Reservation in Arizona. I was living there at the time of my encounter, and it scared me so much that I had to leave. It is scary, not for people with weak hearts or feeble minds.

As you know, I'm from Alaska originally and lived most of my life there until I moved down south to Arizona, where I met my wife. She's part Navajo and has many family members up here on the reservation in northern New Mexico, so we took a liking to it and decided to move up here just outside Farmington, New Mexico.

Everything was fine moving into our new home near Shiprock, New Mexico, for six months or more, but things started changing around our house. It all started with some weird sightings of coyotes, and I thought nothing much of it then, but as things progressed, strange happenings appeared everywhere in our backyard.

When my wife and I would go out into the backyard to do any chores, we'd see hairs hanging in the trees, feathers lying around everywhere, and weird-looking paw prints left behind. These things alone were not so strange or frightening, but what got me freaked out was when one night, while my wife and I were sleeping, I woke up at about 3 a.m. and saw this person standing over our bed dressed all in black! It turned around, stared at me for a few seconds, then disappeared into thin air! After that, I started checking everything outside before going inside, making sure no one was hiding anywhere watching us come or go.

In the late fall of 2007, right after this thing appeared in our bedroom, many strange things started happening in the house just as it started getting dark. Our Jack Russell terrier got sick with something it had never had before and died while we were at work one day. The house was cold even when we turned up the heat to 80+ degrees inside, and all of our food went bad—little worms started crawling out of some of our bread, fruits, and vegetables. It was disgusting sometimes, and I don't even like to think about it.

We heard this constant tapping on the front door every night for about two weeks straight; then all of a sudden, it stopped, which made me feel relieved because I thought whoever or whatever it was had finally left us alone so I could get back to some kind of normal routine again without being scared every night.

We were sitting in our living room, and my wife and I saw this coyote walk up to the back porch, stop for a second or two, and then walk towards the ravine. It was unusually large for a coyote, about twice as big, and it looked like it had some black fur mixed with its tan color. The thing that made me want to scream when I saw this animal was the eyes—they were an amber color instead of the usual green color you see on coyotes. I still have nightmares thinking about that night.

I'm looking for opinions here. Do you think we encountered a skinwalker?

Encounter 6
Submitted By: Anonymous
Time: 2013
Location: Area 51, Nevada

IN 2013, I had a strange encounter with something I can only describe as some kind of skinwalker.

For the sake of this story, let's just call it an anomaly.

It all started one night while my family and I visited Area 51 in Nevada.

I was having fun on the road trip there when I felt this weird sensation like someone was watching me, but no one else seemed to notice anything. As soon as that happened, though, everything changed. The desert started to get dark. The sky went all weird, almost like the sun was blocked out and dark. It was very cold, and I could see what looked like shadows coming closer to the car we were in. As soon as they got close, it seemed like time stopped for a second, and everything froze. That was where things got strange, though; The creatures that came out of nowhere started to look at me through the window, but there was no clear face or anything characteristic about them.

The only word I can use to describe it was emotionless because these things didn't seem alive at all. It's hard to describe how they looked, but if you've ever seen *Silence of the Lambs*, then you know what I'm talking about when I say "emotionless" even though it felt like they were alive. After a while, I got so scared that I just turned my head away and looked at the road we were driving on. Not long after that, everything went back to normal, and I don't remember seeing any of these anomalies again.

A few weeks later, I discovered another anomaly, but this time in Ohio with my cousin, who witnessed them when she started to drive, right before the same thing happened to me.

***Author's note: My cousin told me her experiences are different than mine because she said their faces were visible as if something solid was there.

As far as where I saw them in Nevada, she saw a whole family of them in the mountains when she was hiking with her dog. She said they were there before her, circling and taunting her.

The only thing we have in common is that the things that haunt us aren't making any noise and can appear out of nowhere at any time.

I believe these beings may have something to do with people who go missing because I think they could be taking whoever they want for whatever reason and killing others. "I'm not sure exactly what would happen if one got hold of me, so I'm afraid every night before I go to sleep," my cousin shared.

Encounter 7
Submitted By: Anonymous
Time: 2013
Location: Nevada

ON A BACK ROAD at night in Nevada, I saw something I couldn't explain.

To start this story, I'm pretty open-minded and believe in God, but I don't like talking about my sighting on purpose. Me and two other friends randomly decided to go out one night, so we were just driving around when we went down a back road that had never been there before. We drove for a while, and it was dead silent. Then, as we passed an old run-down house with a white trailer behind it, something crossed the road right in front of us. It moved incredibly fast across the road at what seemed like ten feet in front of our headlights, which was very strange because you could see a human shape very clearly move quickly from left to right, not running, almost more of a jumping kind of motion over the ditch next to the road.

Before we saw this thing, I was very skeptical about the existence of skinwalkers. We were all worried about turning around because you never know what could be back there, so we drove a mile down the road and were still pretty freaked out but trying not to think about it too much.

A few minutes later, we went into a curve and slowed down fast when all three of us just saw something move on the other side of the road from left to right, almost at the same place where we first spotted "whatever that thing was." , The only thing I can think of was maybe a gigantic rat because it moved very similar to one, but what killed that thought is the fact—and we all saw it well in our minds, as we will never forget it—that it held its arms way below the knees kind of like how a monkey walks almost.

When we saw it this second time, it stopped for a solid three seconds before bolting back in the direction it came from.

We still don't know exactly what these things were, but my friends and I have developed some good theories. My first theory is they're outcasts from the Navajo tribe who have gone mad and now are on the hunt to make a revenge killing of some sort. Or another theory could be they are born and bred on the reservation by those who live there; these skinwalkers can change form from anything to a human, deer, coyote, etc. So this is my and my friends' experience with something unexplainable, but I will say this: never go out at night in Nevada or alone anywhere for that matter.

Keep your eyes peeled; just because you don't believe it doesn't mean it's not real.

Encounter 8
Submitted By: Anonymous
Time: N/A
Location: Nevada

I AM a senior at Highland secondary school in 2018, and we did a project about spiritual creatures living in different places around the globe (all over the world), and I'm doing as much research as I can concerning skinwalkers, so if anyone has any knowledge about it, please post a comment and tell me what you know.

Also, an old Navajo legend has been passed down for generations. It tells of a race of creatures that can shape-shift into anything they want or need to be to get what they are after. Shape-shifting was seen as the ultimate achievement one could make; only magic people were able to do this! They would wear animal skins when they became whatever creature their heart desired in hopes of avoiding detection from other magic people who may cause them harm or reveal them if discovered. This way of life went unnoticed by "non-magical" humans until one day; two young boys noticed something odd while hunting with their father. When drifting back on the winds, they could hear the sounds of strange animals and odd hissing noises. One boy became curious; his father knew this, and rather than answer or investigate, he told them he was too old to chase after such things. The young boys decided they needed to see what these noises were, so they followed the sound down a small hill until they came face-to-face with... a skinwalker!

One man (named Russel) claimed to have encountered one of these creatures while driving late at night through some rural area. He declared that it looked like an older Navajo lady in traditional clothing. As Russ approached her on the deserted road, she began walking toward him; as she walked, her appearance changed from that of an old woman into something void of shape, black and demonic looking! If Russ thought that would end it, he was wrong. As she changed into this new form, all sorts of things began flying from her body and flying around his car! After trying to escape, Russ finally outran the creature, who was in hot pursuit for most of the time. When he looked back, he could not see her anywhere even though there were no roadblocks or anything else stopping him from seeing what had become of her.

And in 1995, a family living near Farmington, New Mexico, reported seeing a skinwalker at their front door. The rest of the story goes as follows: "My mother and father had just awakened us after hearing something outside our home around midnight; I noticed something walking on two legs but wasn't sure what it was; I was just waking up, but it did have a humanlike shape, and I remember its face was dark with long black hair. My dad went to the door quickly after hearing my mother scream about 'the porch.' And they all saw him standing at the door, then very fast towards them yelling, 'Get out!!' It scared the crap out of us, and we left that house immediately... never going back!"

There is story after story of these creatures out there, and I don't believe any of this is a figment of my imagination for a second. Something is going on.

Encounter 9
Submitted By: mark I.
Time: N/A
Location: Nevada

I WAS BORN and raised on a reservation in Nevada. This is very true and very terrifying at times. Years ago, my mom told me when she was little, her brother told her to go play in the other room, so she did. She walked back into the living room and saw an apparition of an coyote sitting with her mom. Her brother told her that it was okay. It was just Grandma who had passed away years earlier watching over the family. Grandma was also a witch, by the way. She asked him how he knew about this, and he said, "Nobody told me... I can see Grandma still, too!"

Years later, my mom told me stories of seeing strange native spirits lurking around the house at night under the moon's light. I asked another family member if they could see these men, and she said yes.

I will never forget one time when I was riding in from town with my mother. We took a shortcut through some desert land. As we were driving through this land, there was no trail, but we had taken that road many times. We were stopped, and I looked off to the right side of the car and saw two coyotes sitting by a tree, looking at us. Suddenly, they took off running toward us, my mom floored it, and they ran right next to our truck! She said she could hear their claws on the side of her car as if they might jump in at any second; then all of a sudden, they disappeared into thin air. I'm certain these were evil spirits masquerading as coyotes.

They are very powerful, I don't know much about them, but they are something to be reckoned with.

Encounter 10
Submitted By: Joey
Time: N/A
Location: Nevada

I'VE BEEN READING on the subject of skinwalkers now for more than fifteen years. I'm still unsure what to believe, but it's given me material for many a campfire tale.

One true story that happened recently is that an old ranch hand was working by himself when he saw a strange being come out of some trees near his shack. The person shape-shifted into a coyote and then returned to human form as it came toward. The man, terrified by what he was seeing in front of him went inside and locked up.

Hours later, the boss man came by in his truck with a friend who was some Native American shaman. They wanted to know if he'd seen anything strange. After telling the men what he'd experienced, they expressed that hours earlier, they had been out in the hills searching for some missing cattle and had found dozens of mutilated ones with strange symbols carved into them. That was when the shaman spoke to them and said that evil skinwalkers were doing this, and they were killing ipeople too. The boss told him after hearing this story that he believes there are good Natives who help fight these things, but it has to be a personal mission from within their hearts.

The one commonality among all skinwalker stories is that they all state how powerful their presence is. They're overwhelmingly evil. It sometimes seems impossible and makes you wonder how they could even be real. I know it's hard to believe, but the stories come from all over the world, so something has to be going on that cannot be explained by logic and reasoning alone. These beings are deeply embedded in Native American culture from the sound of things.

Encounter 11
Submitted By: Dawn
Time: N/A
Location: Maverick County, Texas

I HAVE a ranch in Maverick County, Texas. It"s very remote out there, and quite frankly, I"m not sure how I ended up with it,; but the deed is in my name, so here I am. Last year was the first time I'd I've ever been down there. Before that, no one had lived on the land for years, and it was all overgrown with trees and brush and God knows what else, but you couldn"t see any of that from satellite imagery because it was all hidden by vegetation. Anyway, before finally going out there myself, I had spent a lot of time talking to people who knew about the property, some of whom were well versed in local folklore.

The long and short of it is: I didn''t know what to expect. I figured it would be a lot of work, but the payoff could be worth it if the rumors I''d heard were true. And they were! There''s plenty of open pasture out there for grazing and watering livestock. The fences aren''t in good shape, but with time and money, that''s easily fixed. There are also dozens of little feeder streams that lead down into the main creek, which crosses the property, so there is plenty of water for animals. It''s perfect! The whole place looks like someone just plopped down a large chunk of land and forgot to tell anyone about it. One guy even told me he thought at one point, as an isolated ranch, locals would sneak out there at night and drive their cattle across it on the way into Maverick County from Starr County. Remember, I''m talking about a place completely overgrown with trees! Nobody would have been able to see them doing it. I''ve got several hundred acres fenced off for grazing, but in the middle of my land is this little spot untouched by animals or humans. No grass or low-lying plants are growing there – —just hard stone and dirt. It''s an area that measures maybe fifteen feet across at its widest point and is shaped like a perfect square. There was a weird energy that surrounded it. The fact that nothing grew in that spot should have spoken volumes about what it was. I decided to build a little cabin on the edge of the property, right next to the creek. I figured I''d be out there alone for weeks at a time, so I might as well make myself comfortable. I started building the place in the fall of last year, and I''ve been going out there every couple of weeks to work on it ever since. I started hearing the sounds around the same time I started building the cabin. It was a very quiet, high-pitched sound that seemed to be coming from the woods. It was almost like a dog whistle, but not quite. It felt... eerie. I began to feel these strange sensations all over my body while I was out there. It was like I was being watched, but I couldn''t see anything. I started to wonder if I was just being paranoid. I''ve heard stories about people going crazy out in the country, so I tried to keep an eye on myself. I figured there had to be a way to explain these feelings. However, I noticed as I went around the property a lot of the strangeness revolved around that dead patch of ground. Hopefully that makes sense. It seemed like nature itself did not want to be around it, and I started to wonder if that was the reason for the strange feelings. I'd been out there for weeks at a time, and I'd never seen anything. I'd never even seen any tracks. I'd just heard the sounds. Strange bizarre sounds that couldn't be explained. It wasn't until the following weeks where I began to experience bizarre things around the property I couldn't explain. More than what was already happening. I'll start with the sounds. They became more frequent and louder. I'd hear what sounded like screaming and crying, but it was so high-pitched that it was almost like an animal. I'd hear it at night, and it was almost as if it was coming from the woods. I'd hear it one night, and then it would be silent for a few nights, and then I'd hear it again. There would be other times I'd hear what sounded like huge machinery but there would be nothing anywhere. All the sounds seemed to be coming from the same area where that patch of ground was. Over the coming months, I'd then have situations where I'd be seeing black shadows darting in and out of the night, around the cabin that I had there at the time. To save you a novels worth of information, the long story made short is that this property was apparently very haunted. All things pointed back to that patch of ground. Well, after spending some time deep diving and digging, I found out that there as a giant massacre around this area hundreds of years ago. I've had a friend of mine whose full blooded Choctaw that there are evil and demonic shape shifting spirits that reside on this ground. He doesn't even like coming onto the property. He even used the term skinwalker but I don't know anymore. This is all so crazy. The activity had been ramping up with the world in 2020 and I decided to move out for the time being while I decide what to do.

Encounter 12
Submitted By: Anonymous
Time: N/A
Location: Sonoran Desert

I GREW up around many Navajo and Apache Natives who have shared with me many ancient tales and warnings not to travel into certain blacklisted regions in the deserts because of what evil lurks there. This evil destroyed people who started villages and sects of life. The same evil that is said to come from deep within the Sonoran Desert has made its way far north to where we thrive and inhabit.

I am a half Native and try to embrace my culture and belief system as much as possible. There is truth to the wisdom spoken to me through my people and friends. I have a deep love for this nation and do not wish to see it tarnished by the black magic of those evil-doers who wish to wreak havoc upon it. The peace currently being upheld is only because of certain protections and wards against those of the darkness. The great spirit.

I know your channel alerts people that these creatures exist and practice evil out in the world, so they can grow in their power and prey upon the weak. Still, I can share this information with you, and you can share this on your channel. Then, maybe more will become aware of what exists out there and stay away. The more victims these creatures of evil claim, the more power they obtain and the more reign they have.

You have spoken much about the shape-shifters of my land that practice magic and wear the skins of coyotes and other kills. Still, a far more powerful and smaller sect of shape-shifters lies beneath the ground in caverns underneath the Sonoran Desert. The more power they obtain, the more their influence reigns in my region, the Navajo nation, and even farther north. These shape-shifters take the form of large desert serpents and serpent beings that devour dreary wanderers and tourists alive. Or capture them to be taken back to have the life force sucked out of them. I've heard others call this same life force adrenochrome. I believe that's the scientific name for it, but that's what these shape-shifters feed on. They come out once the sun has set in the sky to wander the night deserts, seeking those they can prey upon. They are said to inhibit the bowels underneath the sands.

Many caverns underneath the deserts should be closed, and people should stay far away. Several have already been turned into tourist attractions for those who enjoy underground caverns. This is very dangerous and potentially invokes the presence of these beings.

I'm still not clear whether this sect of shape-shifters is even human beings or something far eviler. Unlike the shape-shifters here, these entities possess great strength and can hide away much easier, revealing themselves only when they want to. They will even go as far as camouflaging themselves as regular Natives to try to lure persons from nearby tribes away. I don't think it to be a coincidence that these shape-shifters are the only things to come out of that area of the desert. My people have talked about flying demons living beneath the desert sand. I believe these align with these shape-shifters, or possibly are even under their control, to scout the area, looking for victims.

I'm giving you this information because people who want to tour the area or are just passing by need to be extremely aware and understand that driving through the area at night is dangerous. You wouldn't even believe me if I told you how many people go missing who are taken captive by these beings and are written off as lost to sex trafficking. It's horrendous. I'm trying to keep my people safe by informing the uneducated. Please, it would mean the world to me if you could share this message; at least many who listen to it would take warning and understand the true dangers that lie outside beneath the sands.

Encounter 13
Submitted By: Anonymous
Time: September 2018
Location: Arizona

MY UNCLE, a Navajo nation police respondent, came across a group of teenage girls huddled together in the morning hours of September 1, 2018, startled, crying, and frightened by something. They were far out in the desert, miles from the nearest road, and claimed to have been driven there by what they described as a man who turned into a demon.

The man was unlike your typical skinwalker and did not wear animal skins and religious garments. He dressed in a loincloth, with black clay covering his entire body, and then he changed into this demon, they said. With eyes so black, they were almost white, if that makes sense. This man or demon intended to kill them, so it chased these girls far out in the desert in the middle of the night. It grabbed one of the girls and ripped a clump of her hair out, and she had a huge clump of hair missing. Blood ran down her scalp. One of the girls with them was reported missing and never found, even after a thorough investigation had been in effect. The four girls claimed this demon man took this girl and took her away. They had no clue where he took her.

The girls were questioned about why they were there and what they were doing. The nearest road was a few miles away, so they were en route to going home after a party in the early morning hours when they got a flat tire. While changing the tire, they were approached by a fierce man who came out of the desert and threatened them with rape and violence, which led to him physically chasing them into the night, where they ran for a long time. The slowest of the girls was also the youngest, at fourteen years old, and was the one grabbed and taken away.

Stories like this happen all the time here on the rez, and it's kept very quiet, so it's not often word gets out. Encounters with beings like skinwalkers and evil spirits are a far more common thing than just drunks and thieves. It's a dangerous world out there, and it's currently not welcoming to visitors, even if they are Navajo.

Encounter 14
Submitted By: Dirk
Time: N/A
Location: Bryce Canyon National Park, Arizona

MY STORY TAKES place in the Bryce Canyon National Park in Arizona. I encountered a handful of strange creatures, or what I would like to call desert witches, that can shape-shift into reptilian beings, I would later find out from experienced Navajo men and women of the area. At the time, I was with my ex-wife, my current wife then; for the story, I will call her Jamie. I also need to point out that even though the canyon isn't quite on the Navajo reservation, it borders it, and many Navajo have experienced wandering through this canyon. Their experiences are very grim, or so I have heard. They claim this to be the territory of shape-shifting witches. Not the same thing as a skinwalker, I'm told.

On this day, we were some of the only few people on the trail, and nobody else was around us. The isolation was bittersweet. Although I rather enjoyed the privacy, it made the situation so much more heightened.

On this day, we had made our way about a mile and a half down into the canyon before this strange lady was walking in our direction and muttering some strange things under her breath at us... we got a really weird feeling, and she kept muttering to herself. She wore a strange veil over her face, and her clothes seemed out of place. I can't quite place the description that accurately describes what she wore, but it reminded me of Middle Eastern clothing. We soon forgot about her and walked past and kept continuing.

Shortly after, we heard strange sounds behind and around us. My wife, Jamie, at the time began to express to me she felt uncomfortable like she was being watched. I told her to look around and that there was nobody out there. She still couldn't budge the feeling, though.

We soon found an area to sit down, take a break, have water, and collect ourselves. We were in conversation for only a couple of minutes before we started hearing what I would describe as religious chanting. It seemed to be coming from all around us and nowhere at the same time. Behind us, around us, up in the air, and below us.

I thought we were hallucinating, but it kept getting louder and louder. Jamie and I could hear it as we were frantically looking around, trying to find the source of this noise, when this chanting evolved into something much more disturbing. Roars and growls. The chanting began to fade as the growls and roars took over, and then it was just roars and growls. It sounded close by but also far away; with the rock structures of the canyon, I know that sounds can reverberate and play tricks on your ears, making you think something is much closer than it is. Now there was no more chanting, but it sounded like twenty lions trapped behind a couple of rocks somewhere, and it was seriously giving us the creeps. I didn't even have to motion to Jamie for us to get out of there before we ditched.

Later that day, after we left, I told a friend of mine, who's full-blooded Navajo and knows the area around the reservation and the canyon and multiple other areas very well, what had happened. He seemed scared when I told him what had happened and told me I had witnessed a shape-shifting ceremony. He described this to me: they were shape-shifting witches who go down into the canyon, and they usually sacrifice humans or animals, drink the blood, and turn into these creatures. He did not exactly specify if there needed to be a sacrifice for them to shape-shift, but he made it clear that they would get together and have a ritual ceremony and turn into creatures of the night. That would explain the loud roaring I heard and growls. It was terrifying. It would also explain the religious chanting that I heard. It very well reminded me of something you would hear from the occult or something along those lines, just in another language. This can be marked as easily one of the scariest experiences I've ever had, but I can't explain what it was.

Encounter 15
Submitted By: Berney Osmond
Time: N/A
Location: Southern Arizona

I'VE NEVER BEEN one to buy into the whole skinwalker nonsense that's talked about in many Native cultures and heard around the Southern United States. But I have something that genuinely happened to me that terrified me. Let me explain this to you. I was driving in the later evening in Southern Arizona, far away from any Indian reservation. This is one of the things that is a red flag in my head because it doesn't make any sense. I guess I realized that they're everywhere in this region and don't pertain to one specific reservation.

So, I was driving, and there were no other cars on the road. It was getting pretty dusk, so the sun was setting. By the way, if you have ever been to Arizona during sunset, it is gorgeous. That's the only positive side note for the story. I was coming up to a bend in the road, or should I say a hill? When I went up it, blocking the road just up ahead was probably what I could make out to be about six or seven coyotes just sitting in the middle of the road, facing my oncoming vehicle. "WTF?" I whispered to myself. "Why are there coyotes sitting there in the middle of the road?"

But as I pulled closer, I realized something was wrong. Not only were these coyotes much larger in size than your average coyote, but they all looked terrible. They were disfigured, emaciated, and looked like they had terrible mange, but they also looked deformed. Before I even came to a stop, I got a bad feeling in the pit of my stomach, and I felt like I needed to turn around and leave. There was nobody else on this road, so all six of these coyotes turned their attention toward me. That was when I noticed something even more terrifying. All of them had solid white eyes. No iris, no pupil, nothing. There was nothing feral about them, and the feeling in the pit of my stomach grew worse and worse with each second, but I sat in this situation. I hadn't even fully stopped the vehicle before quickly swerving in a 180 and hauling it out of there.

I can't say for certain that this was a pack of skinwalkers, but I find it very weird that you have a pack of six of them all looking deformed and covered in mange, an emaciated and grotesque small group like that. The way they all turned their heads to look me right in the face, and uneasy was beyond creepy. They weren't just looking at my car; even though I had my headlights on, they were looking through my windshield directly at my face. I could just feel it. I sensed they were looking at me. Man, did it give me the heebie-jeebies, and even typing this out makes me relive that horrible memory. Now I get freaked out every time I'm driving down there, which I do frequently still because I have family and friends who live down there.

I've heard of all sorts of weird stuff going on in the desert—like UFOs and all things alien and weird like that—but I never in my life would have imagined skinwalkers stopping me like that in the middle of the road. As I said, it may have just been a coincidence, but I don't think I would have got that feeling in my gut had they just been six regular coyotes. There was just something so off about it. I trust my gut instinct when it tells me there's something wrong, and boy, my entire body was screaming *get out of there*.

Anyway, I hope this email isn't too long for you to read, but I just wanted to share with you my skinwalker experience. Stay out of Arizona if you can; it's not meant for people like us.

Encounter 16
Submitted By: Anonymous
Time: N/A
Location: Navajo Reservation

SO A COUPLE of my family friends have some Navajo in them. I'll call her Sarah for the sake of her identity being shared. Sarah is fully Caucasian, but her husband, Mark I'll call him, is full-blooded Navajo. We live in the Pacific Northwest, and his parents are from the reservation. They came up here when he was much younger, and he grew up with them, eventually moving back to the rez. He decided to stay up here and start his life while they still lived back down there. Every once in a while, Sarah and Mark still go down there and visit his family, who are full-blooded Navajo, mind you. They are enriched in their culture and in the Navajo tradition and very religious.

Sarah has plenty of skinwalker stories and even recites them by their actual name, which I will not repeat for my own protection. Silly or not, I don't care what anybody thinks after the stories Sarah told me. I don't want to be at the mercy of these things. Even though she's shared several with me, I'll tell you one that sticks out.

Sarah and Mark had gone down for a week to visit his family, and if you didn't know, there's virtually zero cell service down in that reservation. I think there's a special cell phone service for that reservation. I digress, anyway, she's down there at night, smoking a cigarette, and her whole family is telling her that's a bad idea. If you throw the butt down of the cigarette, these things will come.

I can't remember what Sarah did off the top of my head, but she attracted one of these things because later on, when she went to bed, one of these things came up to the house, and she said you could feel its energy approaching. She said it was the most eerie scary sensation she had ever felt, and this is a girl who grew up in a house with a poltergeist in it. She said she fell into a sleeplike spell and had horrible nightmares of this black smokey shape that crawled into her room through the window, clung to her ceiling, and terrorized her for the entire night.

The very next morning, all of Mark's family was doing rituals and prayers to ward off this potential skinwalker that she had accidentally attracted from approaching the house.

They take these situations very seriously because, to them, a skinwalker isn't just some mysterious cryptid creature that walks up and terrorizes a family. These things will hunt family members down and cause ill luck and fortune to happen to people. Even casting spells on good people makes them sick and ruins their lives. Skinwalkers are dangerous beings of darkness. Sarah told me it's true, they are crawling all over the reservation, and you just have to be aware of what you say and do to avoid drawing them near. It's also very common for people unfamiliar with Navajo tradition just coming on the reservation to accidentally attract these creatures and bring bad luck and fortune upon themselves in the process.

Encounter 17
Submitted By: Anonymous
Time: N/A
Location: New Mexico

SO I WANT to start this email by saying that I'm not too familiar with any of the areas in New Mexico, so I can't fully recall where exactly I was. I drive a crappy 1998 Honda Civic, and of course, out of all the times, it decided to poop out on me when I was on this smaller road. Well, I was driving semi-cross country. It was a hot day in the New

Mexico desert, and I had to walk my happy ass through a very small stretch of the desert because the road I was on was leaving in the opposite direction. Luckily for me, I still had a signal, and my GPS worked, so I just figured I would walk the few miles through the small section of the desert to get to where I needed to go to get help.

Here's where things get creepy. Off to my left was a small bluff that I did not notice immediately, or at least did not notice what was on it. I felt like I was being watched, and I got uncomfortable. I shook it off at first, thinking the heat and the sun were probably just getting to me, and as I was looking around, I happened to turn and notice this dark figure watching me from on top of this bluff. I wasn't far away from it, so I could make out some minor details. It looked very slender and had on black torn robes from what I can describe. Whoever it was had a large animal skull on top of its head with horns, they were covered from head to toe with this tattered black robe, so I couldn't exactly see who it was watching me, but they were very slender, I mean like Ethiopian starving and haven't eaten in three weeks slender. It gave me the creeps, so I kept walking, but this person kept watching me the entire time.

I would periodically check over to see if this freak kept watching me; at one point, it disappeared. This made me feel even more nervous like now this person was going to pursue me and chase me, so I quickly picked up my pace double time. I didn't know who this thing was, their intentions, or why they were watching me so closely, but I was not comfortable being their *Truman Show* entertainment. The only thing I knew about the desert was Las Vegas and Area 51. All sorts of creepy, freaky stuff happens. Oh, I forgot about the Roswell crash. I don't even think I was more than fifty to a hundred miles away from that area, if I'm not mistaken. Either way, screw what happened here. I didn't want any part to play.

I eventually made the four-mile trek and made it to where I needed to go to get help for my Honda Civic, but that was probably one of the creepiest times I can ever recall happening in my life. There is an upside, though; I'm very thankful that this happened to me at 1 p.m. in the afternoon. I can't even imagine, nor do I want to think about, if this would have happened to me at 10 p.m. when it's pitch black outside. I think I probably would have just called for somebody to pick me up or waited for hours or something for an Uber. I'm never walking in the desert at night, let alone during the day. Especially after something like this happens, you can count me out.

11
THUNDERBIRD ENCOUNTERS & SIGHTINGS

THUNDERBIRDS ARE A RELATIVELY new concept to me as a narrator and hobbyist in cryptozoology.

The idea that a bird larger than a grown man can exist and is said to have supernatural powers to bring storms and rain with it—what's frightening is there are many northern tribes that detail stories of birds just like this: bringing storms, or swooping down and picking up grown men and women off the ground to be eaten. In fact, I did a video a while back about one of the most terrifying thunderbird accounts I've ever heard of from a man named Jim.

While there aren't as many of these kinds of stories and encounters, I'll do my best to provide you with what I have so you can be the judge on what is true and what is not.

Encounter 1
Submitted By: Anonymous
Time: N/A
Location: Slatesprings, Mississippi

I'M GOING to give some context. I used to live in Slatesprings, Mississippi, as a kid. I lived in the middle of nowhere next to a giant meadow/field about five miles long by seven miles wide (I looked up my old house to ensure it's correct). Our closest neighbor owned some of it and stored giant cylindrical hay bales there.

It was my birthday, and it was very cold outside. I'd just turned seven and was playing on my little plastic four-wheeler, and I got a stick stuck in the wheel, so I got off and picked it off. I remember getting up and looking up to see a giant bird fly over the giant field in front of my house and land on a hay bale, almost three times the size of the hay bale. I remember freezing and then watching as it took off, almost crushing the bale.

I ran inside crying, but my parents thought I was talking about a raven or something. Has anyone else seen something similar? About a month ago, I told my dad about it, and he said he remembered the neighbor saying something about a bird.

Encounter 2
Submitted By: Anonymous
Time: N/A
Location: N/A

ONE NIGHT WHEN I WAS, like, seven or eight, I went on to the roof of my house with my dad and brother to lie down; after about thirty minutes of talking and looking at the stars, we heard a noise that sounded like flapping. Then we saw a huge bird; I mean, this thing was massive with a wingspan of maybe twenty-five to thirty feet. It flew overhead and into the distance. We never saw it again though we were pretty spooked. We thought it might have been a condor since they have a pretty massive wingspan, but from doing some research, we found out there are no condors in Texas, and they don't get as big as the bird we saw, so we weren't sure.

We often tell this story to friends. Obviously, some don't believe or don't want to, and others are intrigued by the whole thing. One of them even said what we saw sounds similar to the "Thunderbird," which is a creature from Native American legend whose "wings are responsible for causing thunder." I don't know about that, but the sound of that bird's wings flapping still gives me chills to this day.

Whether it was a Thunderbird or a condor or some species of a giant bird, I'm not sure, but I know what I saw. As cliche as that is to say, it's the truth, I don't know what it was, but I'm more curious than scared. Did I see the Thunderbird? A new species of a giant bird? It was heading west, from what I remember that night, towards New Mexico, Arizona, Nevada, etc. So maybe its home is in the valleys, cliffs, and caves over there? As I said, I don't know.

If anyone has any information on this or has had a similar experience, I would appreciate it if you shared it. I don't know what to believe. Honestly, there's that part that wants to believe in the stories of the Thunderbird, but the other logical side is trying to tell me otherwise. But there's always that what-if? What do you think?

Encounter 3
Submitted By: Harlyn
Time: 1996
Location: N/A

BACK IN '96, I and my then-girlfriend saw what we believed to be a Thunderbird. Being from nearby and traveling a lot through the surrounding states, you tend to pick up some information and learn a few things here and there. Especially from befriending locals and tribesmen alike. The desert is dangerous, and much of it is unknown to man. Even many Natives wouldn't venture to some parts, which is saying a lot. Let me get back to the story.

So back in 1996 I was driving along Highway 85 when my girlfriend tapped me on the shoulder and pointed to her side of the car. She asked me, "Do you see that out there?"

I briefly glanced over, and out in the distance, you could see this large bird flying low to the ground. Far enough away that you couldn't make out specific details, but close enough you could tell it was a bird and a very large size. My first thought was that it was a condor or some sort of bird of prey, but as it ascended back into the sky and flew off in the distance, it was clear this was not the case. This thing had black feathers and resembled more of a large raven kind of bird than anything else. It did look different than a raven now; I want to establish that.

As it ascended, you could make out a little bit more of its body, and I remember clear as day white markings on its tail. The whole sighting lasted maybe ten seconds at most, but it left my girlfriend and me in awe and wonder that birds of such size lived out there. I could have never imagined birds that big to exist. It's really hard to put a size on it, but I could tell it was larger than the car I was in, which was my 1993 Nissan Sentra at the time. It was a very large-sized bird, that's for sure.

Encounter 4
Submitted By: Anonymous
Time: N/A
Location: Phoenix, Arizona

I WAS INVITED to a friend's house a few years back south of Phoenix. He lives in the middle of nowhere, but one of the main directions he gave me was that there was a large cattle farm near where he was. He said that this cattle rancher had a habit of not being careful, and more often than not, he would have cattle wander off and die. It wasn't uncommon to see dead cattle off in the distance. Well, he wasn't wrong. On my way to his house, I probably saw at least three dead cows.

This was the same time that I also saw the largest bird in my entire life. Out not far away from the road was this monstrous-sized white bird eating away at this dead cow that must have wandered off and died. This bird was easily the size of the cattle and was a sight to behold. I couldn't stop staring. I was trying to grasp what kind of bird gets that big and if there are even any. It wasn't trying to conceal itself, just feasting away at this dead cow. Pulling massive chunks of meat off its bones. It never flew away, just feasted on this cow's meat.

I eventually got to my friend's place and told him, "You have giant birds around here that are eating the dead cows." He kind of just gave me a blank stare. I don't think he even knew how to respond to that. Kind of stared at me and asked what I was talking about. I explained what I saw, but I don't think he believed me. Here I just thought I saw a bird that might be a normal thing. I don't think he believed me, to be honest.

Encounter 5
Submitted By: Gregory
Time: 1960s
Location: Southern California

MY GREAT-GRANDFATHER WAS A VERY passionate outdoorsman, hunter, survivalist, you know. The kind of guy who lives for the outside world of exploration and adventure. The kind of guy who regularly spends weeks at a time out on hikes and spends more time in solitude than with others.

He's survived in multiple climates, terrains, states, and even countries. At the age of 103, he's still going for it, incredibly healthy, and has a very alert mind. He's told me about some things he's found on his adventures before, and nothing ever too out there.

In the last six months, I learned of the Thunderbird, which is supposed to be this large bird that is said to show up before and after a storm. I told my great-grandfather about it and my interest in it, and he told me a couple of different stories.

The first was back in the 1960s when he was doing a forty-mile hike through the outback of southern California. I know it's not called the outback, but that's what I like to call the harsh, barren wilderness. This man will do these kinds of hikes to (1) stay in shape and (2) push his body to its limits to prove he can do it.

At one point during his trek, he was attacked by a bird of angelic size that nearly grabbed my great-grandfather in its talons and carried him away. He said this bird even dwarfed a condor or other large birds. He was able to burn it with a torch he had at the time and scared it off. It was clear that its intent was to kill him. Said the bird was large, built like an eagle but had very distinctive features to its face. I thought this detail was interesting: Its claws and beak were black, and it looked to have intelligence in its eyes. More so than other birds. He claims it came down from the higher rocky mountains, probably hunting for a meal for its young.

The second was when he had reached the end of a three-week hiking expedition in southern Nevada and found what he described as a feather the size of his torso. It was the largest feather he had ever encountered in his life. It measured about four feet in length and about ten inches in width. He kept the feather with him for years until he lost everything he owned in a house fire that nearly claimed his life back in the early '80s.

I fully believe him. He's not the type to make up stuff like this and is a very honest and hardworking man who comes from that time era when honesty was upheld. I haven't asked him about Bigfoot, but I might have to pick his brain some more to find out if he's got more stories to tell. He's still out and about doing his thing in the wild, so I don't get much of a chance to talk to him.

Encounter 6
Submitted By: Anonymous
Time: N/A
Location: Northern California

I'LL NEVER FORGET when I went camping with my family in Northern California, where my brother saw something he will never forget. Northern California is home to many things, rattlesnakes, giant redwoods, and even the supposed Bigfoot. Still, I never would have thought this animal existed in a million years. I didn't think much of this phenomenon at the time because I was unaware of it. Well, I didn't spend much time looking into it until my brother told me about it.

See, my family loves to just get in a motorhome, and we drive around to different states and find great spots to camp, whether it be a campground or just off the beaten path. It doesn't matter to us; we'll find a way to have a good time no matter what.

In this instance, we were driving around Northern California, and I could tell you that I remember we were near the Redwoods. I can't quite remember if we hadn't gone through it yet or already did. I probably couldn't even tell you the exact spot because I was much younger, but I remember it was that desert kind of woods. If you're having a hard time following along, just simply Google what the terrain is like in Northern California, and you'll get an idea. It's not thick woods like in the Pacific Northwest. It's more dried out.

We had decided to make our camping spot off this road we were on. There was nobody else around, and we figured it would be the perfect place. As we were getting set up, my parents sent my brother to see if he could find a stream nearby to fetch some water because we were running low at the time. My brother was seventeen then and was already a very experienced outdoors kid. He always carried a knife and was very knowledgeable about the surroundings. It wasn't like my parents sent their kids off into the woods without knowing anything. I think my father had even spotted a small stream just a few miles away on the way up and wanted to see if it wrapped around.

About twenty minutes later, my brother came back as pale as a ghost and said he'd seen the largest bird ever to exist. My parents gave him a puzzled look, but I think they ultimately wrote it off and said, "You probably just mistook a bird of prey or something."

What he explained to me was that this giant raven-like bird was larger than him. It always stood out to me because my brother doesn't get scared, especially being out in the wilderness. We've been out in the woods together since we were little kids; to him, it's just a part of nature. Even when we've come across mountain lions and even bears, he's hardly fazed because he's just accepted that it's a part of being in the wild. But this really bothered him, and I distinctly remember him acting the rest of the day differently. It was bothersome. The day did go on, though, and we ended up getting busy with just camping and living, so before you know it, we're on our way out of there, and life goes on.

One interesting thing is that my family and I did hear what sounded like a very large hawk very close by. If you know the sound of a hawk, you'll probably understand what I mean. Except the sound of this hawk was so loud. Do you know how you can tell when you hear an animal sound the general size of that animal? It's just common sense to know that if it's a larger animal, it's going to have more bass and fullness to its cry, roar, or howl, whatever the animal makes. Well, there were a couple of times in that nearby area afterward we had heard what sounded like a hawk but much deeper and sounded like it belonged to a bird much larger. Again, the best way I can describe it accurately is that it had much more bass and vibration to its cry. I guess if you want to call it a hawk, call it a cry. I thought it was cool at the time, but I don't think I put two and two together.

The years went on and on, and my brother and I got to talking again, and he brought up that event. But this time, he went into far greater detail, explaining that as he traversed down this ravine to look for the stream, he saw what he described as a mixture of a raven and a hawk except very large. He said this thing's legs and talons were easily as big as his forearms and hands. The head and beak were larger than his head, and it was watching him, perched up on a dead tree on the other side.

It scared him because he said he's never got a feeling as he did at that moment. He said it was like that bird was sizing him up and deciding whether or not to come after him. I possibly don't understand how you could feel that from a bird, even if it was a rather large bird of prey, but this is what he relayed to me. The entire time he was in view of this bird, it was closely watching him, almost as if it was calculating its next decision. It never moved from that branch, though, and only moved its head to follow him and his movements. He just got a feeling that it wasn't right, and his gut instinct told him to get out of there.

I'm not sure why I didn't put much thought into this happening when it happened, because this was years and years ago, but for whatever reason, when he told me about this experience of his, it was so much more profound to me. Possibly because I'm older, which would make sense.

He told me he learned there's something called a Thunderbird and that people talk about seeing it all over the United States. When I asked him more about a Thunderbird, he was not quite sure. Some people report seeing a giant white bird; others talk about seeing a pterodactyl-like flying animal.

His belief stands firm that he saw something that he doesn't believe wanted to be seen. He stands by that feeling, especially considering he's never seen a bird of that size and has never heard of a bird that looks exactly like this. It had a large pointed beak that dipped down at the end just like a hawk's and had white markings along the bottom of its neck and chest but looked like a mixture of black and brown. If he was guessing size, he would have said around five feet in height. It never spread its wings, so he couldn't get an accurate wingspan. There are plenty of small wild animals out there, and the area we were in, nobody was around. I think we pulled off on an old road that's no longer used since we were accustomed to just finding random roads that were either deserted or abandoned for the best camping spots. It's where you get the best seclusion.

He's not scared about it now, but it opened up the book for him that there might be things out there that are undiscovered and that we don't know about. Whether it truly was something that had bad intentions or maybe was just an undiscovered bird of prey, either way, it sounded far more intelligent than just your standard bird. Maybe there is some truth to the whole Thunderbird phenomenon after all.

Encounter 7
Submitted By: Charley
Time: 1998
Location: Omaha Reservation, Missouri

IN 1998 I was near the Omaha Reservation along the Missouri River and Northeastern Nebraska. I was told this was one of the hotbeds of Thunderbird sightings, and surprisingly I had my own.

I was with a few hiking partners going up a trail when we saw, maybe about forty yards to the north, a large bird ascend from the treetops up into the sky. We only saw it as soon as we did because of the immediate movement. It was large and white and had an enormous wingspan far bigger than any bird I've ever seen. I'm not exaggerating when I say this bird was probably four times the size of an eagle. Its body and head alone would have been the size of a human torso and head. Maybe larger. It shot up from the treetops and ended far away in the southeastern direction. It didn't make any noise or any calls that birds usually make. My friend and I were shocked at what we saw. I was familiar with animals and creatures of living legends like Bigfoot and Thunderbird, but I never knew that I would see one for myself.

As I spent more time in the area and on the Omaha Reservation, I would learn that this is a hotbed spot for not only Bigfoot encounters but Thunderbird sightings as well, among the Natives, who don't share their sightings with many people outside the reservation. However, if you get a chance to sit down and talk with them, they will share with you story after story of these things in the area.

I wasn't frightened at all and never felt threatened by seeing this creature. It was probably the most majestic thing I've ever seen. Its size alone was impressive. I felt like I saw a Pegasus or something for the first time, something you would feel like is supposed to exist during the time of Greek gods. It was a beautiful sight to see. I feel special seeing such a rare animal.

Encounter 8
Submitted By: Anonymous
Time: June 28, 2011
Location: Southern New Mexico

I SAW a bird larger than any animal you could imagine. It was like a flying bison. It was so large. I could tell you the exact date and time this happened, too. This was June 28, 2011, and I was driving down in southern New Mexico. There were other vehicles on the road at the time of this sighting. It was a very hot sunny day. Clear skies, not a cloud to be seen. Temperatures are soaring down there; if you've ever been in the desert, you know how hot it gets.

I saw this large flying object, what I thought was an object, descend closer to the ground and then fly westbound past some smaller mountains. It glided with ease, and I never saw it flap its massive wings once. I saw as it got closer that it was the largest bird I've ever seen. I watched it the entire time it appeared until the time it cleared the horizon, all while maintaining my composure behind the wheel. I wasn't even sure if what I was seeing was real.

The bird looked to be gray from what I could tell by the way the light was hitting it. I've never seen a bird that looks like that before, let alone the size of an actual bison flying through the air. I'm sure I was not the only one who saw this thing flying because it wasn't a lonely lone road. Other cars were driving around, and since the area I was driving around was very open, anybody with a clear view would have seen it.

I'm going to guesstimate it to be about a couple of hundred feet off the ground. It was very high up in the sky and descended pretty low to probably about a couple of hundred feet and then stayed at that altitude until it disappeared off in the horizon to the west. That was the only time I've ever seen an animal I couldn't identify.

Encounter 9
Submitted By: Anonymous
Time: Spring 2018
Location: Berlin, Connecticut

MY THUNDERBIRD SIGHTING happened back in the spring of 2018. I was just outside the small town of Berlin in Connecticut, alongside Highway 15. I saw what I could only describe as the biggest bird in existence. This thing flew from one side of the road to the other, very low to the ground but still above the trees. It just happened to be passing over as I was driving. It was a clear afternoon around 1 p.m. I was alone in the car but saw it in front of me and almost pooped myself at what I saw.

I saw it for approximately three seconds as it flew from one side to the other, but it looked just like an oversized black bird the size of my small sedan. I saw it had a curvature at the end of its beak that pointed downward, and a kind of gizzard beard thing hung down from its neck, not like an actual gizzard but an extra thing of hair that dangled down. I've been out in the forests and lived long enough to know that was not a normal creature you'll see every day!

Encounter 10
Submitted By: Anonymous
Time: N/A
Location: New York

NOT ANYBODY I knew or know personally, but I just heard things through people I've known. I live outside the city of Kingston, New York, and good old Ulster County. I don't know if you would know anything about this, but it's something I find particularly interesting. I've heard stories of a massive bird that flies down and swoops up cattle. Crazy, ain't it? It's been spotted enough times that people are on the lookout for it, and it's even been shot at on multiple occasions because it steals cows. Imagine a bird of prey large enough that it can steal a cow. I have not seen anything myself; I've only heard stories from people I know and friends of mine.

I guess it was a ranch, from what I heard, about seventy miles from here that lost so many cattle from these things they shut down indefinitely. I guess these birds would fly down, grab the cattle, fly about three to four hundred feet in the air, and drop them to let them fall to their death. Then they would fly back around, take the cattle back up and fly off with them.

Pretty harrowing stuff, if you ask me. I can't make this stuff up. I know it sounds like it's straight out of a horror fiction novel, but I'm hearing from multiple different people the same kind of stuff. And I guess it's not just around here; it's even more common than you think it is as you go closer towards the Midwest like Ohio, Michigan, that area.

We got this to deal with just when times could not get any crazier. I guess there was an older gentleman somewhere along the way who ended up killing one of these things, and he kept its skull around, but it's gossip, and who knows who has it now and where it's really at. If these creatures do exist, well, I guess it won't be long before I see one myself.

I just wanted to say I'm a huge fan of your channel and watch all your videos. I thought you might eat this information up. Thanks for sharing so much.

Encounter 11
Submitted By: Anonymous
Time: N/A
Location: N/A

I'M NOT GOING to claim to know anything about birds because I don't. But I'm pretty sure birds don't come out at night unless it's an owl or bats. However, this one night, we came across the largest nocturnal bird, but I'm pretty sure it was not an owl judging by its shape. And its size, of course, because owls don't get to be the size of a human if not larger. Let me explain.

This was just in the fall of last year. Walking around outside with my dad at night at probably about 10 p.m. That was when we heard a huge crash near us in the trees. My father and I looked up, and perched on one of the tree's larger branches was this massive shape that resembled a bird. It was humongous and blacker than the darkness around it. I think that was one of the reasons why it stood out so much and why we could spot it right away. It moved its head, and my dad and I just felt like it was staring at us. I couldn't see any eyes because of how dark it was. It was just this large black shape that resembled that of a perched bird.

Here's the issue that I have with it. Birds don't get to the height of six to seven feet. This thing perched on the branch was larger than my father or I, and right as we heard the crashing, the thing immediately folded its wings up, so neither of us truly saw its wingspan. If it was a bird that large, then its wingspan had to have been massive.

I felt it was probably a good idea to back away from this animal because I did not feel safe. My dad, without breaking eye contact on this thing, whispered to me quietly, "Back away slowly." We backed away to the house without ever breaking the sight of this bird, and its eyes followed us the entire way. It never broke its eye contact either, and it stayed perfectly still.

We made it back to the house. We were both going nuts the entire time thinking about what we just saw! What kind of animal was that? Was there even such a thing as nocturnal birds of this gargantuan size!? Did we just see something new? About an hour went by, and my dad stepped back outside to see if he could still see it. The spot that it was in was empty, meaning it was gone.

Still one of the weirdest things to ever have happened. I didn't know there were such large nocturnal birds, but I guess I do now.

Encounter 12
Submitted By: Anonymous
Time: N/A
Location: N/A

SO I GOT the chance to reconnect with some of my friends over in Colorado who are also of the Sioux tribe and Arapahoe. These are the people who shared with me the tales. Recently I've seen dogmen and Bigfoots waging wars against each other to be able to eat the Arapaho tribe that was defending themselves against these beasts.

I need to watch your channel, and they wanted to share more stories with me. These are stories they have obtained from their chief, which have been passed down through generations, and more tales from their tribe that they would like to share with you. My other friend, who is part Sioux Indian, also has very similar tales from his tribe, dealing with not only Bigfoot and dogman but what they consider the Thunderbird. Especially more so in the Great Plains area.

Certain places were off-limits for hunting and foraging for any sort of food and supplies because these large birds patrolled the perimeter of the area. Usually, it was part of the mountainside, but other times it wasn't. Supposedly somewhere along the way, one of the chief's daughters befriended a Thunderbird and was able to ride it before it tricked her and knocked her off its back while up in midair, and she fell to her death.

From what I've gathered, Thunderbirds aren't nearly as hostile as dogmen and Bigfoot, but they would take pride in stealing kills from hunters by swooping down and taking the deer whole or waiting for the kill to claim the body.

Unlike other birds, they had a very distinctive call, like a hawk or even an eagle. You could hear it from far away and know exactly what kind of bird it was. I wasn't told any story about a Thunderbird having any conflict with a Bigfoot or a dogman, but I'm sure it has happened. They were more elusive than the other two creatures and were not as hostile or aggressive. They were not attacking villages but waiting and watching most of the time. Many times they would show up in full view of villages; they would bring upon them full storms, droughts, famine, and worse. They almost acted like an omen, and even though they weren't seen as much, there's a reason they were named the Thunderbird. Although the Arapahoe and Sioux Indians had their name for them just like they did the dogman and Bigfoot, and I don't think the name they had for them directly translated to Thunderbird. But it did mean something very similar.

One friend of mine who is a Sioux Indian shared with me some stories about back in the early 1800s, these giant black birds with white markings on them would fly out of the mountains in South Dakota, fly down, and pick up villagers, hunters, and even white men and fly high up in the air and drop them to kill them. From the sounds of it, these things didn't fly into the village, but anybody who wandered into a specific area was generally targeted. This leads me to believe that among my friends who shared very similar stories, the Thunderbird is a very real cryptid but, like the other two, dogmen and Bigfoot, very territorial beings. While seeming much more elusive, they still can be just as dangerous since they can just as easily pick up a person and drop them from a hundred-plus feet up in the air to their death.

A couple of hunters had found a large bird nest they described near the base of one of the mountains they were near and found many human skulls and bones. It wasn't entirely clear if these cryptids would pick people up and drop them from the sky to kill them and then eat them or if it was just a killing tactic to eliminate threats. The feathers from these creatures were humongous. These creatures persisted even when white men started traveling to the area and colonizing. They, too, became victims and knew the ferocity of these cryptids. Muzzleloaders and guns didn't seem to be effective against these kinds of flying cryptids, and there were certain areas they would not venture into for fear that these things would grab them.

I'm almost wondering if states with very rocky terrain with lots of mountains and hills make the perfect environment for these kinds of cryptids. Plenty of places to hide and more than enough places to have a nest without anyone bothering you or discovering who or where you are. Even today, there are still miles and miles of wilderness all over the United States that remain uncharted or too thick for us humans to venture off into. It's possible that these things have made their nests and places impossible for us to get to, especially with the vast mountains and cliffs all over.

I recently listened to one of your other Thunderbird stories where a gentleman climbed down a cliff, if I remember correctly, and discovered what he thought was a Thunderbird nest. Well, his description was close to what my friend's story matched up with. And in his story, I believe they were animal bones, but in the story that I got from my friend, they only found human remains.

I don't tend to find much evidence based on what I know about these things on the East Coast. However, the sightings I heard about that happened on the East Coast resemble that of a pterodactyl. Those sightings go down to Southern Florida and even into Cuba. No, it's not a Thunderbird, but there seems to be a continuity with these large flying birds like cryptids all around the United States.

Going back to that Thunderbird encounter you posted about the man who went down the cliff in Northern California, and I have heard of other Thunderbird encounters around that area before. When you mix mountain cliffs and forests, you create a perfect environment for these things to thrive. I believe that's why there are so many good sightings in Colorado, such as reptilians, Bigfoots, dogmen, Thunderbirds, and more.

I find it very interesting that several of the supposed encounters and sightings that many Natives recall of this Thunderbird are usually all large black birds. They all talk about some distinctive white markings on their body that never seem to coincide with a specific pattern or shape. I've heard some descriptions that talk about it being very similar-looking to a stark black eagle and others that say it looks more raven-like. I've even heard others say it looks like its own bird entirely with a pointed-down beak at the end, like a falcon. Either way, we need to keep a close eye on the skies around us when we're out, and if we see something large flying our way, we know they are near.

Encounter 13
Submitted By: Anonymous
Time: 2004
Location: Florida

A FAMILY FRIEND of mine operates a small seaplane business in the Florida area where people pay a small sum of money, and he takes them on tours throughout and overlooking the Everglades. It was my birthday, and I had never been on a plane before. Shocking, I know. Just so you can get an idea of how small these seaplanes are, they are practically two-passenger planes, the ones that fly over water. They're small compared to commercial airlines but large enough for you to get around. They aren't luxurious by any means. I'm not a plane girl by any means; I just know they are called seaplanes. If I had to guess, I'm going to say twenty to thirty feet from the front nose to the back. I have no idea how big the wingspans are.

As I was saying, this family friend took me out for my birthday, and we were flying over the Everglades when he started panicking and pointing out in front of us. Flying a little underneath us and flying perpendicular to us was the largest bird I've ever seen. I'd vaguely heard of a creature called the Thunderbird, but I didn't know what it is.

I don't know if a Thunderbird is real, but I do know now there are very large birds out there that far exceed any size of bird we know about. The bird I saw was an extremely large predatorial-looking bird, all gray to smokey charcoal in color.

This bird has a wingspan that easily matched the size of the plane we were in.

I couldn't believe it; my friend and I were in total awe and could not stop staring at this thing. It was flying relatively low, only a little higher than the tips of the trees. It never once seemed to look up in our direction or even care that we were flying over. It didn't come across like it was in a hurry, just calmly flying in the direction it was heading, which was south. It was all he and I could talk about the rest of the flight and even after. We had no idea what kind of bird it was, and we were convinced that we had discovered a new species of swamp bird. I know now I probably more than likely saw a Thunderbird.

12

WENDIGO ENCOUNTERS & SIGHTINGS

IN NATIVE AMERICAN FOLKLORE, the wendigo is a malevolent spirit that can possess humans and turn them into cannibalistic monsters. These creatures are said to dwell in the coldest parts, and their victims are often those who have become lost or stranded in the wilderness. There have been many reports of wendigo sightings over the years, but most of them have come from remote, rural areas. Reigning primarily in the cold north and northeast, the wendigo is yet another prevalent entity causing terror to many. Unlike dogmen (to my knowledge) I've not come across any reports of wendigos killing or harming anyone that I can recall.

While many people believe that the wendigo is nothing more than a myth, there are those who are convinced that these creatures are real. There have been several sightings of wendigos in recent years, and some people even claim to have been possessed by one of these spirits. I don't have as many stories on these as skinwalkers, but they do provide a very interesting perspective into indigenous cryptids that aren't just shape-shifters.

Encounter 1
Submitted By: Clarissa
Time: Summer 2007
Location: Northern Michigan

IN THE SUMMER OF 2007, I worked at a camp on Lost Isle, a small island off the coast of Northern Michigan. My job was to run the kids' program, which involved taking kids out on wilderness adventures for the day or leading them in arts and crafts.

That summer, I had a couple of kids talk to me about seeing a monster. This was not uncommon. At that camp, the woods were very mysterious and scary, so it was not surprising that kids had seen ghosts, monsters, and other weird things. I was always skeptical about these stories for the same reason adults tell children not to talk to strangers—because adults don't believe in ghosts and monsters. But these kids were insistent. They told me they had seen a monster with yellow eyes and a face with a long snout. I didn't believe them at first, but then I noticed other kids talking about the same monster.

Soon that monster was all anyone was talking about. One kid said he had seen it during an adventure in the woods, and another said she had seen it from her cabin window. At that moment, I started to believe that this monster was real. I just didn't know how real until one night, as I was lying in my bunk, I heard something step on the roof of the cabin behind me. It was extremely loud, like a person stepping on a tin roof. I jumped out of my bed and ran outside. I looked up but could see nothing, so I went back inside.

But the next night, I heard the same thing. After that, I was scared to go to bed. I eventually confronted one of the camp counselors about the monster. I asked her if she had seen it, and she said no, and explained that the kids had just made it up to deal with the fear of being away from home. At that moment, I decided to investigate the monster on my own.

I followed the same path the kids had been taking when they went to the bathroom at night. The trail led through the woods and eventually to the top of a hill. I waited until it was late at night and snuck out to the top of the hill. There was nothing but a small forest, and it was too dark to see anything. I walked down the other side of the hill through the woods. I was not sure where I was going, but I kept walking.

Eventually, I found myself standing at the edge of a forest. I had no idea where I was, but I felt like I was being pulled into the woods. I took a step forward and heard something in the woods. I turned around, and there was a face with yellow eyes and a long snout in the darkness. I knew right then that it was the monster. It was as if I could feel its energy; I knew it had seen me.

I stood there frozen, and then I heard something else. It sounded like a voice, but it was nothing I had ever heard. It was like a combination of a roar and a whisper, and it was right behind me. I turned around, and I saw the monster. It was standing right next to me, staring straight at me. I don't remember what happened next. I think I blacked out.

When I woke up, it was morning, and I was sitting on a log. I felt like I was in a dream, but I knew I was not dreaming. I looked around, and I was still in the woods. I knew that it was still early, so everyone would still be asleep. I walked back to camp, and I told no one about what had happened. That night I couldn't sleep. I was too busy thinking about the monster. The next day I just felt so different. It's hard to explain. Even days and months after that incident had occurred, I never felt quite the same. Like something inside me changed. The kids still kept talking about seeing this monster, and a couple of weeks later, everyone began referring to it as a "wendigo."

So I'll leave it up to you to decide. Was this just some massive nightmare plaguing our camp? Or did we all encounter a wendigo?

Encounter 2
Submitted By: Anonymous
Time: N/A
Location: N/A

YEARS AGO, a group of close friends and I were about seventeen to nineteen. Some of us drove; others didn't. To add some quick background, I've never experienced anything like what I will share before and typically didn't believe in the paranormal. I haven't experienced anything strange in the woods since, and I've continued to hunt, track, and spend time outdoors. I have no explanation for the events that would occur on this night.

It was a hot August evening when a group of friends and I were sleeping in a small cabin out in the woods. The place was old and run-down, but it was the only shelter from the elements. The cabin was owned by my best friend's father, who had the place for years and years but was too darn lazy to do the proper upkeep on it. Sure, it did the job, but it desperately needed much love and TLC.

The night started out like any other night. We were sitting around the fire and telling stories. I can still remember the feeling of the fire; it was so warm and comforting. I thought nothing of it at the time. Around 9 p.m., the group of us went to bed. We were going to scout for good spots for deer stands the next day and wanted a good night's sleep. We were all exhausted, so no one was alarmed at the fact that we all went to sleep at the same time. After all, the drive up here took three hours, and I'm sure you know how taxing long car rides can drain you mentally. Unfortunately, we didn't sleep so peacefully after that... because something happened only an hour after going to bed.

I was awoken by a loud thud from the kitchen, followed by a loud scream. I immediately jumped up from my bed and ran toward the kitchen. The rest of the group did the same; we were all awakened and terrified at what was happening. Whatever this was. My best friend and his father were in the kitchen. Both of them looked like they were terrified and were staring wildly at the back door. Sometimes his father would drop by early in the morning and crash out in the main room, so it wasn't a surprise to see him there. We all asked them what was wrong and why they were screaming.

Soon after, I heard the sound of something coming from the roof. All of us, in unison, turned our attention to the roof, where we could hear something heavy walking across the cabin. Then it let out a terrifying screech, and I remember it was the exact same sound as an owl when it screeches, only ten times louder. The screech was so loud and piercing that it hurt my ears, and I remember I had to cover them with my hands to stop the pain. The screech was also very deep in pitch and sounded like you took an owl and were choking the life out of it to get that kind of noise. It was horrible.

I remember looking at my friends and my friend's father, and we all had the same face of terror. I remember someone saying, "What the hell is that?" and someone else saying, "Is it a monster? A Bigfoot?" Then the screeching stopped. We then heard this loud thud, dropping from the roof and hitting the ground at the side of the cabin. It sounded like whatever it was must have weighed about five hundred pounds. It was heavy. But the screech continued for another minute, and then it was silent. I remember forcing myself to leave the safety of the kitchen and walk out into the main room.

I remember being in that cold old cabin with the moonlight shining through the windows. Imagine that you are in the middle of a scary movie and try to put yourself in that situation. When we were overcome with dread and fear, I believe I was able to speak for all of us together. My friend's father opened the front door and shone his flashlight outside to take a look after it went completely silent. You could hear the night outside was so quiet; there were no crickets, noise, or anything else. This was in the late summer when the forest is usually pretty alive at night. It was incredibly eerie. We all had this lingering feeling that something horrible would happen.

One of our other friends, perhaps in a fit of craziness or for no other reason, suggested that the four of us go outside together to figure out the cause of that noise. I'm sure most of us yelled at him, "Are you crazy?" Even my friend's father had a worried expression on his face and was pacing the room while repeating, "This isn't good, this isn't good," and doing his best to reassure us and keep us inside the cabin. He told us we needed to wait it out until morning. And we were going to have to cancel our hunting trip. I don't know if he was more scared than we were, but his reaction was to force us to stay in the cabin until morning.

One of the friends in the group, who was possibly the craziest of us all, decided that he would go outside and search around in the dark to try to locate the source of that noise. He was certain that this was nonsense and intended to prove his point. We all tried to stop him, but he was having none of it. He ran out of the cabin with one of those high luminous flashlights in hand. In less than five minutes, he came running back in and slammed the door shut. He was screaming and crying and looked like he had seen a ghost. He kept repeating, "There's something outside. It's so big, and it's walking around out there. I saw it!" He was pale, paler than you get if you are sick.

My friend's dad tried to comfort and redirect him to one of the small cabin rooms to calm down. We kept the door locked that night and did our best to sleep, while others thought it would be best to stay up and watch.

The rest of the night wasn't as eventful. Still, among a couple of others who decided to stay up, I kept hearing something big walking around the cabin out in the dark. We were all too terrified to even dare shine our flashlights out there at whatever it was walking around. It reminded me of the film *Jeepers Creepers*, honestly. It seriously creeped me out. I have no idea how my other friends even managed to get any sleep, but somehow, they pulled it off. My friend's dad was among us who stayed up all night to help keep watch to ensure we were safe.

As soon as it was light enough, we all hurriedly grabbed our belongings and immediately began loading our car with minimal conversation. We woke up those who were sleeping and resolved not to spend any more time in that cabin than was absolutely necessary.

My friend's dad drove back in his car and told us he would meet us all back at their house since that was where we'd all met up the day before to load up and go. The three-hour-plus ride back seemed like a blur because the previous night's thoughts wouldn't stop replaying in my mind. We got back to the house, started unloading our stuff, and got ready to go in our separate vehicles. I then asked my friend's dad what he thought it was. Was it a cougar?

He seemed very hesitant to talk about it, but after some prying, I got him to open up. He started telling us that he'd run into it before and knew what it was. Then he asked us, "Have you guys ever heard of a wendigo?" We hadn't. He explained to us that it's a cannibalistic spirit that has taken physical form and will stalk you if it finds you.

One time when he was hunting up by that cabin about four years ago, he felt like he'd ventured a little too far to the west, where this thing's territory must have been, and claimed that it followed him back to the same cabin where we were staying. It was like it had our scent and was waiting for us to come back to that cabin to show ourselves. Even just typing this out gives me the creeps hardcore. I cannot stop reliving it. I'm not sure why it never tried to get into the cabin, but maybe if we had stayed longer. Perhaps it was looking for weak points. We're not sure. Maybe it was just trying to scare us off.

Encounter 3
Submitted By: Keith S.
Time: May 2008
Location: Rocky Mountains

MY STORY HAPPENED in May of 2008. I was camping in the Rocky Mountains of Alberta with my family and friends (about twenty of us) in Banff National Park. We were driven out of our campsite by some sort of animal (we suspect a bear), and we ended up in a place called Johnston Canyon.

It was the middle of the night, and a windstorm was going on. The wind was howling, it was raining, and there was thunder and lightning. My friend and I were in the same tent. About three o'clock in the morning we heard a noise that sounded like something walking around outside the tent. My friend told me to turn my headlamp on, and I did.

I shone the light out of the tent, and from the corner of my eye, I saw something moving around. It startled and scared the living daylights out of me. This thing was about eight feet tall and covered from head to toe in long, black, matted hair. It had yellow eyes that glowed in the light from the headlamp, and it was staring at me, and I tried to scream. This thing was ugly. Its face looked like it could have been that of a dog or a deer. It even had a pair of small horns perched on the crown of its head. Compared to any other face that comes to mind, this one looked more like a decomposing skull with bits of tissue stuck to it. I wouldn't notice until afterward, but this horrible odor of rotting meat lingered around our campsite for hours after the event.

When I shined my headlight into its face, it immediately raised its arm to shield its face, and then it vanished into the darkness of the night. Either that or I turned my head away out of sheer terror and began screaming. My friend and I both saw it. Most of the other people woke up due to my frantic behavior. Now they were yelling at me through their tents, asking what was wrong, and what was going on!? I told them right then and there that something was walking around our campsite. And that it wasn't an animal and it wasn't human. I don't know what it was, but it scared me badly. The rain was heavy right about then, so we all just stayed in our tents. Many of them went back to sleep. But my friend and I decided we should stay up and keep an eye out in case this thing came back. I didn't have a weapon with me. However, he had brought his Colt .45. He firmly believes that if you go hiking, you need to carry a powerful weapon in case you run into a dangerous situation and need it.

After that thing left, the rain and the storm intensified as if its mere presence angered the storm. At some point, I passed out from exhaustion and woke up sometime in the early a.m. I think I was the first one up. I woke everyone else up, explaining we needed to move and not stick around in case whatever that thing was decided to come back. I'm glad my friend stuck up for me and convinced my family and friends that what I saw was verifiable and not just mistaken identity. They were convinced I saw something, although I'm not sure what. We loaded up and packed out of there as quickly as we could.

Now, moving forward in time a little bit, I kind of forgot about the whole event until months and months later. This same family friend and I were sitting down over a beer, and he brought up that time we saw that thing camping. I immediately remembered and had flashbacks to it. It scared me to even think about it. He explained to me, "Yeah, I tried to do some research on what I think we saw. I'm pretty sure it's not a Bigfoot. Didn't look or act like one. It had to have been a wendigo."

As a further point of connection, the friend who reminded me of this event again brought your channel to my attention and suggested that I get in touch with you for confirmation. Is what we saw a wendigo, or was it something else entirely?

Encounter 4
Submitted By: Ricky
Time: N/A
Location: Ohio

MY BROTHER and I were hunting back in the foothills of Ohio when we found ourselves in a small cave. Driven by curiosity, we were no seasoned spelunkers, nor did we have the proper equipment to explore safely, but we didn't care. We were young on a thrill-ride mission.

We were on a steep incline and found a large cave opening. It had a strange smell, and I had a sense of terror the farther down we got. As we neared the bottom of the steep incline, my brother pointed to me and said, "Look at this!" And all along the bottom were dead birds. All were in varying states of decay. Some were freshly dead, some completely rotted and skeletal, while others were in the process of rotting. You can imagine the smell was just lovely.

While trying to put together why there were so many dead birds down there, we both got this horrible feeling that something was watching us from inside the cave, and we shouldn't continue. We turned around to start making our way back up, and as we did, the feeling got stronger and stronger. We started moving as fast as we could up the incline and didn't dare look back until we got well out of the cave opening. We got to the top of the hill, and we both sensed something dangerous was down there.

We were both spooked, but we knew something was watching us, and we should've never gone in there. So we turned around to look back into the cave, and as we did, an enormous, hulking shadow appeared in the opening. We both said, "What the hell is that?" As we watched in amazement, the shadow seemed to stretch and grow, its arms and head reaching out; then it stopped. It stood at the opening, its body hidden in the darkness. It was completely motionless and silent. We felt it was watching us.

Then it started to make a sound. It was a haunting, long, deep howl. It was guttural and coarse. It carried deep into the air. It was a low, moaning growl like a wild animal would make. It got louder and louder until it was louder than our voices when we were talking. It was so loud it was echoing off the mountains, bouncing off the hills. It was the most terrifying howl I've ever heard. It was a wailing howl of pure desperation and hunger. There was something about it that was just so compelling and so very wrong. I can't even begin to describe how it sounded, and it was something you have to hear for yourself!

As it was echoing out this horrendous howl, my brother and I didn't need more time to decide that we needed to get as far away from there as possible. Let's just say we cut our day short and still talk about that day even now. It was hands down the scariest thing I've ever dealt with while in the woods.

Encounter 5
Submitted By: Anonymous
Time: Summer 2020
Location: Northern Michigan

THIS WAS in the summer of 2020. My friend and I were sitting around a bonfire with other friends. We were all fifteen or sixteen at the time and noticed a strange, pale, gaunt figure staring at us through the trees beyond. We didn't think much of it, as it looked somewhat human, and we assumed it was some kid or young adult who perhaps had been drinking and stumbled into our campground. We ignored the figure for a while, but it kept staring at us. It was not particularly tall but was very thin. It was wearing what appeared to be a torn, dark brown robe, and it had pale white skin with very long, dirty stringy black hair hanging in its face. There was nothing distinctive about its face that we could see that would have caused us to be alarmed, even though I'm probably making it sound that way. But that was in the beginning.

After a while, the figure disappeared from the trees. My friend and I were the closest to the tree line and could hear something moving quickly in the woods, coming in our direction. This made us both incredibly uneasy, as it would anyone.

~~Note: This is where I have to insert a disclaimer that I'm not suggesting that what I saw was a wendigo. Also, I'm not trying to mock the idea of the wendigo either. I merely want to share my own experience. I realize there is a lot of controversy surrounding the concept of wendigos. If you don't believe in them, that's perfectly fine. I'm not trying to change anyone's mind. Just share my story and be done with it.~~

I have to tell you, this is the point in the story where I began to question my own sanity. The next thing we knew, we could hear it behind us, and we both turned, and all of us around the bonfire now saw this thing in full sight. The figure appeared and was now very tall, at least eight feet. Its hair was long, very long, and it looked sunken in, emaciated, and sickly. It wasn't a human, at least any I'd ever seen, and it just stood at the tree line watching us. Several of us began screaming, running back towards camp, while others were downright frozen where they were standing.

I do not know what my friend and I were doing. We were in a state of shock for sure. I remember turning and running and being so afraid I would fall and that the thing would grab me. I did not see or feel anyone behind me, but I only made it as far as the firepit of our camp. I stopped and turned to see what it was doing. It had started to run towards me and was now much taller and larger. It was charging at me. I remember looking up at it when it was no more than five feet away from me. And in that moment, it looked at me with lifeless eyes. And somehow, its face had contorted and changed. It had no face. It was just a black void with eyes. I can't even begin to explain. I screamed and fell to the ground. I think my friend was screaming too, but it's a blur to be honest. I don't remember.

The next thing I remember, I was sitting on the ground, looking at my own hands, which were covered in dirt and blood. When I looked up, I was surprised to see my friend next to me. He was frantically looking around, trying to get me to go before this thing came back. I think I must have blacked out for a moment or two because it's like my brain just lapsed that moment in time entirely out of my memory like a voided check.

We made it back to camp; everyone was freaking out and crying as we told our parents what we had seen. They just listened and tried their best to calm everyone down, trying to prove there was nothing spooky out in the woods, and we had no reason to fear. But I convinced them, or at least I tried, that something was there. We saw something, and there's no denying that.

They weren't really buying it, so I just gave up after a while and kept it to myself. I know it might sound bizarre, and I want you to bear with me through these feelings. I strongly feel that whatever I saw that night somehow attached itself to me or marked me in some way. I don't know how to explain or describe my feelings. It's like it marked me. I feel different. Not just about my sighting, but I physically feel different. I feel like this thing is a part of me now. I haven't felt right ever since this happened. I don't know whom I can talk to about it. My parents and family don't want to hear any more about it. And my friend who was there with me listens, but there's not much he can do. Understandably so. What do you think happened to me? Can you provide me with some answers?

Encounter 6
Submitted By: Anonymous
Time: N/A
Location: N/A

I WAS out camping in the woods for a few days at the time with my friend and cousin. We were sitting by this lake around midnight when we heard branches snapping and footsteps headed towards us. Then a weird guttural growl, sounding like a cross between a wolf and a bear or something. Anyway, my friend said he'd go take a look, and I told him not to, but he did anyway. He was gone for about twenty minutes when I heard branches and twigs snapping. He returned with this freaked-out look on his face. "We need to go now!" was all he said, and we grabbed our gear and ran off.

Later that night, we were all in my tent when I heard branches snapping and footsteps, so I quickly unzipped the tent and yelled,

"WHAT!?" There was no response. But we kept hearing the sounds for the next half hour.

We all heard this strange voice calling all of our names. I thought someone was playing a prank on us, but the voice sounded wrong. It was all distorted and crackly. Like it was coming from an old FM radio or something. I looked out of our tent, but I didn't see anyone. I tried my best to ignore it. We were all pretty spooked by what we were hearing.

It wasn't until later that next day when I was taking a piss in the woods that I noticed feathers and blood on the ground around me. There were no birds or animals around that I could see, so I wasn't sure what to make of it other than maybe a bird had been eaten there. I zipped up and returned to hanging out with my friend and cousin.

Then we heard that low growl, followed by a strange humming noise again.

Now, all three of us started freaking out, and looking over to the woods, we saw a strange creature watching us from the trees. I can't begin to tell you just how terrified I was by seeing this creature, whatever it was. We all booked it out of our camping spot and ran towards where we had our truck parked. Without wasting a second, we all jumped in and flew out of there so fast. We would go back and collect all our stuff in a couple of days, but nothing could have prepared us for what sort of dark, sickly-looking creature we saw.

It was ugly. It kind of looked like a Gollum, troll-looking thing. I don't know. It freaked all of us out badly. I don't even like to talk about it, to be honest, because it brings the memories right back.

Encounter 7
Submitted By: Anonymous
Time: N/A
Location: N/A

I'VE HEARD many stories about wendigos, but they sound like a mix of Native American folklore and tall tales. I know the wendigo creature is part of Ojibwe or Anishinaabe (or Nishnaabeg) culture from north-central North America, namely in the Midwestern United States and eastern Canada.

My only knowledge of a wendigo was when my grandmother told me a scary campfire story when I was a young child. The story, which took place around a campfire, involved a group of children who got lost in the woods and were eventually killed by a wendigo.

It sounds like this thing is supposed to take on the form of other things in order to lure people away from safety into the woods, but I've never seen it.

Wendigo sightings aren't just restricted to places like Canada and the Great Lakes area. They've been reported as far away as Florida and California, where Native American folklore likely wouldn't reach or influence people so much. I think that's odd and makes these sightings seem a lot more credible.

As I understand it, a wendigo is basically a man or woman who has been possessed by an evil spirit and turned into sort of an ogre or demon. The creature's skin becomes what we call wah-pee-tah, which apparently is alsoa type of snow that clings to the ground even in warm weather. The wendigo is said to have a tall, lanky body and long arms, and it's often described as very gaunt-looking with bony knees and elbows. The creature usually has no hair or only sparse clumps of grayish hair on its head that look like lichen or even moss growing on rocks.

And wendigo sightings seem to be increasing. It was also described as having a deathly pale, white face with stringy black hair and a large mouth that looked like it contained fangs. Sometimes the wendigo is said to have glowing red eyes or even blue ones.

I know this isn't really a story and more just information, but I'd be curious to look more into the research side of things. What are your thoughts on wendigos?

Encounter 8
Submitted By: Drew
Time: After Halloween, 1991
Location: N/A

THE TIME WAS JUST after midnight on Halloween, 1991. To this day, I still have no idea what I saw out there in the woods. However, only one thing really matters: whatever it was (or maybe still is) out in those woods most assuredly wanted to be seen by me.

The location where it took place is very far away from even the nearest town, which is only a few miles away from where I saw whatever it was. Because of the remoteness of the location, it is doubtful, if not downright impossible, that anyone else has ever discovered the creature's lair.

The setting is one of those "lost frontier" places where local kids used to do drugs and have sex because we were too far from town for anyone to hear us. The woods were vast, with large trees and steep ravines all around us.

The night was chilly. We were riding around in my pickup truck with the windows rolled down only halfway to help keep us warm while we drove through the darkened woods. The night was getting darker around us as if a storm was coming. The entire night I had been drinking hard liquor on an empty stomach, so by the time this occurred, I was already drunk.

I was driving rather slowly, just following the dirt road we had been on many times. I thought I saw something moving in my rearview mirror for a second. I made a concerted effort to clear my vision by blinking rapidly, then looked again into the woods behind us, where I thought I'd seen something. But there was nothing.

I sensed something out there in the woods off to my left. I looked out the driver's side window directly into the woods, then over my right shoulder at my friends in the truck. Suddenly, this huge ripple of darkness—like a wave rolling through the forest—passed right past us down the hill from where we'd just come. It went from left to right, then ended and disappeared from sight on the right side of us as quickly as it had come.

I stopped the truck. Then turning to my friends, I said, "What the hell was that?"

I've never been a fan of horror movies or scary stories. I don't like being scared by things that exist in real life—things that I can imagine happening to me, and it goes against my nature, and I don't like it.

The following is the thing that gives me the most chills: "The knowledge that all of us are vulnerable, no matter how brave or self-confident someone might believe themselves to be. Anything can happen to anyone at any time—and if you think you're ready for it when it does, there's a pretty good chance that you're about to get the living crap scared out of you."

The woods looked dark and foreboding, much darker than they should have. Something had changed in them. As if whatever was out there was closer now than before—and this time, I knew we couldn't escape it.

I looked in the direction where I'd seen whatever it was disappear.

It wasn't there anymore. But at least this time, I saw what had caused the ripple of darkness through the trees: a shadow passed over a large tree behind us and began moving forward, coming toward us up the hill.

The three of us sat in silence as we watched this large, dark figure come closer and closer to the road where we parked. I remember having an overwhelming sense of fear, as if something was pulling me toward the darkened woods. The darkness felt like it was calling my name—wanting me to come to it. Whatever I had seen out there on the edge of those woods, it wanted something from me—and that was when I knew: Whatever it was out there in the dark, whatever it had been that had made that dark ripple through the forest—it wasn't human.

The thing came closer to us, then stopped just at the edge of the headlights' light and looked up at us. Its eyes were yellow and bloodshot, as if from a fever.

Its face was contorted into an appearance that I cannot even begin to fully describe; it looked almost like the face of an evil being. But with a wilder look, the skull's appearance looked like some wild beast instead of a normal human face underneath its skin.

I remember saying out loud, "Oh God, no." I was shaking and crying.

The thing that had been stalking us turned around and walked away into the darkness of the forest without making another sound. I knew it was keeping an eye on us. Nothing will sober you up quicker than coming in contact with entities from other dimensions.

When the creature had gone, I remember grabbing my pistol from under my seat and checking it. It was loaded with hollow-point rounds, and I made sure that they were seated properly in the chambers.

We all sat there stunned. Then one of my friends said, "Who would ever believe us? We can't tell the police about this, and they'd think we're crazy."

We figured it was best if we headed back into town, where we'd be safe, and just sort of let the alcohol get out of our systems. I started the truck and turned it around, looking back at where we'd been. I could see that whatever it was, was now hiding in the shadows under the trees—watching us. A small part of me understood what I was seeing. Still, another part of me didn't want to believe that anything this horrible even existed on this earth.

There was something in the darkness that night, and it wasn't going to let us go until it got what it came for: something from one of us—possibly all three of us. I figured we'd be safe once we made it back into town, though—nobody could hurt us there, and there were too many people around.

As I drove back into town—suddenly feeling soberer than ever, accompanied by a worse feeling: being followed—I kept glancing in my rearview mirror at whatever it was following us. I could see it moving along behind us through the trees. This massive silhouette. It was trailing us, moving from tree to tree.

I kept driving faster and faster along the dark road back into town. My friends were panicking, trying to make the truck drive faster, but this thing was a podunk, beaten-up truck, and it could only go so fast. "FASTER!" my friend screamed at me, and I tried pushing the old truck harder. It was going about 60 mph by now, but whatever it was behind us didn't seem to be faltering. Finally, it vanished after pursuing us for a while.

We were successful in making it out of the portion of woods we were in and back into town. Now it was around one in the morning. We had been drinking, so we didn't want to report what we had seen or experienced to anyone, but let's be honest here. There is NO amount of alcohol that will allow you to experience what we did. Even today, I'm still friends with those guys who experienced that with me. All of our stories remain the same. No details have changed. We all saw the same creature or being.

One thing I wanted to mention about this entity is that there was this evil that emanated from it. You could feel it wanted to harm and do bad to us. You know how you can just feel certain things from people? It's our natural human discernment. That's what we all felt off this being.

Afterwards, we all felt really weird for a while too. One of those friends got horribly ill for the next few days, fever and all. Over the next few days, we'd all felt drained.

Sorry for the long story, but it's important that I share every aspect of what happened on that night back in 1991.

Encounter 9
Submitted By: Larson
Time: 2001
Location: Wisconsin

THE FOREST behind my house is so scary. I have always heard stories about a wendigo living there, which always gave me the chills.

Once, when I was eight years old, we were hiking through that part of the woods and saw something huge in the distance. It looked kind of like Bigfoot but more humanlike with glowing yellow eyes. My dad told us to stay out of that back area of the woods because we had no idea what we were playing around with, and we needed to be very careful. He told us there were bad spirits back there.

My dad knows a lot of the history around here, and supposedly there's an old Indian burial ground nearby. Still, I've heard that old tripe before, and I don't know if you can trust that.

Once, my grandma was in the hospital, and I had to spend some time with her. She's always been a little different. She told me about this weird creature that the Indians used to worship. She claimed it was a spirit of nature or something like that. She said if someone destroys the land too much, it will upset the balance of nature. It'll make scary monsters that take the shape of animals, trees, rocks, and even weather to get revenge on whoever did it. My grandma died shortly after we got home from visiting her at the nursing home, and I think one of the spirits possessed her and killed her.

My father claims that we've been targeted because we went back there in those woods. And as long as we stay away from that area, we should be okay.

Encounter 10
Submitted By: Mikael Vanders
Time: N/A
Location: N/A

LAST TIME I was up on the mountain, I saw something, something that made me think the stories about a wendigo in these woods are true.

I never used to believe them, but now... well, I'm not so sure.

It started as just another regular hike: nothing different about this one from all the others before it. My friends Mark and Ian had both decided to come with me that day. We were heading out early in the morning to catch some good footage for our documentary "The Mythical Creatures of Appalachia." As much as I'd like to believe we got good footage, we didn't film near as much as I'd hoped. That's okay, though.

We spent much time at the summit and felt like someone was following us. We tried to keep all our thoughts on the wendigo so that it would stay away. Let's just say we cut our hiking trip in the mountains short from dealing with this creature. We wanted to get back to town and out of the woods, so we started walking as fast as possible. We kept looking behind us, thinking we were being followed by someone, but there was never anything there, just trees. It made me feel like I was going crazy; it really messed with my head.

We were almost ready to give up when a small patch of tall grass swaying in the wind suddenly stopped moving. My friends and I froze right where we stood, afraid to move another inch for fear of whatever could be in those bushes seeing or hearing us come closer...

The three of us turned around slowly with our lights pointed towards the spot where the movement had stopped... and that was when I saw it!

I froze like my friends did when I saw a pair of glowing red eyes staring right through those bushes. It was hard to see, but I could tell this thing had long, stringy black hair covering its body. Mark whispered behind me, "Do you guys see that?" We all nodded without taking our eyes off what we were looking at. "What do you think it is?" Ian answered by saying it was likely some kind of coyote with rabies or something... but he sounded so unsure of himself that even I felt uneasy about his answer.

All of a sudden, that patch of grass started moving again. We couldn't move if we wanted to; we were just standing there in shock as this figure slowly came out from behind the tall blades of grass and into our sight. I don't think any of us could have even blinked at that moment for fear of not being able to see this thing up close... and believe me, none of us really wanted to miss seeing it!

As soon as it stepped through the thick bush line, it stopped dead still on its hind legs and let out a sound that sounded like a combination of a man's voice and a high-pitched dog's yelp. It shook its long stringy black hair from side to side as it let out another ear-piercing screech. We couldn't help but move backward a few steps, but we stopped when none of us wanted to turn our backs on this thing just yet.

This... thing was standing right before us so close that I could almost reach out and touch it! I can't explain how it looked except to say that it resembled some sort of cloaked figure from the movies. It had long stringy black hair covering its body, as Mark said earlier, but there were parts of its face and arms exposed. Think of an upright coyote or something with bad mange mixed with a feral human being. Utterly shocked at what we were seeing, I think all three of us just reacted out of fear and ran away from this creature.

I don't think any of us knew then, but Ian tripped and fell to the ground not too far from where we were standing. My mind was filled with fear as I ran back towards my friend to see if he was okay. When I turned around to look at it again, it was coming after both of us and picked up speed. The look on its face seemed frenzied, like it was out for blood! It looked down at Ian on the ground and let out another screech. It sounded like a mixture of laughter and pain all put together.

As I tried lifting Ian off the ground, something caught my eye behind this creature making its way closer to us. What appeared to be five other figures emerged from somewhere back in those bushes next to us; they looked almost just like the one coming right for us. They all began slowly coming out of the brush, moving in our direction. I yanked Ian up and caught up with Mark, who was already ahead of us.

In that instance, the thing directly following us dove right into the forest on our left, keeping parallel the entire time. It didn't seem right, so I stopped running and turned around... just in time to see it pounce on top of a deer that had emerged from the forest without us knowing about it! The deer let out a high-pitched scream that sounded like the creature's screech from before; it was as if this thing was playing with its food.

I don't think we realized it until later, but we kept moving pretty fast, trying not to turn our backs on that monster or those other five things. We were running faster than usual, desperate to make sure none of them got too close. After what seemed like forever, we all stopped for a second and looked back at where we came from... nothing! I feel terrible for saying this, but thank god for that deer. I think that deer distracted these things away from us.

As I said, we safely made it back and cut our trip short. I have never in all my years come across anything remotely similar to the strange creature we all three saw that day. I firmly believe it was a wendigo, but I can't be too sure. It looked like a large man covered with thick fur from head to toe. The face wasn't that recognizable or unique, but this thing had these big bulging yellow eyes that stuck out and were hard to look away from.

Even now, when I try remembering our day's experience, my body still shivers thinking about what we saw in those deep dark forests on the mountainside. This is one of those moments where you can say, "I never believed in a wendigo until now."

I don't know if any of us will ever return there again... who would want to?

Encounter 11
Submitted By: Frank
Time: 1990–1998
Location: Canada

YOU CAN CALL ME FRANK. I'm a paranormal researcher up here in Toronto. I wanted to write to you about the strange things and sights that have been happening up here in this beautiful country.

Something eerie is happening in the forests of Canada. A hideous creature that can best be described as a malevolent monster with supernatural abilities has been sighted. It is known to the Native Americans by a name from their folklore—"the wendigo."

It would not be correct to say it resembles an apelike creature because it stands erect like a human being instead of walking on all fours.

One Canadian province alone had more than sixty sightings reported over an eight-year span (1990–1998). And this number only represents those people who were brave enough to report what they saw in writing.

Some eyewitness accounts claim that the wendigo possesses powers that could rival shape-shifting aliens, vampires, or even witches—including mind control. According to Native American folklore, this creature is said to have a magnetic personality similar to the dark spirits or aliens that are also believed to be around. And they use humans for sustenance purposes such as blood by luring them into their tight grips, either through hypnosis or just plain force.

On rare occasions when the wendigo was encountered in rural areas, they were known to take small children who were left unattended even for short periods. In some cases, they appeared out of nowhere and snatched kids because their parents were not paying attention.

Most child-snatching cases occurred on sunny summer days

when the kids would do something like leaving their homes unsupervised. At the same time, their mothers would be tending to household chores or would be busy cooking in the kitchen.

One story involving a stolen child is as follows: A woman who lived in the forest far from any neighbors called the police, saying that her five-year-old boy named Timmy(name changed) was missing. And they should hurry because it was getting dark and there were wild animals like bear and wolves in this area. When authorities arrived at the scene, she told them that while she was making dinner for "Timmy," he said he had to use the bathroom and then ran out of sight to go play against his mother's wishes. She immediately looked for him, but could not find him anywhere around their house. It's as if he had simply vanished.

The police searched extensively, thinking maybe he had fallen into a nearby river or something. Still, after their search yielded no results, they started to get skeptical because of the woman's peculiar attitude.

The local police were about to call in the government investigators when one of them noticed fresh tracks near a tree hollow that was close by. Although he had no idea what type of animal left those marks on the ground, he felt 100% sure that whatever made them wasn't human.

But before they could investigate deeper, their radio got a call from a nearby town saying that another child had been snatched by something big and hairy that looked like "a giant troll" running past their houses. It was reported that the kid's parents were watching television while he played outside, but when he came back in through the front door, asking for a glass of water, they saw this unkempt-looking beast standing on two legs with its arms reaching out, and it took the boy in front of the parents Remember though, this is heresay.

Another eyewitness who lived next to a wooded area claimed she saw a tall creature run across one side of her lawn one night and then disappear into the trees on the other side. She claimed it looked like "a large troll," and it wasn't a bear. Still, she didn't tell anyone what she saw because she was afraid someone would think she was crazy after admitting to seeing a terrible creature such as described in fairy tales.

Another local woman called in saying that the dog started barking like crazy at one point during her night-shift job because it saw something moving outside the window, causing her to get curious and look out too. She claimed to have seen a tall hairy monster run across the road in front of her house while carrying something a dead deer. She believed it was a Wendigo spirit.

It's pretty evident that something is going on around here up in Canada. I know we have our fair share of cryptids, just like the United States. In my opinion, I believe much of this is the work of a wendigo demon, not that of a Sasquatch.

As a cryptozoologist and a paranormal researcher, I feel it is my duty and job to pursue these creatures further to seek the answers we're all looking for, for better or for worse.

Encounter 12
Submitted By: Anonymous
Time: N/A
Location: Canada

I USED to live out in the country up north in Canada, out in the sticks. You had to bike or drive to go anywhere aside from a small little taco stand. At night it would get pretty dark too. With my mother and stepdad, we had a few small dogs and a cat, and I was often left in charge of all of them. I was resentful for all the work on top of the schooling and homework. But I loved the animals, so I couldn't blame them too much. Unless they made a huge mess, then I'd be pretty ticked, but that's not entirely relevant. What is, is that I would routinely take them all out before going to bed, and I would go to bed very, very late at night, like any fourteen-year-old with such lax parenting.

My dogs usually stayed in the front yard, a vast acreage of flat land with a tiny ditch. It was easy to see the small dogs and call them back in. Sometimes the one dog would wander, my mother's cairn terrier had a bit of a rebellious side to her, but it wasn't her who took off this night; it was the cocker spaniel. She was protective and had a watchful eye, while the others were mostly divas. Frustrated, I ran after her to the back of the house, which is a steep slope toward a water bed that is an offshoot of the Red River. What I saw slowly sprawling across the slope, coming in our direction, still gives me chills.

These things were about chest height to me and twenty feet away. They were very grotesque looking like they were covered in rotting dead flesh, but on all fours with long legs that were longer in the back. They turned their almost rotting faces toward our direction at the top of the slope. Their eyes were large and glowed like big white marbles in the faint back porch lights. Luckily my dog had stopped moving; we both were frozen in the movement, her hackles raised like a hyena. The creatures were still walking and pacing around, keeping an eye on us like we were a newly discovered threat. I grabbed the dog by crouching quickly, frightened we'd be attacked, and bolted around the side to the front again, calling for the others to come inside. The other two dogs were already sitting at the door, waiting for us. I guess they figured it was too chilly for them to stay out so long, but truthfully my out-of-shape self was boiling from the adrenaline.

After this incident, I refused to take them out after dark, which unfortunately resulted in plenty of messes I had to clean up. I would occasionally see those strange things wandering outside our house after that, and it gave me the creeps. They'd only look up at my house if I had the lights on and was obviously moving in clear view.

Another night I woke up, radio flashing 1 a.m. or something close to that. I wasn't sure why I woke up until I realized I wasn't alone. I slept in the basement at that time. My window overlooked the backyard, but only slightly. It was under the back porch, which could be walked under if you simply stooped. One of those things, with what appeared to be a rotting-flesh skull-looking face with dead sunken eyes, looked in through my window. I froze. I'm not sure if I moved at all after waking up. It pressed its head against the glass briefly and snorted real loud. I got the feeling it was scanning the darkness for someone, me. After a minute, it pulled its head back and resumed the direction it was walking in.

To this day, I have no idea what they were. They looked very skinny and appeared to have what I would describe as rotting flesh all over their bodies, and it was putrid looking. They acted and moved very strangely and walked on all fours, sometimes alternating to just two legs. They had long legs and arms, and I didn't see any claws.

The only thing I could find when looking up any sort of myth was cryptids like the wendigo or skinwalker. But a skinwalker is usually only a Navajo Native thing. And up here, it's not very likely. I don't know what a wendigo looks like, although I know they're cannibalistic creatures. I just don't know if they're depicted as looking like they have rotting flesh. Aside from simple distance making it hard to discern their faces, they stuck around long enough for me to get a good look at their form. So what was I seeing out there?

Encounter 13
Submitted By: Alexander
Time: Summer 2015
Location: N/A

DURING THE SUMMER OF 2015, I had the most terrifying experience of my life. I've always been a rabid outdoorsman and have been obsessed with camping. Really anything involving nature, actually. I would go out camping with a couple of very close friends of mine who were also part Native and knew a lot about the wild around them.

We had gone hiking on different trails, land, and areas. Even areas deep within my friend's reservation where most people don't have the proper permission to go out. That's what makes rez land so great. It's generally uncharted because many of the Natives living on it themselves don't bother to go far into it. The area was thick with wild game, like deer, black bears, and cougars.

On several occasions, we had gone far out into the wilderness on his tribe's land for miles, sometimes going as much as we could in one day just to see how far we could make it. The forest was always so full of life, especially out there where white men like myself never got the opportunity to venture into. They held this place sacred and would even hold off on hunting it unless they needed to.

Usually, on every trip, it would just be me and a couple of his family members I was close with. But the one time I went with him, I noticed something very eerie. We were probably four hours into a long hike when the forest had gone completely silent. I know we have cougars around, but generally, this isn't the case with a cougar of the woods being silent. I waited as quietly as possible and surveyed my surroundings meticulously. The sun was still bright in the sky and burning as hot as ever on this warm summer day. It was weird to have so much light and so little sound.

That was when a very creepy thing happened. I heard my name being called out close by. It didn't sound normal, though. It sounded weird. It sounded like someone trying to mimic my Native friend, who was right next to me at the time, and the voice sounded distorted. It called out my name, telling me to come here. My friend looked at me, and he was sweating bullets. He said something in his native tongue and urged me that we needed to leave now. He kept telling me not to respond to it no matter what, and we began to turn back the way we came.

Whatever the thing was that called out to me was close by in the woods, and it was following us as we made our way back. My friend started becoming incredibly nervous and kept whispering in his own language. I kept asking him what was going on, and what was calling my name, and he wouldn't respond directly. Just kept telling me he'd explain later when we were safe.

This went on for about a couple more miles until we passed through a large creek that it did not pass through, but it continued to call out to me through the woods. It never revealed itself, whatever it was. We came to a spot where there were these strange wooden structures, if you wanted to call them structures. They were hanging from the trees, and I was told those are border markers. Border markers of the wendigo. We hadn't seen them before because when we'd crossed the creek earlier, it had been an entirely different location of the creek. And that area didn't have these markers, so we didn't realize what lay ahead of us.

We made it safely to the other side and, within no time, actually made it back to where he was staying at the time, in just a few more hours of hiking. So maybe we were definitely more than four miles out.

Once we got back and I could get him to thoroughly calm down and relax, he explained to me that what had happened was we came upon a wendigo's territory in the woods. He should have known by the feel of the energy around us but chose to ignore it because he thought his gut was misleading us. Wendigos are cannibalistic creatures that lure you in and then devour you whole. Many have been lost to these creatures, even more during the night. They can read your thoughts and mimic those close to you to lure you into their trap where they get you. It would've gotten us if we had gone just a little farther into the woods.

He had me freaked out by telling me all this stuff. His brothers and family confirmed this to be true with me and told us it's very dangerous to be in that area of the woods. There's a reason many of their people will not venture out into those places; that's wendigo territory. That is why his people and family only go out there hunting for food if they absolutely have to. Because they know there is such a considerable risk involved in going to certain places.

Thinking back on it, the utter silence of the woods was incredibly disturbing to me. I've been in those situations where a mother bear was around with small cubs but never like that. And I don't recall the woods going silent as they did there. You could hear a pencil drop. It was so quiet. I can't be 100% certain of what I encountered to this day, wendigo or not. Could it have only been a bear or maybe something else, and my friend was overreacting? Possibly. But if that is true, then what was calling out my name in his distorted voice? And why was it following us so closely back to the creek where there is a supposed territory marker? It just didn't make sense. That was one of the last times I went far into the deep woods, and I probably won't be returning anytime soon.

Encounter 14
Submitted By: Silvia W.
Time: Spring 2010
Location: N/A

I WAS HIKING in the woods of Western Michigan with my dog, a German shepherd/Labrador mix (who was also my best friend at the time) when I came across a very large, thin man lying on the ground. There was a good distance between us, so I tried to make out if it was an injured hiker or maybe a deceased person. As I got closer, I saw he was tall and very thin, with long, thin arms and legs. He had very pale skin and very dark hair. His eyes were a bright, blood red. I saw him from about twenty feet away, and I saw all these details as he immediately shot up off the ground and began walking toward me. At first, I didn't see those details, so I thought the man was sickly and needed help.

I realized he was not only naked but not a man. the revelation felt instantaneous and I was very shocked. It was sudden, and I didn't even have time to react. I only knew this because growing up here, I'd heard countless stories about Wendigos and their looks, etc. I just knew what this was. I also knew this was very bad. I knew I had to get out of there immediately, so I picked up my dog in my arms and began running. I ran as fast as I could, hoping to get away. I ran into a clearing and then turned around to see if he was following me. I did this because I was worried about him chasing me. Quickly, this thing began zooming through the woods with very twitchy stiff movements.

Luckily I got away from him carrying my dog, and he disappeared, but that was easily one of the scariest experiences I've ever had in the woods. Never had that happened before in my life.

AFTERWORD

I hope you enjoyed this book full of sightings and encounters with cryptids. I certainly had a blast pulling open the vault and digging through to find these stories! I hope it's opened your eyes to the possibility that these strange and terrifying creatures may be out there, just waiting to be discovered. I'm going to keep this short and just wanted to say thank you again for the support.

If you enjoyed this book, be on the lookout for VOL 2, which will be out sometime in the indefinite future! Also, be sure to subscribe to my YouTube channel because I will be telling many of these accounts in full presentation! Look me up: What Lurks Beneath. https://www.youtube.com/channel/UCvwo7ZoeSMpbyMSBE4Iryrg

As always: I love you all, keep an open mind, and I'll catch you guys in the very next book. :)

ABOUT THE AUTHOR

Josh Nanocchio is a full time entertainer running the YouTube channel What Lurks Beneath. When he's not doing production or filming, he's spending time with his wife and four children enjoying life. Josh is passionate about the supernatural and creating content that makes his viewers think outside the box.

Made in United States
North Haven, CT
28 February 2024